THE NEW NATURALIST

A SURVEY OF BRITISH NATURAL HISTORY

THE BROADS

The aim of this series is to interest the general reader in the wild life of Britain by recapturing the inquiring spirit of the old naturalists. The Editors believe that the natural pride of the British public in the native fauna and flora, to which must be added concern for their conservation, is best fostered by maintaining a high standard of accuracy combined with clarity of exposition in presenting the results of modern scientific research.

THE NEW NATURALIST

THE BROADS

by

E. A. ELLIS

WITH 47 PHOTOGRAPHS
AND 68 MAPS AND DIAGRAMS

COLLINS
ST JAMES'S PLACE, LONDON
1965

Printed in Great Britain
Collins Clear-Type Press
London and Glasgow

CONTENTS

Except where otherwise indicated, the author is E. A. Ellis

PLATES

PLATES

TEXT FIGURES

EDITORS' PREFACE

Ever since the *New Naturalist* series was projected nearly a quarter of a century ago the editors have hoped for a book on the Broads under the leadership of Edward A. Ellis, himself a Broadsman by adoption. Mr. Ellis owns Wheatfen Broad, and lives there, and ever since he came from Guernsey to Norfolk as a boy in 1920 has been challenged by almost every aspect of its wetlands' complex and fascinating natural history. Readers of this book will soon appreciate just how much of it he has mastered.

It is an ill wind that blows nobody any good. Friends of our series have for years inquired anxiously about the progress of a book they knew was under way. The delays have been unavoidable; and they have also been benign—for in the last decade our contributors Joyce Lambert, Joseph Jennings and C. T. Smith have, in a series of finely co-ordinated researches, proved beyond all reasonable doubt that the Broads are not a natural lake-system, but human artefacts. They are, in essence, waterlogged pits left by medieval turf-cutters. This was a reversal of most previous views on the subject.

Much indeed would have been false in this volume if we had published it fifteen years ago, as was originally planned. As it comes now, it is a balanced and up-to-date assemblage of the natural history of an area of National Park calibre—even if it has never attained this official status. The book, of course, owes all to the complementary talent of some of the cream of field naturalists of a county that—through the long history of British natural history—has perhaps provided more cream than any other.

Early in his Norfolk career, E. A. ELLIS came under the influence of that inspired amateur naturalist, the late A. H. Patterson. Using, as we do, the word amateur in its proper sense (enthusiast), we greet Ellis as Patterson's mantle-wearer, and as much besides. For nearly thirty years he worked at the Norwich Castle Museum as assistant naturalist and later Keeper of natural history. Now he has retired, to read the living book of the Broads and to write, and to be an active member of the Norfolk and Suffolk Broads Plans Committee and River Board, and of the Norfolk Naturalists' Trust (the oldest local conservation trust in the country). He is recorder for East Norfolk to the Botanical Society of the British Isles.

The veteran naturalist, J. E. SAINTY, can most properly be described as the senior amateur geologist and prehistorian now working in Norfolk.

JOSEPH JENNINGS, one of those who has so boldly and recently solved the mystery of the origin of the Broads, is now in Australia as a senior lecturer in Geography in the University of Canberra, a post which he has reached *via* Cambridge, where he has been both student and lecturer.

CHARLES GREEN is one of East Anglia's most prominent and active practising archæologists, with vast experience of excavations (often for the Ministry of Works) from the Roman port of Caister, near Yarmouth, where he lives, to Saxon and medieval sites all over Norfolk.

JOYCE M. LAMBERT, now a lecturer in Botany to Southampton University, is Norfolk born and bred; her great experience of plant ecology (including her pioneer and definitive study of the pond-grass *Glyceria maxima*) made her the perfect colleague for Jennings and C. T. SMITH, an historical geographer at Cambridge, in their joint assault on the problem of the Broads' origin.

The late ROBERT GURNEY was a paragon of naturalist virtue of the classic Norfolk stream. Originally a marine zoologist, he came to specialise in Broadland water zoology, in particular crustaceans. With his brother Eustace, he established a pioneer fresh-water laboratory at Sutton Broad in 1906; and he lived and worked for many years at Calthorpe Broad.

A. E. ELLIS, biologist at Epsom College until his recent retirement, lived in Norfolk for many years, and wrote the standard work on British snails soon after he left Oxford in 1926. ERIC A. DUFFEY, now a Principal Scientific Officer of the Nature Conservancy, with special experience of East Anglian ecology, is an all-round naturalist with a particular interest in the ecology of spiders. The late B. B. RIVIERE, for many years a medical practitioner in Norfolk, was the greatest twentieth-century scholar and historian of its birds.

Finally, the late RAINBIRD CLARKE, Norwich-born archaeologist and son of another great Norfolk naturalist (W. G. Clarke, who wrote *In Breckland Wilds*), when Curator to the Norwich Castle Museum entirely reorganised its archæological collections. His colleague HORACE BOLINGBROKE for many years took care of Norwich's Strangers' Hall Folk Museum, which was originally presented to the city by his father.

THE EDITORS

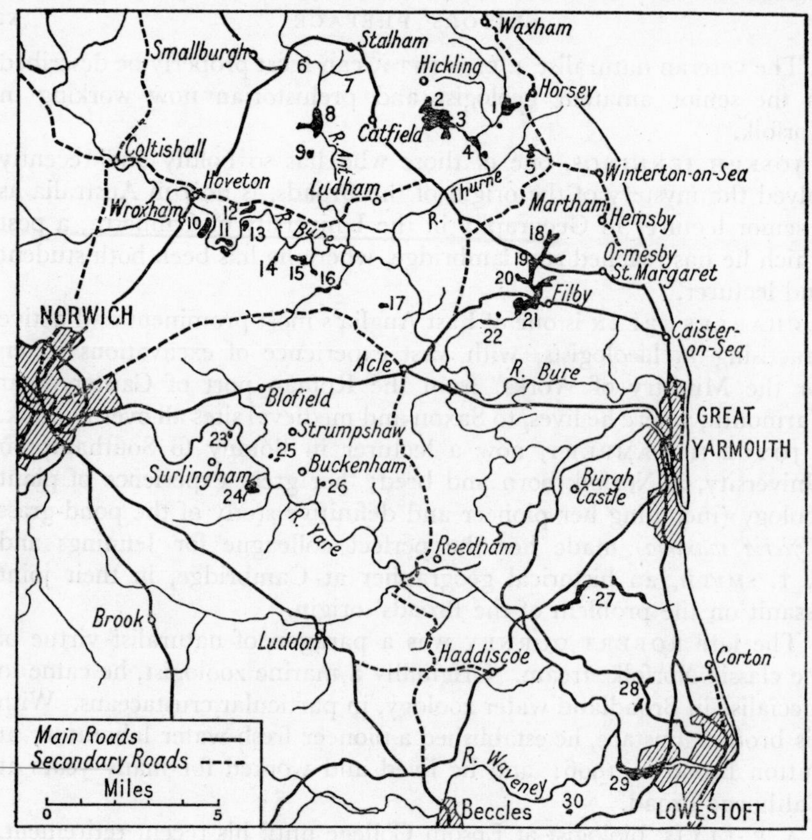

THE NORFOLK BROADS

KEY

THURNE
1 Horsey Mere and Blackfleet B.
2 Hickling B.
3 Whiteslea
4 Heigham Sounds
5 Martham B.

ANT
6 Dilham Broad Fen
7 Sutton B.
8 Barton B.
9 Alderfen B.

MIDDLE BURE
10 Wroxham B.
11 Hoveton
12 Hoveton Little
13 Decoy
14 Cockshoot
15 Ranworth and Malthouse
16 South Walsham
17 Upton

FLEGG
18 Ormesby
19 Rollesby
20 Lily
21 Filby
22 Burgh

YARE
23 Surlingham
24 Rockland and Wheatfen
25 Strumpshaw
26 Buckenham and Hassingham

WAVENEY
27 Fritton Lake
28 Flixton
29 Oulton
30 Barnby

INTRODUCTION TO THE BROADLAND SCENE

by E. A. Ellis

The broads are shallow, reed-fringed lakes associated with rivers that wind slowly through the lowlands of east Norfolk and neighbouring Suffolk to flow into the North Sea through a common harbour at Great Yarmouth. Their waters are often ruffled by sea breezes and salt tides affect them from time to time; indeed, but for coast defences, they and many thousands of acres of adjacent marshes would be at the mercy of regular sea flooding. It used to be thought that they were relict pools of an estuary clogged by centuries of silting and reclaimed by the spread of marsh vegetation; but the recent researches of Dr. J. M. Lambert and her associates have proved (see chapter 3) that although estuarine conditions have prevailed temporarily in the lower parts of the east Norfolk river valleys on more than one occasion in the past, the broads originated comparatively recently as peat-pits, flooded and linked by artificial channels with the rivers, as the general water-level rose in late historic times.

Thousands of people spend summer holidays afloat on the broadland waterways. They sail, cruise and fish in surroundings that give a sense of freedom and peace and of remoteness from the conventional life of towns. There are crowded yachting centres at some points, but between these, miles of unspoiled and largely wild country delight the eye and refresh the soul of the voyager. Here, as nowhere else in England, a vast system of lagoons lies open to exploration by amateur watermen, and its attraction lies in the beauty of its landscape revealed at every bend of every river, under a wide-horizoned sky. While the broads themselves are pure wilderness, sprinkled with lilies and palisaded with reeds, and the rank fens behind, bushy and sedgy, have a primeval appearance, much of the marshy country has been embanked and drained to form vast green pastures on which cattle graze in summer. The uplands flanking the wide valleys are gently undulating, with low contours, and are a many-coloured patchwork of arable farms, marked out by hawthorn hedges and plentifully endowed with wayside oaks and small plantations serving as game coverts. The flint towers of churches, many of great size and beauty, suggest that this has been a well populated and flourishing part of the country in the past, while the brick towers of derelict windmills are a reminder of strenuous efforts made by reclaimers of marshland in the 18th and 19th centuries, before modern electric pumps were invented.

The holidaymaker sees some evidence of native industries when he visits the village staithes; there will be reeds harvested in winter and stacked for the thatchers, or bulrushes and osiers collected for basket-making. But the major waterside industry now is that which caters for yachtsmen and there is an ever-growing number of boat-building and boat-letting yards. The traffic of wherries, the black-sailed barges peculiar to broadland, has ceased within living memory; but these well-designed craft used to carry much of the farm produce and most of the household supplies to and from the waterside villages and towns (see chapters 15 and 16).

So far as the economy of the wilder parts of the broads is concerned at the present time, there are riparian interests in reed-cutting and wildfowling, while many large areas are owned and managed by charitable Trusts as nature reserves. Navigation interests are looked after by the Great Yarmouth Port and Haven Commissioners, and the East Suffolk and Norfolk River Board deals with flood-protection, pollution and fisheries.

As will be shown in chapter 1, broadland occupies part of East Anglia in which many changes in the relative land and sea levels have occurred in the last half-million years, while the alternating advances and retreats of the ice-sheets have left their marks on the landscape and built up a unique series of deposits, which are to be seen in the local cliff-sections and sand and clay pits. Here, classical studies have been made of the Norwich Crag, a shelly marine deposit of the early Pleistocene, by Searles V. Wood and F. W. Harmer. The early interglacial fauna and flora of the forest beds exposed from time to time along the coast have attracted the interest of famous geologists throughout the world since they first came to notice some two hundred years ago. The alternating strata of sands and boulder-clays, often strangely contorted and containing rocks and fossils brought from far afield by moving ice, tell the story of violent up-heavals and inundations suffered by this now tranquil part of England.

Following the last retreat of the ice from East Anglia, arctic conditions gradually gave place to temperate, with minor variations in warmth and rainfall, as well as in the relative levels of land and sea, during this post-glacial period of some 10,000 years. Evidence of these changes is to be found in the deep beds of peat in the river valleys of east Norfolk, which preserve relics of the changing flora in vertical succession, interleaved with intrusive silts that mark periodic inundations by the sea. This period of transition is dealt with in chapter 3.

The vegetation of this area today comprises a magnificent graduated series of aquatic and fen communities, fuller and richer than that surviving in any other part of Britain. The waters hold species of charophytes and the stagshorn weed (*Naias marina*), unknown elsewhere in these islands. The broads are the chief remaining home of plants like the water soldier and cowbane, and nowhere else are there such massive ranks of the tall marsh sowthistle along miles of riverside. The fen orchid and round-leaved wintergreen linger in the mossy fens and the great spearwort raises its yellow heads between the reeds. Plants of ancient lineage in these eastern valleys hold their places in the ever-changing pattern of swamp and carr and provide the botanist and plant geographer with rich material for study. In the humid shelter of tall marsh vegetation, countless little fungi thrive almost as in a tropical jungle, attacking plants alive and dead and parasitising millions of insects and spiders.

The waters, because of their varying salinity, support a remarkable range of planktonic animals, including many curiously specialised crustaceans, and freshwater polyzoa flourish greatly. The more calcareous regions are very rich in molluscs and the riversides yield an interesting series of brackish-water species along their lower reaches.

The insects include the British swallowtail butterfly, surviving in abundance nowhere else, and two dragonflies which are restricted to this region. The beds of reed, sedge and rush are the haunts of many rare and local moths, especially the wainscots, and as recently as 1961 a new British footman, *Pelosia obtusa*, was found near one of the broads. Whereas most of the ancient fenland of Cambridge, Lincolnshire and Huntingdonshire has been drained out of existence, almost all its specialised insects and other invertebrates, as well as its plants, are represented in the broadland region.

There is a wealth of bird life at all seasons. In summer, the chinking notes of bearded tits may be heard among the reeds almost everywhere and bitterns, for many years absent as breeding birds in this country, are well established. At the time of writing, the marsh and Montagu's harriers are suffering from a recession, but they flourished here for many years until very recently and may return to nest again. Every broad has its elegant great crested grebes, and from time to time spoonbills alight to feed and flocks of black terns make a call on migration.

A South American rodent, the coypu, has become established in great numbers everywhere on the broads in the last twenty years and it has wrought many changes in the waterways and marshes (see chapter 13).

Finally, there are the people living and working in the marsh country. The history of their establishment and ways of making a living out of the wilderness is told in chapter 14, and details of their tools and river craft are given in succeeding chapter 15 and appendix c.

In presenting the story of the broads anew, with a stress on much very recent scientific research, it is fitting that tribute be paid to the many fine naturalists of the past who have investigated the geology and wild life of this region. The first was Sir Thomas Browne, back in the seventeenth century, reporting on the 'bittaurs' and other remarkable creatures of the weedy wilderness. Botanical exploration was carried out by such Norfolk worthies as Sir James Smith, Sir William Hooker, Dawson Turner, and Sir James Paget, and in the early years of the nineteenth century the Rev. John Gunn of Irstead (1801–1890) was tireless in his search for forest-bed fossils. The Norwich geologist Samuel Woodward suspected an artificial origin for at least some of the broads as long ago as 1834.

The birds were studied intensively by Henry Stevenson (1833–1888), author of the classic three-volume '*Birds of Norfolk*', and the two John Henry Gurneys, father and son, together ranging over a century of local ornithology from 1819–1922, gathered much additional information. The Yarmouth and broadland naturalist A. H. Patterson (d. 1935) produced a number of delightful books on the wildlife and human characters, especially of Breydon, the Yarmouth estuary.

The setting up of a freshwater biological station at Sutton Broad by the brothers Eustace and Robert Gurney at the beginning of the present century resulted in much scientific information about the aquatic fauna being collected and it was very regrettable that their efforts were brought to a close by the First World War.

In recent years, the Norfolk Naturalists' Trust has acquired large areas of water and fen at Alderfen, Barton, Hickling, Ranworth and Surlingham Broads, while Horsey Mere and the surrounding marshlands have become a responsibility of the National Trust. The Nature Conservancy has assumed an important role in the area, by negotiating management agreements for many of the broads, by carrying out research and by co-ordinating local interests with a view to making the best all-round use of the area as a whole in the future, under a balanced plan of management. Under provisions of Town and Country Planning, the Norfolk County Council exercises control over certain types of development on the broads and in this it is assisted by a Broads Joint Advisory Planning Committee, representing a variety of local interests. The maintenance of the rivers and navigable channels across the broads is the responsibility of the Great Yarmouth Port and Haven Commissioners, while the local River Board deals with the upkeep of river banks and the main drainage; it also looks after angling interests and copes with the problems of pollution.

Since this book was first planned the broads have been studied and discussed more actively than ever before as a focus of interest in the English countryside. The authors have carried the story forward a little, partly by their own discoveries and partly by summarising the knowledge of wildlife gathered patiently by fellow spirits over the years. All are most deeply aware that exploration in many fields has scarcely begun and that future work in this unique region will prove as interesting and exciting as anything done in the past.

Geology and Physical Background

CHAPTER I

THE EARLY GEOLOGY OF BROADLAND

by J. E. Sainty and E. A. Ellis

Studies of the deep structure of East Anglia are still very imperfect, but borings made at a few strategic points, together with seismological tests, have shown that far down, the ' floor ' of the oldest (Palaeozoic) rocks slopes gently downward from south to north. Over it lie Mesozoic deposits of varying thickness, ranging from the Bunter sandstones to the Lower Greensand exposed in west Norfolk. Above these and much more thoroughly known are the Cretaceous deposits, comprising the Neocomian sands and clays, the Aptian Carstone and the Albian Red Rock and Gault Clay (Lower Cretaceous) and the Lower, Middle and Upper Chalk series of the Upper Cretaceous reaching a thickness of 1,400 feet in Norfolk and forming a chief ' bed-rock ' of the area.

In the broads district of east Norfolk the surface of the Upper Chalk slopes downwards from west to east from above river level at Norwich until it lies at a depth of approximately 450 feet in the neighbourhood of Great Yarmouth and Lowestoft, but its surface rises again northwards towards Cromer, where the youngest of all Chalk beds to be found in England is exposed at sea-level at Trimingham.

Capping the Chalk beneath Great Yarmouth are sands and clays comparable with the Reading Beds, and some 300 feet of London Clay (Eocene). In later Tertiary times the land to the south appears to have risen slightly and a westward-extending bay of a sea occupying the present North Sea basin advanced northwards, depositing shelly sands, gravels and clays of the well-known East Anglian Crags, formerly thought to be of Pliocene age but now taken by most geologists to belong to the Pleistocene, except possibly for the deepest-lying Coralline Crag of Suffolk.

Many Crag shells are of kinds common in the present North Sea (cockle, mussel, oyster, whelk and winkle); some are found living now only in Arctic waters, while others are characteristic of warmer waters and yet others have become extinct. It has been observed that modern and cold-water forms increase in proportion upwards in the series of marine and estuarine shell deposits. Thus there was a progressive chilling and shallowing of a northward shifting gulf of the Crag Sea and in this region a vast delta came into being.

There followed a period during which rock fragments of Scandinavian origin found their way to the estuary, probably in seaborne ice. Clays and gravels were deposited in the delta and formed the Cromer Forest Bed, now exposed periodically at a few points on the coast and containing a rich assortment of animal and plant remains. The basal portions of the Forest Bed are well known for their bones of extinct mammals, many of which were probably borne to their last resting place by river and sea from distant sources. These include early horses, the great southern elephant (*Archidoskon meridionalis*), hippopotamus, the Etruscan rhinoceros (*Dicerorhinus etruscus*), all representing the relict fauna of a warmer period, together with remains of contemporary Arctic species such as musk ox and walrus.

For a time, the sea-level became lowered sufficiently to allow land plants and animals to colonise the former domain of sea and estuary in this region and there came into being a country of forests, swamps, pools and streams. Successive deposits yield evidence which enables us to recognise the pattern of a glacial-interglacial sequence in them. There is an early cold phase, indicated by the presence of birch and pine; these trees give way to mixed oak forest, followed by hornbeam and spruce and finally, with cooling conditions, there is a return of pine. During the warm-temperate phase a rich assemblage of mammals flourished. An extinct giant beaver (*Trogontherium cuvieri*) inhabited swamps in which grew the water chestnut (*Trapa natans*), a plant no longer found wild in Britain. Many kinds of freshwater molluscs became abundant; these included modern forms living in company with several species that have since become extinct.

Traces of a deposit of marine sands, containing an Arctic lamellibranch mollusc, *Yoldia myalis*, have been found above the Forest Bed of the Norfolk coast, suggesting that the sea-level had risen towards the end of the interglacial period. Higher still in the succession is found the Arctic Freshwater Bed, containing northern plants such as the Arctic willow (*Salix polaris*) and dwarf birch (*Betula nana*); therefore land must have reappeared and the sea retreated.

A period of severe glaciation followed. The first great ice advance came from the north-west, to leave deposits of brickearth and the much contorted Cromer Till, containing rocks of Scandinavian type, spread over the eroded surface of the Forest Bed. A period of climatic amelioration seems to have followed, during which there was a rise in sea-level sufficient to account for the presence of the current-bedded and in parts shelly marine or estuarine sands known as the Corton Beds, which are a notable feature of many cliffs and pit exposures in broadland. Subsequently, a second ice sheet advanced from the west and fanned out northward and southward as it reached this district. It left extensive deposits of chalky boulder clay (the Lowestoft Till) containing flints, hard chalk, Jurassic fossils and an assortment of rocks derived in part from earlier ice advances. The weathered surface of this Till is now exposed to form much of the arable land of this area and except in parts of the river valleys, where terrace gravels appear, little evidence has been discovered of later Pleistocene material being deposited within the bounds of broadland. An Acheulian flaking site in terrace gravels of the river Yare at Whitlingham, near Norwich, is indicative that Man came here during the interglacial period immediately succeeding the glaciation which culminated in the Lowestoft ice advance. At Hoxne, adjacent to the Waveney valley, coeval interglacial lake beds studied by R. G. West have been found to contain successive zones of late glacial, early temperate, late temperate and early glacial vegetation.

No later ice advance appears to have left deposits round the broads, but the Gipping Till, spread over much of Suffolk following the interglacial of Hoxne and elsewhere provides evidence of a third glaciation in East Anglia. In Suffolk, also, R. G. West's investigation of the Bobbitt's Hole lake deposits near Ipswich has yielded knowledge of a further interglacial phase represented in the region. Finally, in the last glaciation of the Pleistocene to affect Britain, and in the early years of the ice retreat following, many changes in local topography were brought about through the gradual thawing of a deeply frozen land.

ZONES OF THE PLEISTOCENE IN EAST ANGLIA

(*features recognised in broadland are marked with an asterisk*)

Deposits are listed from the oldest to the most recent and the correlations given in parentheses refer to glacials and interglacials recognised in (1) north-west Europe and (2) the Alps. In some instances there is not full agreement over these correlations and they must be regarded as tentative.

CRAG: Waltonian, Newbournian, *Butleyan, *Icenian.

CROMERIAN INTERGLACIAL: *Cromer Forest Bed, Arctic Freshwater Bed.
(? 1st interglacial—pre-Elster, Günz-Mindel.)

LOWESTOFT GLACIATION: *Leda myalis* bed, *Cromer Till and *Norwich Brickearth, *Corton Beds, *Lowestoft Till.
(2nd glaciation—Elster, Mindel.)

HOXNIAN INTERGLACIAL: *Outwash and terrace gravels.
(2nd interglacial—Elster-Saale, Mindel-Riss.)

GIPPING GLACIATION: Gipping Till, *outwash deposits, *gravels.
(3rd glaciation—Saale, Riss.)

IPSWICHIAN INTERGLACIAL: Bobbitt's Hole Lake deposits. Freshwater Bed.
(3rd interglacial—Eeemian, Saale-Weichsel, Riss-Würm.)

HUNSTANTON GLACIATION: Hunstanton Till and *solifluction deposits.
(4th and last glaciation—Weichsel, Würm.)

It appears probable that the main river valleys of east Norfolk were cut during the interval between the Cromer and Lowestoft ice advances, when the sea-level was high; but many modifications have taken place since, during and between successive glaciations of the area. Advancing glaciers, melting ice sheets and alternating transgressions and retreats of the sea have again and again erased old features of the landscape and created new ones.

With the termination of the succession of Ice Ages a more settled era began, but as will be seen in the next chapter, further changes in the character of the broadland flood-plains have taken place in the post-glacial period.

CHAPTER 2

THE PHYSIOGRAPHICAL EVOLUTION OF THE EAST NORFOLK RIVER VALLEYS SINCE THE ICE AGE

by J. N. Jennings and Charles Green

Apart from the intense scientific interest of the varied plant and animal life of broadland, the general geographical pattern of the region has an individuality which intrigues the student of relief and drainage. There is indeed little in our country to compare in detail with the complicated pattern of winding rivers and associated stretches of open water found in the wide alluviated Norfolk valleys, and it is not surprising, therefore, that this region has been the object of recurrent discussion since the early years of the nineteenth century, with attention particularly focused on the problem of the origin of the broads themselves. There is not space here, nor is there need, to set out all the theories which have been offered to explain their nature. Many of the early theoretical conceptions ceased to have any real interest when officers of the Geological Survey mapped the rocks of this part of East Anglia in the closing decades of the last century. Their maps revealed that all the broads lay entirely in the formation called " alluvium," [1] or were at least held up on the downstream side by alluvium, even if along other sides their waters came into contact with the rocks of the upland, the Crag or the glacial drift. So it is clear that before we can consider the geographical status of the broads in any detail, we need some background knowledge of the structure and relationships of the alluvium itself, laid down in the latest division of geological time, the Postglacial. Chapter 1 brought the evolution of the physical geography of the region forward to this final critical phase, which now calls for consideration.

[1] Strictly speaking the term alluvium should be applied to deposits laid down on land by rivers, but it has come to be used in this country as a convenient ' portmanteau ' word for a variety of sedimentary deposits, which from their disposition relative to the glacial deposits, are known to have formed since the Pleistocene Ice Age.

Certain essential facts about the alluvium of the broads' valleys were already recognised at the end of the nineteenth century. First, mineral alluvium—clay, silt and sand—predominates in the seaward parts of the valleys. These are deposits of marine and estuarine conditions; indeed the inorganic mud shallowing Breydon Water today is typical of them. On the other hand, the inland parts of the valleys are characterised by peat, the accumulation of decaying plant material where it has been growing, and organic mud, the water-laid remains of plants and animals, sometimes calcareous. These are the deposits of freshwater lake, swamp and fen. This contrast is typical of coastal alluvial lowlands as, for example, the Somerset Levels, and is usually accompanied by a fall in general surface level inland from the coast. This is due to the fact that tidal range gets less in this direction and so salt-marsh clay may be built up on the coast to a high water mark many feet above mean sea-level. But the tidal range at Yarmouth Bar is only small and, because of restricted entry, is already reduced to four feet at springs at the head of Breydon Water. Thus the silty clay grazing marshes about Breydon at one to three feet above O.D. are at much the same level as the undrained peat fens farther up the valleys. However, between these two areas there are lower-lying grazing marshes at one or two feet below O.D.; this is due to the oxidation of surface peat after drainage. In this way a former peat cover has wasted away from many grazing marshes to expose the underlying clay.

A second major fact, which impressed itself early, was the considerable depth of alluvium to be found in these valleys; this was known from various well sinkings, excavations and borings for bridge foundations. Thus in a well for Lacon's Brewery at Yarmouth were found sands and clays down to 150 feet below O.D., which were interpreted as recent estuarine deposits. It is possible some part of these beds belongs to the Crag. Nevertheless Postglacial beds just behind Yarmouth reach down certainly to 69 feet below O.D. There were other undoubted deep records such as a depth of 39 feet at Potter Heigham railway bridge. The conclusion was that there had been considerable depression of the land in Postglacial time, drowning the lower parts of the valleys of the Yare and its tributaries and turning them into branching estuaries. More recent bores have shown the valley-bottom at Acle Bridge to be 63 feet, and at Ludham Bridge 41 feet, below O.D.

How extensive this transgression of the sea had been was less easily agreed upon. Some were inclined to think that the sea reached

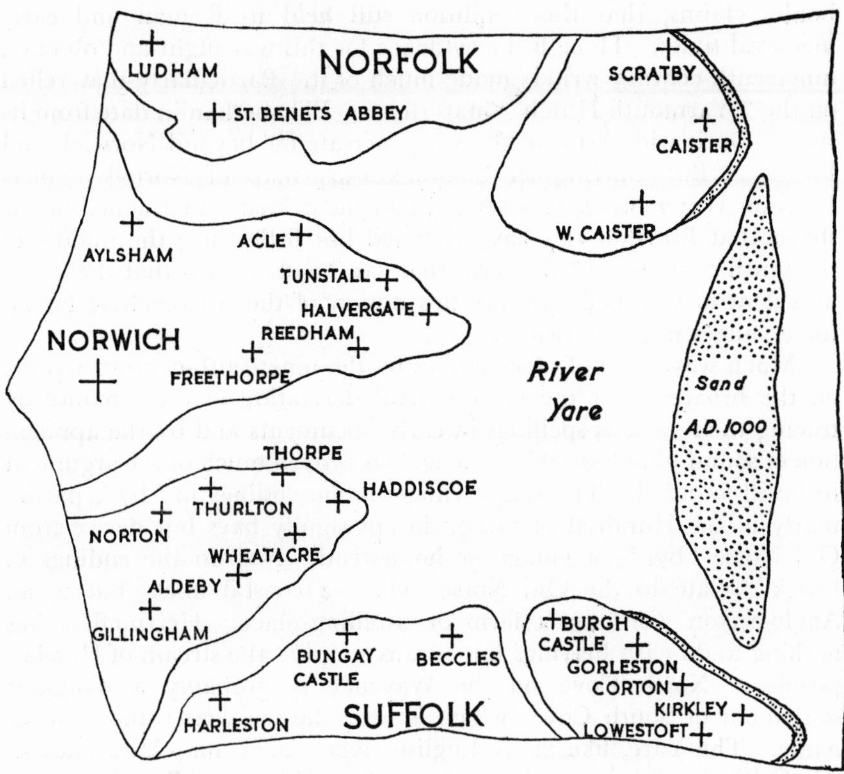

Fig. 1. Coastal outline and settlements from the Elizabethan "Yarmouth Hutch" map

over the whole of the alluvial flats at least as far up as Norwich, Bungay and Wroxham and that the sharp break of slope at the foot of the upland represented the old shoreline. Many visitors to the broads will have seen the map representing such a condition which has hung for many years in the porch of Ranworth Parish Church. Other investigators pointed to the completely fresh water and terrestrial nature of the peats found in excavations dug in the alluvium below these towns, e.g. in the Yare below Norwich. From this it was argued that the more inland parts of the broadland valleys were not reached by salt water, indeed had been merely fen.

During the last century there was also much discussion as to the time to which this estuarine state, extensive even in the conservative view, persisted. Many thought, as the map in Ranworth Church boldly claims, that this condition still held in Roman and early medieval times. Though the evidence for this was slight and obscure, nineteenth-century writers made much of it. Particularly they relied on the "Yarmouth Hutch" map (fig. 1), Elizabethan in date from its style. On it wide arms of the sea penetrate far beyond Norwich and Bungay. But Christopher Saxton's 1594 map of Norfolk depicts Breydon Water much as it is now, and the evidence mentioned below shows that Breydon can have changed but little since the middle of the ninth century. So the most that can be claimed is that there was prevalent in Elizabethan times this notion of the sea reaching far up these valleys not long before.

Much was made of place-names by the nineteenth-century writers on the broads. But the more careful derivation of these names by tracing their various spellings in early documents and by the application of sound philological knowledge has proved much of the argument to be ill-founded. The many village name endings in 'by', particularly in the Hundred of Flegg, do not signify bays but derive from Old Norse 'byr'—a village or homestead. Nor do the endings in 'wick' relate to the Old Norse 'vik'—a coastal inlet—but to an Anglo-Saxon word for a farm or dwelling-place. Herringfleet has nothing to do with herrings but means simply 'the stream of Herela's people'. North Cove on the Waveney is probably a daughter settlement of South Cove (which is near the sea coast) and took its name. The Yare, like many English river names, may hark back to the Celtic language and have a root 'gar', to cry. But the strong rush of ebb and flow of the Yare at its mouth is surely enough to explain it being called the 'roaring river', without any implication of the breaking waves of a great sea arm. The various 'holms' of the Bure and Thurne valleys, e.g. St. Benet's Holm, the 'ey' of Horsey, the 'ay' of Bungay, do mean 'island'. Yet very many examples scattered through England show that these place-name elements were as often used for small knolls in fens or partly surrounded by streams as for true islands. Most important of all, the place-name 'Breydon' itself serves to show, as has been said, that during the ninth century Breydon Water must have been in size and shape very like the Breydon Water of today. For 'Breydon' is a Danish name used also in Norway and Denmark to describe the 'broadening' of narrow rivers exactly as we now see it. As the Danish settlement in this area was made in A.D. 879 or within a year or two later, the condition of the old estuary must have already so changed that the areas of land and water cannot have differed much from those of today, except that the river Bure still found its way to the sea between Yarmouth and Caister-on-Sea by a dwindling channel known in medieval documents as 'Grubb's Haven' or 'Cockle Water'. Finally, in 1347, due to the changes which had taken place, this shallow shrunken channel was artificially closed and the river was diverted into its present-day channel which turns south near Caister and empties into the Yare–Waveney at the outlet from Breydon Water. Indeed it is probable that much of the Bure's water had already been flowing in this new channel, for that part of the Yarmouth Spit, which today joins Caister to Yarmouth Town, was already forming about the time of the Norman Conquest and must have impeded, as it grew, the direct flow of the river to the sea.

Until recently archæological sources had little evidence to offer. Earlier writers such as Blomefield mistakenly considered that the various 'burghs' well up the valleys—Burgh St. Peter, Burgh St. Margaret, Smallburgh and Tasburgh—had been Roman forts. These attributions were quite without real justification. But in the last few years a series of archæological and other excavations in the Yarmouth district (fig. 2) has provided evidence to transform our picture of these estuarine conditions. The first of these excavations, at Caister-on-Sea, has revealed the remains of a busy Roman port, a walled town which stood here from the early days of the second century to the latter part of the fourth. It seems to have had a sheltered harbour, not on the open sea coast, but on the northern shore of the estuary, a harbour where Roman ships could lie at anchor. On the southern shore of the estuary, a little farther from the sea than the Caister town, stood, and still stands, the Saxon Shore fort at Burgh Castle, which was built in the second half of the third century, and continued in occupation during the fourth. It appears to have been placed there to protect a naval dockyard which apparently lay in Belton Fen, a little to the south, where a sheltered creek would have provided the necessary facilities. By this time much of the estuary contained silt-banks, which were perhaps not all water-covered even at high water, but there seems to have been a channel from fort to town, linking the broad 'stream' of the Yare-Waveney with the more northerly one of the Bure, while between them at the seaward end, a 'middle ground' was slowly accreting. The completely water-filled estuary was by these times a thing of the past.

Other excavations within the line of the old Yarmouth town wall have shown traces of this late Roman middle ground. One in particular, cut to examine the foundations of the town wall itself, revealed

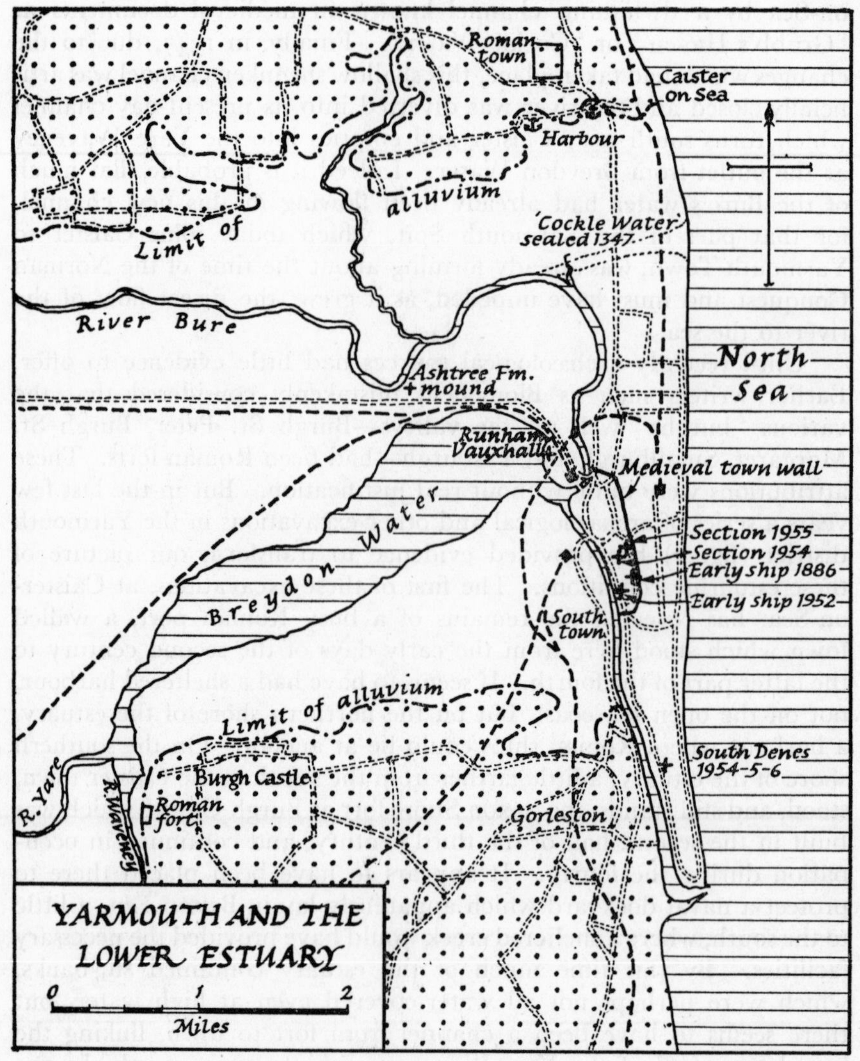

Fig. 2. Map showing the sites of the more important excavations in the Yarmouth area which have provided archæologically-dated evidence of the relative changes of land- and sea-levels during the last 2,000 years

that these foundations had been set in a band of silt laid down in late Roman times on a bank of sand which stood above the water at low tide. As this section of the wall was built about A.D. 1300, great changes must have taken place in the intervening thousand years. Farther south, near St. Peter's Church, excavations for a sewer exposed a Viking-type ship of Late Saxon days resting on a beach just above mean sea-level. In late Roman times this would still have been below mean sea-level and so the southern end of the Roman middle ground must have lain a little to the north. More recently the cuttings for another sewer running along the South Quay exposed part of another ship, apparently of the fourteenth century, which lay across a small bay in the eastern shore of the Haven. Just beyond, the contemporary shore lay exposed with a slipway for boats and the foundations for early buildings, all close to or at today's mean sea-level.

Most important of all have been the vast excavations for the water-cooling system of the new electricity generating station on the South Denes at Great Yarmouth. This work, carried out in 1954–6, has given ample evidence that, about the time of the Norman Conquest, the changes had continued so that a beach now well below low-water mark stood then well within the intertidal zone. But the full explanation of this and other evidence, which can only be explained by inferring changes in the relative land- and sea-levels, can better be discussed with other evidence from the river valleys.

The conception that geologists such as Woodward, Harmer and Gregory at the end of last century had of these changes was in terms of a single deep drowning of these valleys by land subsidence after the Pleistocene glaciation, with the alluvial infilling envisaged as a subsequent process. Even at that time the records from bores and wells demonstrated that the story had not been so simple, for peats were encountered beneath and in between clays and sands bearing estuarine shells. There had been halts in the subsidence, possibly reversals of that movement. But techniques suitable for deciphering the more complex sequence of events had not then been developed to their later pitch. The present century has seen the elaboration of new methods, which have found a particularly effective field in this study of Post-glacial deposits.

Perhaps most important has been the laborious but rewarding study of the micro-fossils of such deposits, the diatoms, the plant pollen and the foraminifera. Of these the greatest advance has come from studying the pollen content of peats and organic muds, most important because it provides a means of relative dating of deposits and events since the last Ice Age. The ordinary method of determining the relative ages of rocks is by the species of the fossils in them. As time has passed, the plants and animals have evolved from one form to another and so the rocks of each particular period of time have their own characteristic assemblage of fossil species. But in the Postglacial this method falls down because there has hardly been time enough for the extinction of old species and the development of new ones. The changes in flora and fauna in the deposits are brought about by migration in response to changing environmental conditions, not by evolution in the organisms. Of the vast amount of pollen and spores dispersed into the air from plants, most falls on to land and water surfaces. If they happen to be incorporated in growing peat deposits in bogs or fens, or in muddy sediments beneath water, the waterlogged conditions prevent their decay, at least of the outer walls which retain characteristic features and sculpture. As the deposits continue to accumulate, they will preserve through the pollen rain a record of the changing vegetation cover of the neighbourhood.

This record can be reconstructed; samples are taken at close intervals from top to bottom of the peats and muds which have accumulated, and by a series of chemical and mechanical operations the pollen from each can be isolated and mounted on slides for microscopic examination. The different kinds of pollen are identified and counted. For the Postglacial period in north-west Europe it is usually satisfactory to count all pollen and spores until a total of 150 tree pollen is reached, each of the tree genera or other pollen types being calculated as a percentage of the 150. The results from the different samples can then be plotted in graph form (fig. 6, p. 29) to show in an imperfect yet valuable manner the changing vegetation cover during the period of time represented by the deposit concerned.

The changes in vegetation are due to a variety of causes; simple plant succession unassociated with general geographical changes, changing level of land and sea in the case of coastal deposits, forest destruction by men, are all factors to be reckoned with in interpreting pollen diagrams. But it is clear from hundreds of diagrams from north-west Europe that certain sequences of changes are fundamental to all and can only be attributed to climatic change. As a result it is possible to divide up a pollen diagram into a series of zones, each characterised by certain proportions of the different tree pollen and corresponding to given phases of the climatic history and dependent forest history. In this way is obtained a relative time scale, which can be applied to other events than those relating to climate.

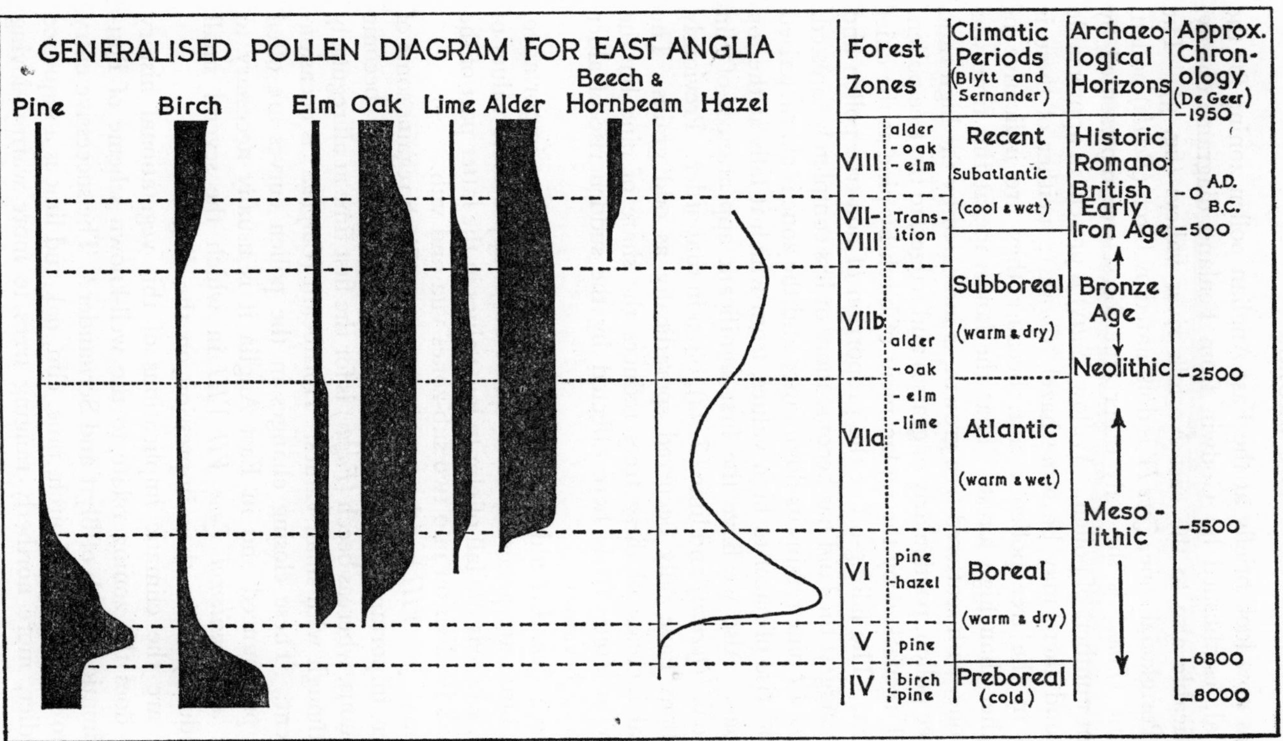

Fig. 3. Generalised pollen diagram for East Anglia for the Postglacial period, showing the forest zones correlated with archæology, Blytt and Sernander's climatic periods and De Geer's varve chronology (Based on Godwin)

Let us now look briefly at the East Anglian pollen zoning for the Postglacial, established by Godwin from Fenland diagrams chiefly, but applicable also to the east Norfolk river valleys (fig. 3). The earliest, Postglacial zone, *Zone IV* is dominated by birch (*Betula*) pollen, whilst pine (*Pinus*) is the only other true forest tree represented by significant numbers of pollen. Willow (*Salix*) is present in appreciable amount and there may be some hazel (*Corylus*); neither of these is included in the tree pollen count, because they are indicative of scrub rather than high forest. That the landscape at this time was an open one, with scattered tree growth, is indicated by the high ratio of non-tree pollen, particularly of grasses and sedges, to the tree pollen.

Zone V is marked by the replacement of birch by pine as the chief tree pollen. The falling-off of the proportion of non-tree pollen and of willow suggest the land has become more or less completely forested.

In *Zone VI* pine retains its dominance and the zone is characterised by a rapid rise of hazel to high values, from which it falls at the top of the zone. Also we have the first significant appearances of elm (*Ulmus*), oak (*Quercus*) and lime (*Tilia*), often in that order. Previously these pollens have only occurred sporadically as odd grains. The substantial increase of these trees reduces the share of pine but the transition to Zone VII is here effected by the sudden rise of alder (*Alnus*) to high values.

Through *Zone VII* alder and oak remain of greatest importance, pine and birch are generally low. Lime keeps appreciable values of its pollen, whereas the fall of elm to low values in the latter part of the zone allows its division into two sub-zones VIIa and VIIb.

The final *Zone VIII* has three main features. Birch regains some of its former importance, the lime curve declines and may become discontinuous, whereas beech (*Fagus*) is for the first time at all regularly present, though with small values. Hornbeam (*Carpinus*) is occasionally present. These closing changes in the pollen curves are often not very pronounced and in East Anglia it is usually necessary to recognise a *Transitional Zone VII–VIII* in which the several small shifts gradually make their impression on the diagram.

What are the climatic implications of this vegetational history and how does the zoning relate to the well-known scheme of Postglacial climatic periods of Blytt and Sernander? The successive entry and rise to importance of birch, pine, elm, oak and lime is a sequence from hardier, more northerly ranging trees to more warmth-loving ones. It is a reflection of climatic amelioration, of recovery from the cold climate of East Anglia during the last Pleistocene Ice Period.

Zone IV thus corresponds to the Subarctic or Preboreal division of Blytt and Sernander. Zones V and VI cover the Boreal period, with increasingly warmer but still dry and continental conditions. The sudden rise of alder, which follows, is not thought to be due to further increase in temperature, because it is not more exigent in this respect than some of the trees which expanded previously, but rather, from the alder's prevalence in damp habitats, to betoken a sharp increase in rainfall. So in Zone VII occurred the most favourable climatic conditions for forest growth; in the pollen curves this Postglacial climatic optimum is marked by the greatest values for lime, oak and alder, and the least for birch and pine. Zone VII covers the Atlantic (warm, wet) and the Subboreal (warm and dry) phases of Blytt and Sernander. Evidence for a dry Subboreal is not well marked in East Anglian pollen diagrams, though the decline of elm in the latter part of the zone may be interpreted in this way, since the elm favours wet, oceanic conditions. The decline of lime and the resurgence of birch in Zone VIII point to decreasing warmth, to the climatic deterioration and vegetational reversion of the Subatlantic (cool and wet) phase.

The pollen zonation provides only a relative time scale but it has been possible to link it with more precise time scales. Thus in western and northern Europe close correlation between pollen sequences and the archæological record has resulted both from chance finds in peat and by deliberate excavations. In northern Europe the relative time scale of the pollen history has been linked to Baron de Geer's geochronology, an absolute time scale based on 'varves' (annual bandings in clays laid down in lakes fed by glacial meltwater rivers). By such correlations rough dates in terms of centuries have been given to the forest history and these in recent years have found support from the C-14 dating technique based on the fixed rate of decay of radioactive carbon in fossil wood, peat and shells.

Knowledge of the stratigraphy, i.e. the vertical and horizontal arrangement, of alluvial deposits has also advanced in the last half-century through changes in technique; in particular systematic hand boring for scientific purposes has been resorted to instead of reliance solely on chance commercial bores and excavations. In Norfolk Clement Reid and M. Pallis were pioneers whose early efforts in this respect were not followed up for a long time.

By now the general arrangement of deposits in coastal alluvial lowlands in north-west Europe such as the fenland or north-west German marshlands is well known (fig. 4). Peats are intercalated with silts and clays; the latter wedge out landwards and the former

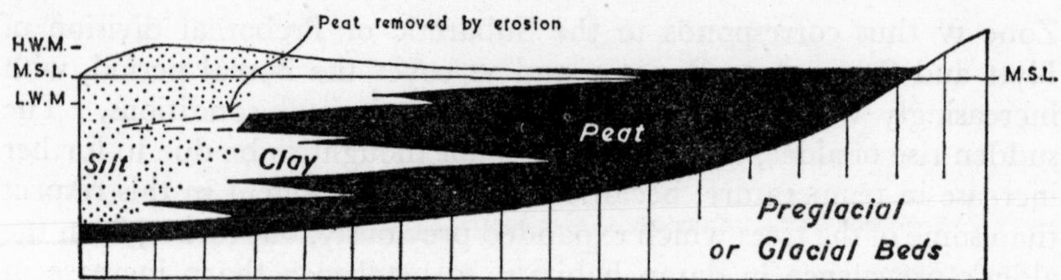

Fig. 4. Diagram to show typical arrangement of marine and freshwater deposits in the coastal alluvial lowlands of North-West Europe

peter out seawards. The clay and silt wedges represent phases of rapid submergence, or estuarine and marine transgression, whereas the extensions of peat over them indicate halts in the submergence, in some cases periods of emergence. The seaward parts of peat layers are often removed by wave erosion in a succeeding transgression.

Such an alternation of conditions is typical and it is now widely recognised that the oscillating changes in the relative level of land and sea in areas like north-west Europe, which were heavily glaciated in the Quaternary but which lie away from the tectonically unstable belts of the earth where mountain building is still in progress through folding and faulting, have been due to the interaction of two factors, the *eustatic* and the *isostatic*. The water locked up as ice in glaciers and icesheets comes ultimately from the only great reservoirs of water, the oceans; as the masses of land ice have extended or retreated, sea-level has fallen or risen in sympathy. The Quaternary Glacial Periods have been times of low sea-level, the Interglacials and Postglacial of high. These shifts in sea-level are called eustatic and are uniform in amount and simultaneous in operation throughout the intercommunicating oceans and seas of the world. In a second way icesheets affect the relative level of land and sea; they represent great loads on the earth's crust, which bows down beneath their weight, most of all where they are thickest. On the melting of the ice, the land recovers; but slowly and with some time-lag. These are the isostatic shifts of the land itself and they vary in amount according to distance from the main ice centres. From this it will be clear that the changes in the relative land- and sea-levels will differ from one place to another. Thus although the Postglacial changes have been worked out in considerable detail for the Fenland by Godwin, it would be wrong to assume that the story has necessarily been the same in the broads region only forty miles away. There will be much in common but they will not be exactly similar.

Sufficient general background has been given for a review now of the present state of knowledge of the Postglacial evolution of the east Norfolk river valleys; it is still very imperfectly known for only recently have beginnings been made in applying some of the modern techniques to the area.

Indeed the story must be begun outside broadland itself on the floor of the North Sea. From the early days of trawling on Dogger Bank, loose masses of hard, dark, fissile peat, known as ' moorlog ', have been torn by the trawl from the sea floor at depths of eighteen to twenty-nine fathoms. C. Reid examined several samples for the larger plant remains and identified birch, sallow and hazel amongst trees and a number of fen grasses, sedges and herbs. The peat undoubtedly formed in fresh-water fen and carr, with a more northerly climate than that of East Anglia today. Warmth-loving trees were absent and the dwarf birch (*Betula nana*) was present as well as the silver birch. These conclusions have since been confirmed and more closely defined by pollen investigators. Nearly all the samples have virtually no tree pollen other than birch and pine, sometimes with the former preponderating, more often with pine; thus they belong to Zones IV and V of the forest history, (*c.* 8000–7000 B.C.). One sample at nineteen fathoms from the Leman and Ower Banks, only twenty-five miles from the coast of broadland, is slightly later in age. Pollen counts show additionally high hazel values and significant amounts of oak; they can be referred therefore to the transition from Zone V to Zone VI. This sample is of particular interest because it was trawled from the same locality as a block of ' moorlog ', raised by the trawler *Colinda* and which broke open to reveal a Mesolithic bone harpoon of Maglemose type. Thus during Preboreal and at least early Boreal times the floor of the southern North Sea was a land of fens and of open birchwoods, replaced later by pine forests, over which primitive hunters and fishermen wandered freely from the continent to what is now the island of Great Britain. The sea lay north of Dogger Bank during this time. There is a thin peat bed at sixty-eight to sixty-nine feet below O.D. beneath the Breydon Viaduct, recently demolished which probably belongs to this phase.

Since ' moorlog ' belonging to later zones has not been dredged from the North Sea banks, it seems that the sea floor was submerged in Zone VI (c. 7000–5500 B.C.). In fact extensive submergence in late Boreal times has been established for various parts of the British coasts and of the continental shores of the North Sea. So widespread does it appear to have been that it is regarded as a eustatic transgression, a rise of sea-level the world over through the melting of the glaciers in their last big retreat to approximately their present extent. Furthermore when this rapid submergence slackened off in early Atlantic (Zone VII) times, it had brought sea-level nearly up to its present position and the North Sea had reached more or less its present size. It is likely that this sudden flooding of the southern North Sea basin in Boreal times made the climate of the surrounding lands so much more oceanic as to permit the quick rise to importance of the damp-

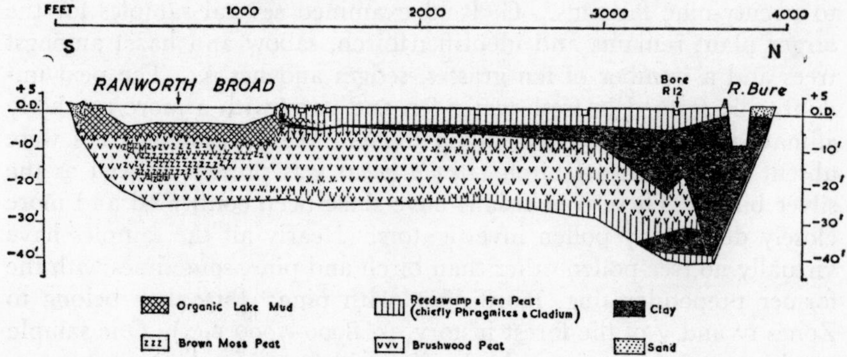

Fig. 5. Section through the alluvium of the Bure valley at Ranworth (Vertical exaggeration: × 20)

loving alder in their forest cover, a change reflected markedly in the pollen curves at the Boreal-Atlantic transition.

Let us now transfer our attention to some evidence from within broadland, to a section (fig. 5) through the Bure valley alluvium, running south from Horning Church to cross Ranworth Broad and a pollen diagram (fig. 6) from a bore near the river in this section. The oldest deposits occur in the deeper, narrow channel, cut into the flatter, broader part of the buried valley floor. At the bottom is a thin compressed peat; rather muddy and containing remains of the common reed (*Phragmites communis*), it betokens a swampy river course. The pollen diagram from the peat covers Zones V and VI and the beginning of Zone VII. During this time then, the river ran along a narrow, peaty channel between rising banks, whilst the wide valley floor and upland slopes were clothed first by closed pine forest with patches of birch, then the birch was replaced by hazel scrub and finally there came the invasion of mixed oak-lime-elm forest (largely to replace the pine) and of alder in the wetter parts.

Allowing for some compression of this peat, its great depth (its top is more than thirty-seven feet below O.D.) tells us either that the sea-level was very much lower than it is now or that the land was higher. Now the former assumption does not tally with the claim made a little earlier that water had returned from the ice-sheets to the sea sufficiently to bring sea-level practically to its present position in early Atlantic times. That the land itself has been moving is made clear if we compare the present level of the Boreal-Atlantic transition (Zone VI–Zone VII) boundary here at Ranworth at thirty-eight feet below O.D. with its level at three feet below O.D. in the Somerset Levels, in deposits which must have formed close to sea-level. Thus there has been tilting between west and east in southern Britain since the beginning of Zone VII (c. 5500 B.C.). In fact Godwin has shown that north-west Germany, Holland and the Fenland have been warped down compared with southern Sweden and the west of Britain in this period of some 7500 years. There has been isostatic depression of the southern North Sea basin and broadland has partaken in it.

Above the lowermost peat in the Ranworth section there comes a lower clay. This soft, grey-blue clay, with reed remains in its top and bottom parts, contains foraminifera, which show it formed in slightly brackish water. In the middle, large numbers of *Chenopodiaceae* pollen, often indicative of salt marsh vegetation, are found. Here is almost certainly the inland tapering end of an estuarine clay transgression. Up the Bure it reaches a little above Horning Ferry but farther upstream only organic muds, with fresh-water mollusc shells, are found in this deep channel. This confirms that the clay does represent a phase of rapid submergence of the valleys, which took place within Zone VII (*c.* 5500–800 B.C.) of the forest history, possibly early within this long period.

Submergence must have been checked, for in the succeeding phase peat formed over the lower clay, indeed over the whole valley floor. The stools of great oaks rooted in the mineral soil and their prostrate trunks were buried by it. In the Bure valley a great thickness predominantly of brushwood peat accumulated at this time. Alder fruits and wood, birch fruits, catkin scales, wood and bark, sallow leaves and hawthorn nutlets have been found in it. It is clear that for some time fairly dry conditions of fenwood or fen carr prevailed over the Ant and middle Bure valleys, though lenses of reed, sedge and moss peat testify to wetter patches from time to time in places.

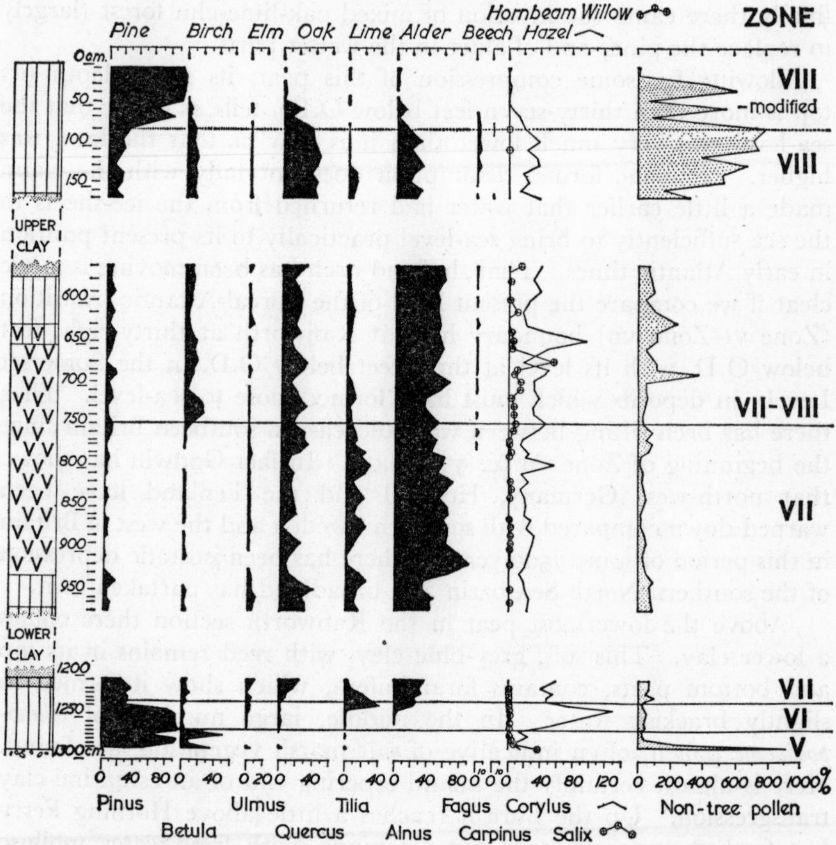

Fig. 6. Pollen diagram from bore R 12 at Ranworth (see fig. 5)
In stratigraphic column on left, vertical ruling represents Phragmites peat, V symbols represent brushwood peat. Each pollen type is expressed as a percentage of the total tree pollen

From the middle Yare valley many sections have a similar brushwood layer but certain of the more seaward ones have on top of brushwood peat much mixed peat, which includes abundant remains of sedges, of hypnoid and *Sphagnum* mosses as well as woody debris. So here the fenwood was replaced by herbaceous and mossy plant communities with only patches of carr. In the Breydon Viaduct foundations, peat encountered between sixteen feet and twenty-six feet below O.D. probably belongs to this same phase.

From the Ranworth pollen diagram the lower part of this peat is seen to belong to Zone VII; alder, oak and lime dominate the tree pollen, pine and birch are at their lowest ebb. But in the upper part birch recovers to become persistently substantial, lime declines in importance though maintaining continuity, beech comes in sporadically with small values. These are clearly the changes heralding the final Zone VIII, the Subatlantic period; at the very least we must allow for part of the Transition Zone VII–VIII (approximately 800 B.C. to 0 B.C.) before the close of the formation of this peat.

What happened to the relative land- and sea-level during this period? The contact of this peat with the lower clay beneath suggests a sea-level of about thirty-three feet below O.D. at the beginning of its formation whereas its contact with the clay above shows that the sea-level must have been about six feet below O.D. when it ceased to form. Thus there was a net rise of the sea relative to the land of the order of twenty-seven feet in this time. It is possible therefore to see in the great thickness of the fen carr peat the effect of continuous but very slow submergence from the isostatic factor mentioned previously. However the story may not prove quite as simple as this for Godwin has shown that there was a regression of the sea in the latter part of Zone VII around the North Sea. This contradictory eustatic fall in sea-level during part of the period of formation of the brushwood peat has to be reckoned with also, and the issue is not yet clear.

Whatever the answer to this question, there is no doubt that a phase of rapid submergence followed to bring in the upper clay of the Ranworth section, which is found to penetrate all the broads valleys. In its more inland reaches, this clay, locally called ' ooze ', is soft and unctuous, blue-grey and free from silt; as it is traced seawards, it becomes more and more silty and of darker hue. At the surface, this silty clay is often buff in colour or mottled buff and grey but this difference may be an effect of oxidation.

We may take its occurrence in the Bure valley as typical. From St. Benet's Holm seawards this upper clay fills the whole width of the valley to a considerable thickness of twenty feet or more and heavily compresses the peat beneath, though small embayments in the valley side such as the one in which Upton Broad is found and tributary valleys such as that of the Ormesby-Rollesby-Filby Broad are not penetrated. Where it is extensive and thick, the upper clay is rich in foraminifera, many of marine habitat though some tolerant of brackish water. More obvious is the fact that it is full of estuarine molluscs. As the spoil from dykes dug in this clay weathers out, there can be seen the shells of cockles (*Cardium edule*), periwinkles (*Littorina littorea*) and spire-snails (*Hydrobia ulvae*, *H. ventrosa*), furrow-shells (*Scrobicularia plana*) and finger-nail shells (*Macoma balthica*). The tiny and rarer *Retusa alba* has also been found. Thus at this time virtually the whole Bure valley about as far up as St. Benet's was open estuary; the Ant to a little way above Ludham Bridge was in a similar state and so was the Yare as far as Cantley.

Above these points, this latest estuarine transgression found a different expression. It is exemplified by the Ranworth section which reveals a deep channel beneath the Bure, reaching down through the brushwood peat to the level of the lower clay and filled in by this upper clay. Already the estuarine molluscs in it have become rare and foraminifera much fewer and all tolerant of brackish water. This deep clay channel is undoubtedly estuarine and it was no doubt the tide which brought up the mineral sediment to form the clay, but conditions were much less saline than farther down the valley. However tidal waters overspilled this narrow channel at high water and deposited fine sediment to the flanks amongst actively growing reeds. Thus were built low banks (seen as flanges in the section) of mingled reed remains and clay, a deposit known from its fœtid smell as 'bear's muck' in the Fenland. Since the reed is primarily a freshwater plant, though surviving under brackish water conditions, this *Phragmites*-clay indicates only the most attenuated of estuarine conditions and it is also a valuable index of former sea-level since it can only have formed near the high-water mark. As these flanges wedge out very generally at a rough level of three feet below O.D., it seems that this submergence brought sea-level to approximately that figure.

Up the Bure from Ranworth the clay channel has been traced, narrowing and shallowing. The flanges also become thinner and narrower; they are found on both sides of the river except where the meanders of the latter bring it directly against the valley side. Thus they underlie and conform to the width and arrangement of the little strips of marsh called 'ronds' separating the river from the broads.

What deposits belonging to the time of this transgression are to be found beyond the limits of the upper clay? If we neglect the broads themselves for the moment, the answer is simple; reed and sedge peats overlie the brushwood peats, as for instance across the full width of the Ant valley at Wayford Bridge. The wetter conditions in the valleys due to the submergence caused a reversion of the vegetation from fen carr to fen and swamp.

Beneath the upper clay at Ranworth there are some six feet of peat belonging to Transitional Zone VII–VIII or later and so the extremely recent date of the onset of this transgression is apparent. The transgression belongs to Zone VIII and in terms of years must have begun after 500 B.C.

To arrive at an idea of when the estuarine phase ceased here, we must consider the upper peat overlying the clay flanges of the ronds. It is not thick, five to six feet at the most, and is usually of reed (*Phragmites*) peat, though, where carr is growing on the surface now, a thin layer of brushwood peat has often formed beneath the carr. Turning to the pollen diagram from the upper peat at Ranworth, the lower part is typical enough of Zone VIII but at 80 cms. from the surface there is an abrupt change to almost complete pine dominance, all else falling into insignificance. Without doubt this final phase of the pollen zonation relates to the time of complete clearance of the natural forest of the upland, when hedgerow and plantation trees would supply most of the pollen rain. For this area we know from the Domesday Book that by the end of the eleventh century forest clearance was virtually complete. Yet the extremely high percentage of pine would seem to link this top 80 cms. to the centuries since Tudor times during which there has been planting of this tree.

But this does not define at all closely the end of this upper clay transgression, nor does it give a very full picture of the ensuing conditions. It is here that the archæologically-dated stratigraphical evidence from the Yarmouth district, summarised above, has proved so valuable. Several closely dated silt, clay and beach deposits, some yielding molluscs such as dog-whelk (*Nucella lapillus*) and mussels (*Mytilus edulis*) and acorn barnacles (*Balanus balanoides*) which define contemporary sea-level quite well, have served as fixed points in the sequence of events. These fixed points, in conjunction with other evidence, have made it possible to outline the story of the estuary during the last two thousand years, which is roughly the period of our written history.

The maximum of the upper clay transgression seems to have fallen in the first century B.C., though this has not yet been firmly dated. During this transgression period the clay-silt deposition in the roughly rectangular lower estuary took place primarily at its western end in the broad area between the two main streams where tide- and river-flow kept the channels clear. These banks assumed a triangular form with the apex creeping closer and closer to the sea (fig 7). Below this apex, in the mouth of the estuary a roughly kidney-shaped middle ground began to form. Then began a slow emergence of the land and

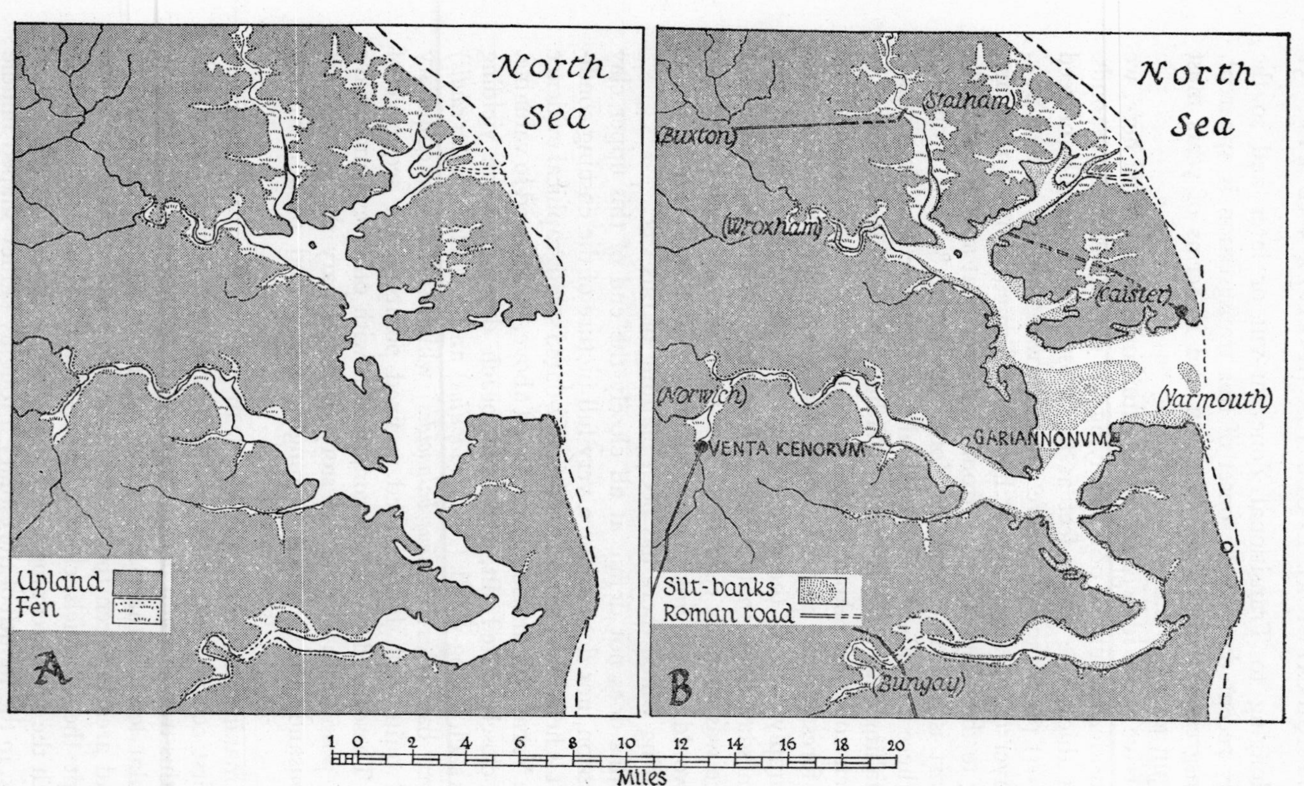

Fig. 7. The broadland estuary
A. The maximum extent of marine transgression in the Iron Age
B. Probable bank—and channel—formation in Late Roman times

the surface of the banks began to be lifted above the water, though the main channels for long remained comparatively unaffected, for the harbour of the Roman town was used throughout the Roman period and, indeed, well into Middle Saxon times, as the remains of a later settlement on the same site have shown. The presence of the Saxon Shore fort across the estuary shows too that the southern channel was also open in late Roman times and the communication between Burgh Castle and Caister suggests that the apex of the emerging banks had not yet joined the middle ground of the estuary mouth. A pagan cremation cemetery, apparently Anglo-Saxon, found many years ago at Runham Vauxhall, lay in the north-western end of the middle ground. Its date cannot be later than about A.D. 600 and the present-day levels make it clear that by that date emergence had so progressed that the land stood relatively five feet or more higher above sea-level than it does today. By the middle of the ninth century the upper silt banks had joined the middle ground as the name 'Breydon' has shown and the emergence was approaching its maximum height. The banks were dry and grass-grown and the eleventh-century Domesday Book shows that they were used as sheep pastures.

By this time the middle ground itself had become the site of the first Yarmouth town with seventy burgesses. North of the town, the sea was slowly building a rampart of sand and shingle against the seaward edge of the silt banks, gradually choking the outlet of the Bure. South of the town, from the tail of the middle ground, grew a long spit which by about A.D. 1200 had reached nearly to Lowestoft. This sealed the direct entrance to the southern part of the estuary, though river and tide kept open a passage between the shore and spit.

And then slow submergence began again. At first this must have been slight, for at the time of the great flood of A.D. 1287, a closely dated level in the South Denes has shown that, at that date, the land surface still stood some thirteen feet higher in relation to the sea than it does today. For a time, the submergence-rate accelerated and the local inhabitants built the banks, known as 'walls', which border Breydon Water and the rivers, in an attempt to prevent the flooding of their pastures. By the seventeenth century the land stood relatively no more than three to four feet higher than today and the submergence-rate was decreasing, a decrease which has continued until the present-day rate is no more than some six inches in a century and the level of the sea in relation to the land is rather higher than it was in Roman times.

Thus the alluvium of these east Norfolk valleys tells a story of fluctuating water levels and of estuarine transgression and retreat against a background of changing climate and vegetation. In Mesolithic times there are at first only narrow strips of swampy land along the rivers where peat and mud are forming, for the coast is as yet north of Dogger Bank and river gradients are still appreciable. Climate is getting warmer and first pine and hazel forests, later on oak and elm, replace more open birch woodland. Then the southern North Sea is flooded by waters from the retreating icesheets of north Europe and north America, and soon repercussions begin to be felt up the valleys. Climate becomes wetter and alder becomes important in the forest cover. And now with sea-level not far from its present mark, the valleys are liable to be flooded by the sea. Either in late Mesolithic or Neolithic times there is an estuarine transgression, depositing clay some way up the Yare and Bure. The sea regresses, but now peat formation is widely spread over the valley floors. The comparatively dry conditions of fen carr are prevalent for some time but it is clear that broadland is being warped down isostatically towards the North Sea basin. Perhaps a eustatic fall in sea-level is offsetting this to some degree during part of the Bronze Age. However the climate has begun to worsen slightly and the birch has resumed a little of its former importance in the forest cover, before submergence quickens and a second and greater incursion brings estuarine conditions and clay deposition much farther up the valleys than previously. This upper clay transgression, probably eustatic in character because submergence is widespread in western Europe at this time, must have begun in Early Iron Age times, reaches its maximum in the century before our era and begins to lessen in Romano-British times. Regression continues throughout the Anglo-Saxon period, and the land reaches its greatest relative height about the time of the Norman Conquest. During the earlier part of this regression, peat of fen and reedswamp once more forms over the clay of the middle valleys while the clay of the lower estuary is slowly lifted to become grass-grown pasture. Once again submergence begins, a submergence which has not yet reached its end. But the rampart of sand and shingle built across the estuary mouth during the Saxo-Norman regression has served to prevent direct transgression by the sea and the activities of modern man have preserved much of the valley-filling from reversion to waterlogged marsh. These various phases of the Postglacial infilling of the valleys have therefore left a pattern of interdigitating peat and clay, and it is in relation to this basic pattern that we must consider the problem of the origin of the broads themselves and the present surface features of the region.

To this end, recent studies of the distribution and relative density of ancient communities in East Anglia provide supplementary evidence. It has been shown that in pre-Roman days the East Anglian population was largely concentrated in the western half of the province, where the light dry soils provided land of the 'primary settlement' type. During this long period the broadland area was but sparsely occupied, with certain areas almost completely devoid of inhabitants. Even in Roman times, the pattern was not significantly altered, for the Roman town at Caister and the fort at Burgh Castle, both sited for specific topographical reasons, stood almost alone in the district. It was not until the Saxo-Norman emergence of this low-lying area was advancing and the Middle Saxon population of west Norfolk began to spread eastward, that a significant change took place. But the determining factor in making these areas the most thickly populated in England, as Domesday Book shows them to be, was the Danish settlement of the ninth century. It was largely to the broadland and Norwich area that these new settlers came, at a time when the emergence had left the area ripe for clearance and farming. And as the later studies in this book will tend to confirm, it was the descendants of these Danes and their English neighbours who, through domestic need of fuel after the woodland had been cleared, began the organised activities recounted below.

CHAPTER 3

THE ORIGIN OF THE BROADS

by J. M. Lambert, J. N. Jennings and C. T. Smith

It is now time to turn to the broads themselves—those enigmatical sheets of open water which lie in the flat, alluvial valley plains, surrounded by wildernesses of fen and carr. Varying in size from the well-known expanses of Barton and Hickling to the few secluded acres of Calthorpe Broad, their very existence poses a problem unmatched elsewhere in the British Isles, and challenges the imagination as to their place in the physiographical picture.

Somewhat paradoxically, this interest arises because the broads in fact belie their name: they are not as a general rule 'broadenings' of rivers, as the derivation from the Anglo-Saxon 'brædan' (to broaden) has been taken to imply many times in the literature. Breydon Water, it is true, does conform to this description, but it can hardly be considered a broad in the strict usage of the word. With its appreciable tidal range, its expanses of soft, black, estuarine clay exposed at low water, and its patches of salt-marsh, it is readily recognisable as the surviving part of an estuary, almost cut off from the sea by the sand spit on which Yarmouth stands. No essential difference exists between Breydon Water and, for instance, the wide reach of the Alde above Aldeburgh, partially isolated from the North Sea in a comparable manner by Orford Ness. Nor have we far to seek to find other examples.

In contrast, the broads in general lie away from the main rivers, either to the flanks in the major valleys (fig. 8)—the by-passed broads, we may call them—or in minor tributary valleys (fig. 9)—the side-valley broads. This point has been expressed emphatically by J. W. Gregory: 'Instead of the river passing through the broads, it kept sullenly aloof from them; as we sailed down the river there was broad to the left of us, broad to the right of us, broad in front of us, but by a series of ingenious twists and turns, it managed to wind through the whole lot of them, either eluding any direct contact with them or communicating only by a few narrow and overgrown passages.' It is this characteristic, combined with their occurrence in flat valley plains, with their surfaces only one or two feet above the mean level of the sea, which gives the broads their geographical individuality in Britain.

Despite the anomalous nature of the region as a whole, there is, however, a general consistency in surface features to be recognised between the river valleys themselves. The three chief broadland valleys—the Bure, the Yare and the Waveney [1]—all possess a lateral series of broads lying progressively farther from the rivers as the valleys widen downstream (Appendix, maps 1, 2 and 3), and a corresponding division of their flood-plains into drained and undrained regions. The similarity of pattern in these three valleys is further emphasised

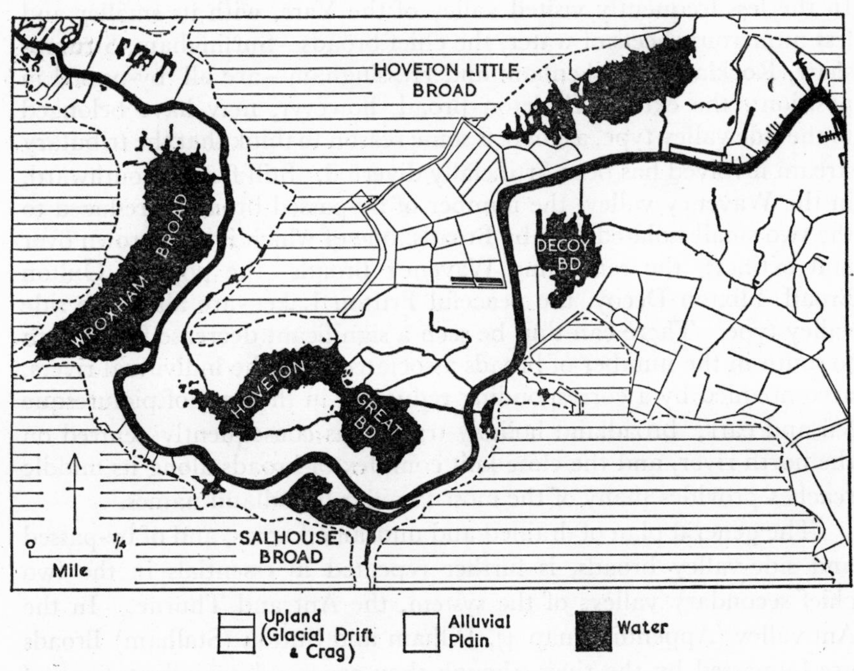

Fig. 8. By-passed broads of the Bure valley
(Open water areas from 1946 R.A.F. air photographs)

[1] Though the Waveney Broads lie just over the Suffolk border, they are few in number and essentially similar to the others; therefore the term ' Norfolk Broads ' is used with a little latitude to include them.

by the fact that the broads are normally confined to their middle reaches, though the north (Bure) and the south (Waveney) rivers possess also big downstream side-valley broads lying well back from their channels.

Within the general framework of this pattern, the valleys themselves show variations in the proportions of their individual parts, both in number and type of broads and in the amount of associated undrained land. Within the Bure, the most northern and best-known valley of the three, the broads are numerous and generally large (Pl. 11). Most of the broads of the Bure are of the by-passed type—Belaugh, Wroxham, the Salhouse and Hoveton Broads, Decoy, Ranworth and Upton; but side-valley broads are also well-represented by Burntfen, the South Walsham Broads, and the Ormesby-Rollesby-Filby series, with the small sanctuary of Cockshoot forming an intermediate type. In the less frequently visited valley of the Yare, with its smaller and less numerous sheets of water, the chief broads—Surlingham, Strumpshaw, Rockland, Buckenham and Hassingham—are all by-passed in position; the extinct Carleton Broad, however, may have belonged to the side valley type, as there is some reason to think that the tributary stream involved has been artificially diverted. Still farther southward, in the Waveney valley, the number of by-passed broads is reduced to the two small isolated Barnby Broads, one of which is now grown over and extinct; the remaining Waveney Broads—the popular Oulton Broad, Flixton Decoy, the peaceful Fritton Lake—are all of the side valley type. There can thus be seen a significant decrease from north to south in the number of broads associated with the individual rivers, accompanied by a corresponding reduction in the area of picturesque fen and carr; broadland holiday traffic has consequently centred on the north river, and the close-knit complex of broads along its middle reaches provides many of the most familiar broadland names.

The general plan of drained and undrained areas, and of by-passed and side-valley broads, is further repeated in essentials in the two chief secondary valleys of the system, the Ant and Thurne. In the Ant valley (Appendix, map 4), Dilham and Sutton (Stalham) Broads are by-passed by the river, though they occupy deep indentations of the upland making them almost side-valley in position; more typical side-valley broads are seen farther down the valley in Crome's and Alderfen Broads. But at Barton the relation of broad and river has been complicated by past artificial diversion of the main channel to run through Barton Broad itself; borings have revealed the former

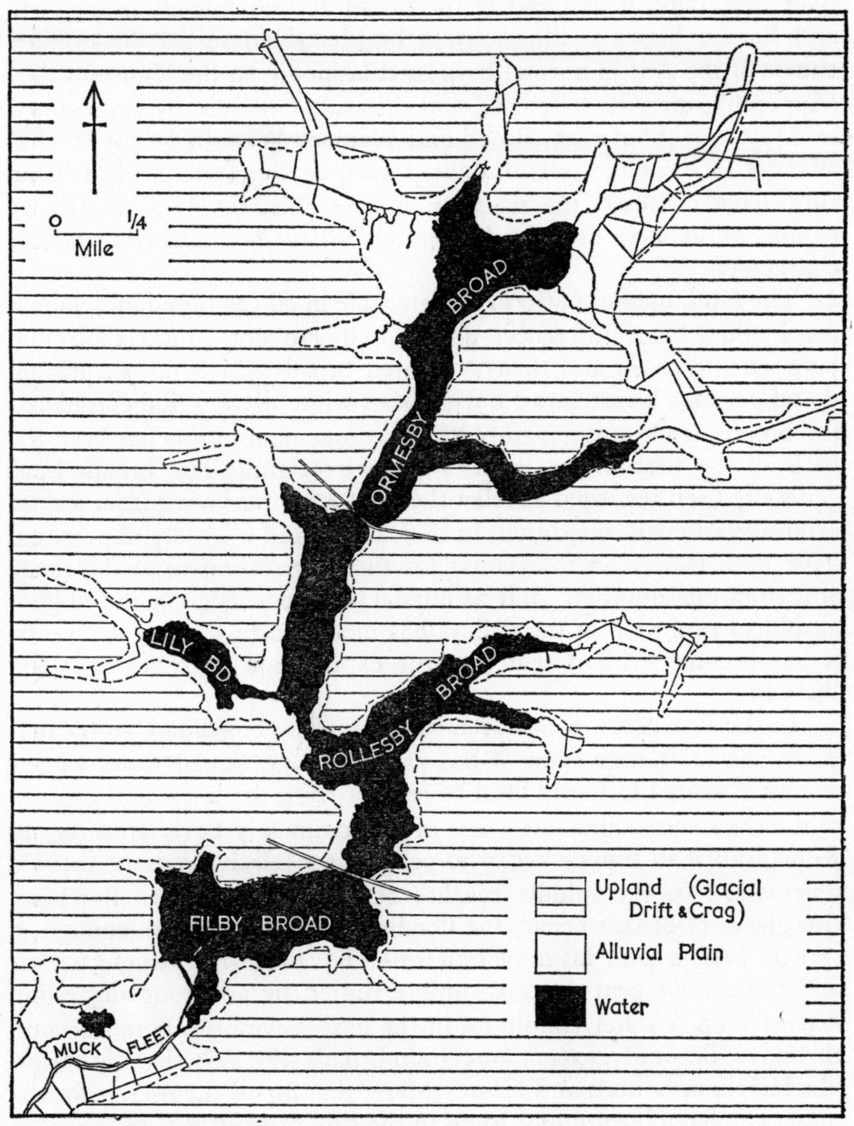

Fig. 9. Side-valley broads tributary to the Bure valley
(Open water areas from 1946 R.A.F. air photographs)

river bed, lying to the east of the broad and completely overgrown, and Barton Broad is thus seen to be placed lateral to the original course of the Ant in normal by-passed fashion. In the Thurne valley (Appendix, map 5), by-passed and side-valley broads are represented by Martham (Somerton) Broad and Womack Water respectively: but changes in drainage relationships, including the making of artificial cuts, have confused the situation in the Hickling-Heigham-Horsey region, while here the broads themselves have an unusually shallow character.

The fundamental pattern, recognisable in all the broadland valleys despite these lesser differences, points forcibly to some causal connection between the rivers and their associated broads. It is not surprising, therefore, that investigators have almost without exception considered the broads as natural geographical phenomena, and this has been the basis of the best-known theories of their origin. The broads have generally been regarded as relict sheets of water surviving from former extensive estuarine conditions in the valleys, and a variety of processes have been conceived to account for their separation from the rivers and from one another. But as our factual knowledge of the physiographical evolution of the valleys has increased in the last few years, it has become evident that the true explanation does not lie along these lines.

In the first place, it has been shown in the preceding chapter that no estuarine transgression of the valleys in Postglacial times was as extensive as had formerly been believed. Even the latest and greatest of the sea's encroachments—that of approximately Early Iron Age to Romano-British times—began to peter out a relatively short distance upstream. In the middle reaches of the valleys, where the main complexes of broads occur, the flooding was not complete enough to spread even a thin layer of estuarine clay over their whole width; and continuous peat deposits, uninterrupted by any zone suggesting extensive open water conditions in the past, have been found beyond this clay. Secondly, except for certain broads with very shallow basins, like Heigham Sounds and Horsey Mere, the broads themselves for the most part have been found to lie to the side or upstream of the main wedge of the estuarine deposits, or beyond the limits of the latter in embayments or in tributary valleys. The number of by-passed broads occurring in the major valleys appears in fact to be inversely related to the extent of former estuarine flooding, indicated by the lateral spread and depth of the clay, in the different valleys themselves.

Hence, by-passed broads are almost absent from the Waveney, where a considerable thickness of clay can still be found well upstream; but they are numerous in roughly comparable reaches of the Bure, where a generally less prominent clay horizon occurs.

We can therefore dismiss the idea of any deep and total flooding, at any phase in their post-glacial history, of the areas of fenland where the present broads now lie. From the detailed evidence which we now possess of the nature of the deposits in the immediate vicinity of the broads, a markedly different scene must be envisaged at the time of maximum invasion of the sea. There can have been no more than a tapering central channel of brackish water, entered by small lateral creeks, and flanked by stretches of reed and swampy fen. Interspersed with the latter were small, extremely shallow, reedy pools, but these were not comparable in the least with the present broads in either area or depth.

Since the stratigraphical facts definitely preclude any general origin of the broads by sub-division of former deep, continuous sheets of water, the basins of the various broads themselves must be regarded as distinct and separate units; in other words, each of the broads which we now know possessed an individuality in the past as well as at the present time.[1] In fact, they lie in hollows separated from one another by great stretches of solid peat, or peat and clay; and it is the relationship of these basins to the general alluvial deposits of the valleys which must next be considered.

The nature and shape of the basins of the broads have been determined by the same hand-boring methods used to reveal the sequence of deposits in the valleys as a whole (chap. 2, p. 13). Lines of close-set bores, carried across the whole width of the open water and into the fenland beyond, have shown that the bottoms of the basins normally extend deep into the alluvium below the horizon marking the level of the latest estuarine transgression. In certain cases, where the alluvium is shallow near the valley margins, the basins may reach right down to the original hard valley bottom, cut in glacial or earlier deposits, so that such broads have a gravelly or sandy slope on their landward side. Usually, however, the broads lie

[1] This does not apply to closely-adjacent broads which are known to have become separated by recent overgrowth of encroaching vegetation, as, for instance, Ranworth Inner and Outer (Malthouse) Broads, which were both part of one continuous sheet of water in the last century (Appendix, map 10). Broads such as these, though known under different names, are here regarded together as forming a single unit.

entirely within the alluvium of the valleys, with their basins walled by peat throughout.

The basins themselves are somewhat variable in depth from broad to broad. In the great majority of cases, the general level of their bottoms lies some ten to twelve feet below the surface of the surrounding peat, as, for instance, in Hoveton Great and Little Broads, Ranworth, Strumpshaw and Rockland, to mention but a few; in other broads, depths of up to, or even exceeding, fifteen feet have been recorded, and this is particularly characteristic of the big downstream side-valley broads, such as Fritton Lake and Rollesby Broad; others are definitely shallower, with maximum depths lying within the seven to ten-foot range (Alderfen, Sutton, Dilham and Calthorpe, etc.); while Hickling, Whiteslea, Heigham Sounds and Horsey Mere are shallowest of all, rarely attaining a bare six feet except where sailing channels have been dredged.

Within the basins are thick deposits of soft, uncompacted organic and calcareous muds, formed by the accumulation of the remains of aquatic plants and animals, so that the present depth of free water in the broads is generally very much less than that of their actual basins. Indeed, in all except the deepest of the broads, the muds now commonly reach to within four or five feet of the water surface, and in parts have been overgrown by encroaching vegetation—by reedswamp, fen and carr.

If we neglect for the moment the accumulated muds, and confine our attention to the shape of the peat-walled basins themselves, a number of striking and most significant features is immediately revealed (fig. 10). In the first place, the basins in general have been found to have virtually vertical sides, except in such places where their waters lap directly on the sloping margins of the valley: but even in these broads with a gravelly slope, vertical edges of solid peat can still be found on their other sides. In the great majority of broads, the original sharp edges are obscured by overgrowth of marginal vegetation, so that they have hitherto remained unsuspected and unrevealed; the abrupt lateral transition from solid peat to deep organic muds beneath the surface vegetation mat can, however, be easily shown by closely-spaced boring.

A second significant feature lies in the presence of steep-sided islands of solid peat in many of the broads. In spite of the fact that deep, oozy, unconsolidated muds impinge directly on all their sides, the deposits under these islands are compact, with their vertical sequence reflecting exactly that of the solid fenland adjacent to the broads. Islands of this nature, bearing reedswamp, fen or carr, can be seen, for instance, in Decoy, Rockland and Surlingham Broads (Appendix, maps 9, 15, 22) and in several others as well. Of still more common occurrence in the broads are well-marked peninsulas of compact, solid peat, projecting outwards into the open water and often continued as ridges below the water surface; and again, though they are steep-sided, with deep muds on either flank, they unquestionably continue the general stratigraphy of the marginal deposits. Peninsulas or ridges of this nature are found in so many of the broads that their presence may almost be regarded as the rule rather than the exception, and numerous examples may be seen in the set of appendix maps.

A close study of such maps, combined with evidence from air photographs and underwater soundings, has furthermore revealed the striking fact that these peninsulas and submerged ridges of peat appear as a general rule to run in strictly parallel lines across the broads, and usually lie approximately perpendicular to the valley margin. Equally significant, in broads where a parish boundary runs across their waters, sets of ridges may lie at a slightly different angle on either side of the demarcation line; an excellent example of this is seen in the oblique air photograph of Barton Broad (Pl. III), where the pattern of ridges, indicated by lines of patchy reedswamp straddling the open water from marginal peninsulas, shows a definite change in direction at the Barton–Irstead boundary. In certain cases, a ridge of peat occurs directly beneath the parish boundary itself. The Sutton–Stalham boundary, for instance, is marked by such a ridge in a long-overgrown part of the original Sutton Broad. Over a century ago, Samuel Woodward noted a similar ridge along the Barton–Irstead boundary in Barton Broad, while another has been reported along the Hopton–Lound boundary in Mill Water, upstream of Fritton Lake.

The widespread presence of vertical sides to the basins, instead of gently sloping margins, is sufficiently striking in itself to cast grave doubts on any theory of natural origin of the broads; these doubts are further heightened by the frequent occurrence of parallel peninsulas and ridges of peat within the basins, and by the fact that in certain cases they bear a definite relationship to historical parish limits. Instead, there is now strong reason to believe that the broads themselves are fundamentally artificial features, set in natural surroundings —in other words, that their basins represent entirely man-made pits, formed by deep extraction of peat (presumably for fuel) at some time

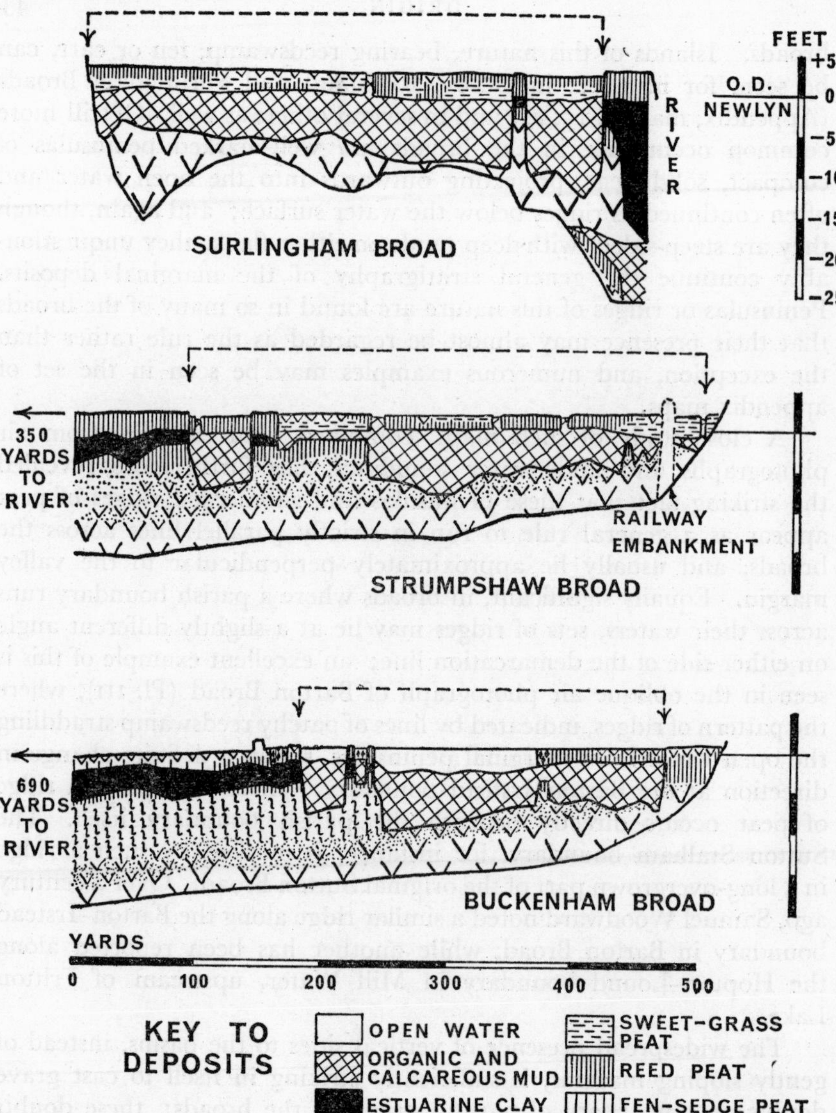

Fig. 10. (*a*). Simplified sections across the basins of three Yare valley broads (Vertical exaggeration—× 20; original limits of basins indicated by a broken line)

Note the vertical sides to the basins, and the islands and ridges of residual peat projecting from the basin floors. The Surlingham and Strumpshaw basins are now completely sealed in by surface peat from recent vegetation along the lines of the sections, while Buckenham Broad is partially overgrown

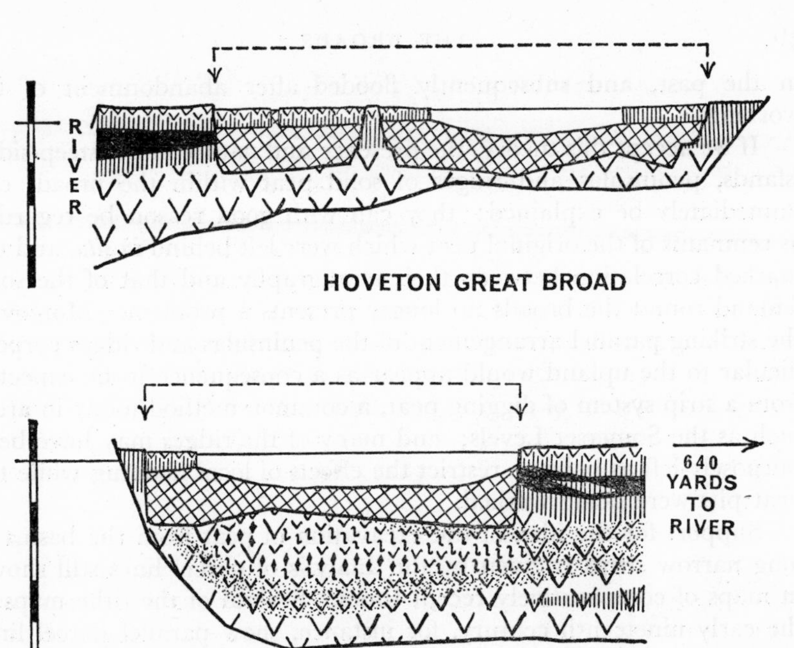

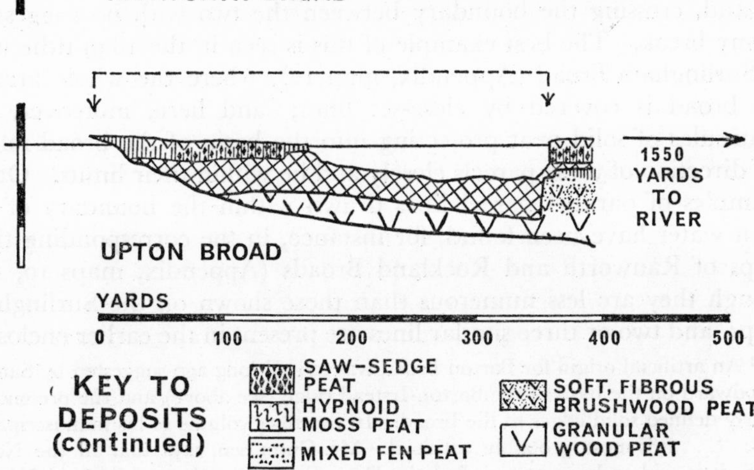

KEY TO DEPOSITS (continued)

SAW-SEDGE PEAT
HYPNOID MOSS PEAT
MIXED FEN PEAT
SOFT, FIBROUS BRUSHWOOD PEAT
GRANULAR WOOD PEAT

Fig. 10. (*b*). Simplified sections across the basins of three Bure valley broads. (Vertical exaggeration—× 20; original limits of basins indicated by a broken line)

Note that the left-hand side of the Upton basin impinges against the sloping valley side. Hoveton Great Broad and Upton Broad are both greatly overgrown, but Ranworth is still fairly open

in the past, and subsequently flooded after abandonment of the workings.[1]

If we accept this theory, the presence and nature of the steep-sided islands, peninsulas and ridges of solid peat within the broads can immediately be explained: they can with good reason be regarded as remnants of the original peat which were left behind *in situ*, and the marked correlation between their stratigraphy and that of the solid fenland round the broads no longer presents a problem. Moreover, the striking parallel arrangement of the peninsulas and ridges perpendicular to the upland would appear as a consequence to be expected from a strip system of digging peat, a common method today in areas such as the Somerset Levels; and many of the ridges may have been purposely left as balks to restrict the effects of local flooding while the peat pits were being worked.

Support for the idea of the excavation of peat from the basins in long narrow strips is given by the analysis of parcel lines still shown in maps of comparatively recent times. Several of the tithe maps of the early nineteenth century, for instance, show parallel parcel lines running across the open water of the broads as well as across the fenland, crossing the boundary between the two with no suggestion of any break. The best example of this is seen in the 1839 tithe map of Surlingham Broad (Appendix, map 12), where the whole area of the broad is covered by close-set lines; and here, moreover, the peninsulas of solid peat projecting into the basin of the broad follow the direction of these parcels closely and lie within their limits. Other examples of parallel parcel lines drawn within the boundary of the open water have been found, for instance, in the corresponding tithe maps of Ranworth and Rockland Broads (Appendix, maps 10, 15), though they are less numerous than those shown on the Surlingham map; and two or three similar lines are present in the earlier enclosure

[1] An artificial origin for Barton Broad was indeed long ago suggested by Samuel Woodward on the basis of the Barton-Irstead ridge (see above) and the presence of clearly defined solid edges to the broad. In the 1834 volume of his manuscripts he says: "... it is most probably artificial. Mr. Gunn Sen. says that in the Norris MSS. it is said to have been called the Deep Fen in the time of Edward III and may have become waters by the continued cutting of turf out of it. ... In fact the borders of the broad are an evidence of it, as they are one solid bank of turf of considerable extent before you gain the soil of high ground—a ridge is also left in the midst of the broad having at this time only about a foot of water upon it marking the boundary of the Parishes of Barton and Irstead—there was no appearance of the bank of turf on the sides extending itself into the water; but its edge appeared very clearly defined as kept in that state by art." There is no evidence, however, that Woodward considered the rest of the broads as other than natural.

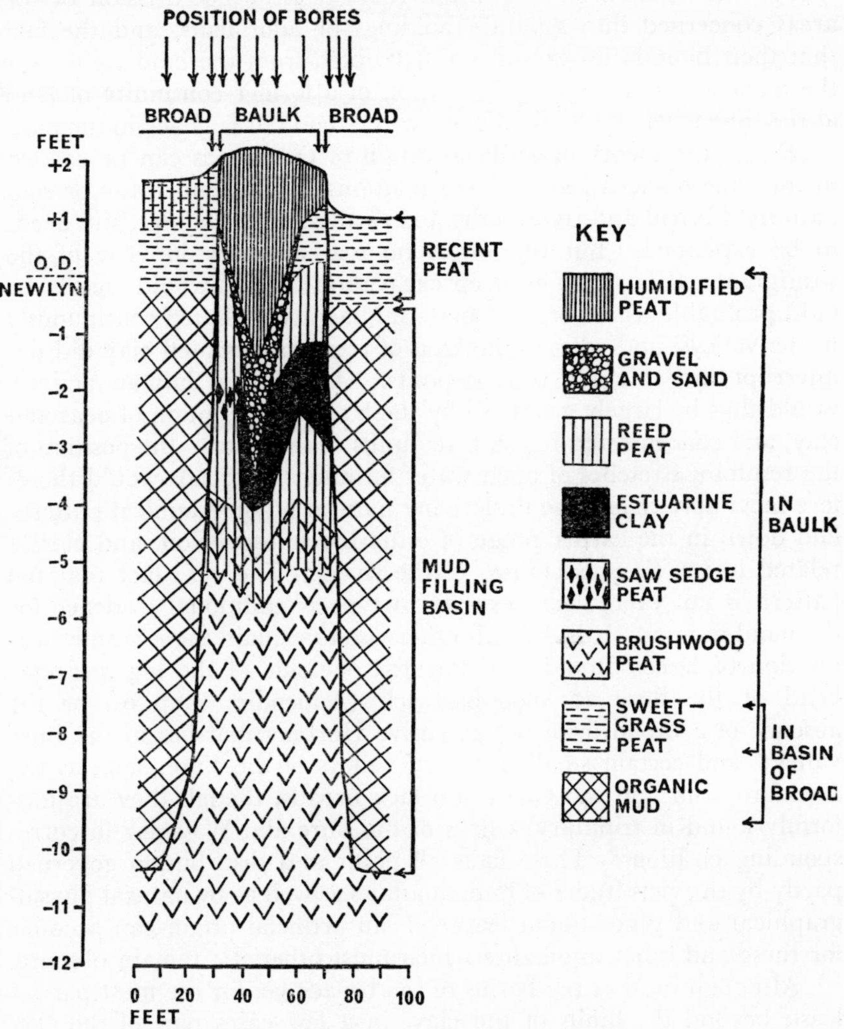

Fig. 11. Vertical section through one of the original peat balks dividing up the basin of Surlingham Broad
(Vertical exaggeration: $\times$ 20)

map of Barton Broad, though they are omitted from the tithe map itself. Such parcels are doubtless relics of a former division of the areas concerned into separate holdings or allotments, and the fact that their boundaries extend uninterrupted from the land right over the open water is a strong indication of a former continuity of land at the time when the original parcels were laid out far back in the past.

Before the theory of artificial origin of the broads can be carried further, the obvious geographical relationship inherent in the present pattern of broad and river, indicated earlier in this chapter, still needs to be explained. But this offers no real difficulty in view of the stratigraphical facts. The deep excavation of peat would clearly be most profitable where organic material had accumulated continuously in the valleys, and where a horizon of reed-impregnated clay did not interrupt the valuable peat deposits. Any site of human activity would thus be largely governed by the lateral distribution of peat and clay, and concentrated beyond the limits of the latter; the position of the resultant stretches of open water forming the broads would therefore inevitably reflect the underlying natural physiographical pattern, laid down in the earlier phase of estuarine transgression, and closely related to the sinuous courses of the rivers. The very fact that the pattern is not everywhere exactly to type is additional evidence for the hand of man. It is difficult otherwise to explain the asymmetrical position of Decoy Broad well towards one side of the big meander bend of the Bure at Woodbastwick (Appendix, map 9), or the absence of a broad from the extensive Horning marshes in the Bure valley; and certain small tributary valleys of the Yare, such as the Lackford Run and the Chet, also lack broads, though they are uniformly found in tributary valleys of the Bure and Waveney in corresponding positions. These facts all point to a distribution governed partly by the vicissitudes of human affairs as well as by natural physiographical and vegetational features: an artificial origin can account for these and other anomalies which must otherwise remain obscure.

Although most of the basins of the broads lie, for the most part at least, beyond the limits of the clay, in a few cases part of the clay flange has been found to have been cut through, leaving a truncated edge (fig. 11). In such cases, small isolated pockets of clay, apparently identical in composition with the clay of the flange itself, have been frequently found at the bottoms of the basins, resting on the solid peat below. It is difficult to explain the presence of these pockets, well below the natural stratigraphical level of the clay, and buried by deep mud, by any theory relying on a natural origin for the broads.

But they can easily be interpreted as waste material thrown down to the bottom of a pit during the excavation of the peat, and subsequently covered by accumulating muds after the pit had been flooded and abandoned.

The general nature of the deposits at the bottoms of the basins—i.e. at the junction of the muds and underlying peats—bears further witness to the general argument. In the deeper parts of the broads, the transition is generally marked by a layer, of varying thickness, of sludgy and disintegrated peat, mixed with some mud and contrasting sharply with the undisturbed peat below. This is exactly the deposit which might be expected to accrue at the bottom of a pit by the accumulation of peat debris during the course of digging. If the basins had been natural hollows, filled by a gradually rising water level during the physiographical evolution of the valley as a whole, we might well expect to find a horizon of reedswamp peat between the brushwood peats below and the commencement of the muds: this would register the gradual transition to the wetter conditions in the same way as the presence of a horizon of reed anticipates the onset of the estuarine transgression in the solid fenland around the broads. The absence of such a zone therefore suggests an artificial junction, at which the peat and mud became mixed by subsequent water movement.

Earlier in this chapter, it was mentioned that some of the broads may lie, in part at least, immediately against the inorganic rocks of the original glacial valley sides. In such cases, a sandy or gravelly bottom is generally found at the landward side of the broad, giving a superficial appearance of a natural sheet of water. Sloping margins of this nature are found in several by-passed broads—for instance, in parts of Salhouse and Martham Broads; and they are particularly characteristic of the big downstream side-valley broads of the Bure and Waveney—i.e. the Ormesby-Rollesby-Filby series and Fritton Lake. But the bottoms of such broads, away from the gravel margins, have been found to show an exactly similar transition from mud to undisturbed peat below as that already described, and one or more of the other features suggesting artificiality—steep-sided peat edges in other parts of the broads, islands or peninsulas of solid peat surrounded by deep lake muds, or pockets of clay at the bottoms of the basins—have also been found in every case. Steep-sided remnants of the original alluvial fill occur in parts along the sides of even the big side-valley broads, whose basins otherwise occupy the whole widths of their valleys and consequently follow the latter closely in outline; and here, moreover, the full complement of compact alluvium—again steep-sided, and with truncated strata—can be found stretching across the valleys immediately downstream of the basins of these broads. The sloping gravel margins can therefore most easily be interpreted as regions where the peat has been removed completely up to the valley side, with subsequent wave erosion of any residual debris, a process which can indeed be observed going on today in Salhouse and other broads. The presence of such margins therefore offers no serious obstacle to the idea of artificial origin of the broads, and the theory can be extended to cover the partly gravel-lined basins as well as those sited entirely in the peat.

The idea of artificial origin gains further support—if in a negative way—by the very difficulty of visualising any natural geographical or ecological process which could have produced, in the well-nigh perfectly flat alluvial plains of relatively limited extent, natural depressions in the alluvium of the magnitude of the basins of the broads. Where flood-plains are marked by natural embankments or *levées* of inorganic deposits, built up by river or estuarine watercourses, the formation of large lakes can readily arise. But such *levees* are lacking in the present surface of the broadland valleys, and the great areas of solid fenland which lie round the broads today are remarkable for their very level surface, with local variations of less than a foot in height. As we have seen, the inorganic deposits of the latest estuarine transgression, which alone could have provided a natural process to account for the lakes, are interrupted or truncated (and thus post-dated) by the basins of the broads in many places, and this transgression therefore cannot have been concerned in their formation. Moreover, for the deep hollows in the peat holding the water to have been formed by natural means would involve the postulation of a most uneven growth of peat over the flood-plains of the valleys in the past: and such irregularity, in areas where peat accumulation is dependent on ground water, is contrary to general observation.

Even, however, if the stratigraphical facts, as well as other evidence, all point to the conclusion of deep peat digging in the past, the practicability of the hypothesis must still be estimated. Anyone familiar with the waterlogged areas round the broads today may well question whether such depths as twelve or sometimes fifteen feet below the surface could ever be attained in early historical times by relatively primitive tools and in the absence of modern pumps. It is a matter of common experience among local marshmen that excavations made in the undrained fenland today, for cutting of dykes or other purposes, rapidly fill with water before any great depth is reached. How, then, can we visualise great peat pits in the past of the size of even the smallest of the broads?

At the present state of our knowledge, the question of ways and means must for the time being remain a matter for speculation. But if we try to reconstruct the probable conditions in the fenland between the limits of the time when the pits could have been made, there seems no inherent impossibility in the idea. The great thickness of muds accumulated in the basins of the broads argues against assigning too recent a period for the origin of the broads: but on the other hand, from the established relationships of the basins to the natural deposits of the valleys, the extraction of peat must obviously have post-dated the period of estuarine transgression by a considerable time, since compact peats overlying the clay flange, as well as the clay itself, have been found to have been cut through. At the time of excavation, therefore, the main regions of operation must have already been separated from the free water of the rivers by a wedge of impervious clay. But whereas the latter is now dissected by numerous man-made dykes, which allow free access of river water to the peat areas beyond the clay, it is possible—and, indeed, most probable—that the clay wedge was still intact and formed an effective barrier at the time when the pits were made.

Moreover, the archæological and other recent data from the Yarmouth region (chapter 2, p. 13) has indicated strongly that the Early Iron Age to Romano-British transgression of the sea up the Norfolk valleys was followed by an appreciable drop in sea-level relative to the land. We have seen that these accumulated data in fact suggest that mean sea-level in Saxo-Norman times lay more than ten feet below its present value, an estimate which accords well with a similar estimate by Dr. H. Godwin for the nearby Lincolnshire Fenland. Lack of marked humification in the broadland peats disputes an upstream drop in water level of similar magnitude, but nevertheless a medieval mean sea-level of several feet below that of the present day would probably be reflected in some measure in the middle reaches of the valleys. Not only would tidal effects in the valleys be diminished and surface flooding eliminated, but the general fenland water table may have been lowered to such a level that only the more compacted deeper layers of peat fell within its range: since this 'compression peat' is far less pervious than the looser surface layers, lateral seepage into the pits would thus be relatively slow. The exact conditions in the fenland at the time when the peat was dug have still to be worked out in detail, but the evidence seems to be tending towards a period of less waterlogging in the past.

The possibility of digging peat to a depth of several feet even today in broadland regions is often underestimated. Provided the area is isolated from tidal flooding, practical experience has shown that depths of several feet can often be attained in places where the general water table is only a foot or two below the fenland surface. For instance, an ornamental swimming-pool was excavated in the Hickling marshes to a depth of more than eight feet entirely by intermittent hand labour without the use of elaborate pumps, with the men working well below the level of the water in the nearby dykes: indeed, the landowner concerned suggests that depths of twelve feet or more could easily have been attained. Similarly, it is reported that little trouble with lateral water seepage through the peat was encountered when the Lound reservoirs were dug out upstream of Fritton Lake, though the base of the workings lay well below the surface level of the lake: most of the water accumulating in the excavations in fact came from a small stream entering at the western end and from springs on the exposed valley sides.

Apart from questions of tidal flooding and lateral seepage, the early peat diggers would have to reckon with drainage water from the marginal upland: but this could be diverted relatively easily by a catch-drain, and the dykes which now run along the valley margins may repeat such earlier drains. Rainwater falling directly into the pits, and ground water seepage outstripping the removal of the peat, could have been dealt with by very primitive baling methods, such as the ladle-and-gantry still in use in the peat workings in the Somerset Levels: simple methods such as these, if maintained regularly in operation, here make it possible to keep deep diggings of fairly large size sufficiently well drained to work even today.

But even if we assume that former conditions in the fenland were more favourable for deep digging than at the present day, there is still considerable evidence that seepage was not negligible and that only limited depths could be attained. The remarkably constant depth of ten to twelve feet established for the basins of the great majority of the broads is sufficient in itself to suggest that beyond this depth conditions generally became too difficult for further excavation, even though good peat deposits could still be found below; and it is significant in this connection that the deepest broads are found in the downstream side-valleys well away from the rivers and separated from the latter by a great stretch of clay; while Dilham, Sutton and Calthorpe Broads, which are found well upstream entirely or practically beyond the limits of the clay, are relatively shallow. The continual struggle against flooding of the pits is also emphasised by the presence of the parallel ridges of peat found in so many of the broads. Though certain of the smaller ridges may be merely relicts of the method of strip-cutting of the peat, in other cases, a narrow bank of peat stretches right across the whole width of the broad, suggesting a sectional excavation of the basin and a deliberate leaving of a balk of solid peat to delay flooding from one section to another. Continuous balks of this nature are seen, for instance, in Surlingham, Wheatfen, Hassingham and Hoveton Little Broads (Appendix, maps 12, 15, 16, 8), and although they are now cut through by narrow channels, the latter were probably made at a later period when the basins had become completely flooded and the resulting sheets of water were subsequently opened up for navigation and trading purposes. Solid bars of peat, with their surfaces only just below the present water level, have also been found at the mouths of individual branches of the great Ormesby-Rollesby-Filby system of broads, suggesting that these were excavated independently and their waters only later linked.

Detailed investigation of some of the steep-sided, solid balks of peat by boring have shown a further interesting feature contributing to the general picture which has gradually been assembled. Sections through two of the balks which stretch from the valley margin out into the now overgrown part of Surlingham Broad (Appendix, map 12) have revealed a layer of disturbed and compacted peat, mixed with much sand and gravel, lying a little below the present surface level, and hidden by recent peat and surface vegetation (fig. 11). In the centre of these balks, the peats below this layer are much consolidated and compressed, giving a V-shaped profile across the width of the balks. This obviously suggests that they were used as causeways by the workers at the pits, with the sand or gravel strewn to give a better surface, and with the depressions in the centre bearing witness to the heavy traffic along them. Patches of sand or gravel have similarly been found on or near the tops of solid balks in other broads, in positions where they cannot be explained by any theory of natural deposition: but they are easily interpreted as the relicts of former causeways by analogy with the evidence from the more closely-investigated Surlingham balks.

Indeed, the whole picture, as far as the evidence can be pieced together, is one of considerable human activity in the fenland of the past. The question may now arise as to why such deep excavations for peat were made, in view of the great areas of available surface peat, which could presumably be dug with much less difficulty and effort. The answer probably lies, at least in part, in the better combustible quality of the peat at the lower levels. Whereas the surface deposits consist predominantly of fairly fresh remains of reed and sedge, often with a somewhat muddy matrix, at the lower depths the compact, humified brushwood and fen peats were uncovered. Brushwood peat, when extracted in bulk, is of a close-set, cheesy consistency, lacking the fibrous coherence of the upper peats, but not impossibly difficult to handle; it has an obviously superior fuel value to the reed peat at the surface, and may well have provided economic returns well worth the extra effort in extraction. Moreover, in some areas, particular land-holders may have exhausted their own surface peats and been compelled on this count also to dig deeper: and it is interesting in this connection that in the big downstream side valleys, near the formerly thickly populated 'settlement islands' of Lothingland and Flegg, most of the peat appears to have been removed in its entirety down to the critical level controlled by water seepage.

The thick deposits of mud now found in the basins of the broads are a clear indication that the deep excavations must have been abandoned and filled with water a long way back in the past, and the question of cause and effect in this is by no means certain at present. Whether the pits became so full of water by increasing rate of seepage or by some catastrophic flooding that they became unworkable, or whether the decreasing demand for peat made deep excavation no longer profitable, is not so far revealed. We know, however, that the use of surface peat from the Norfolk valleys for local consumption, as distinct from the deep digging, was continued up to very recent times, even up to the beginning of the present century. Successive maps and old records, together with evidence from borings, show that a great deal of the fenland between the broads has been superficially cut for peat at one time or another. Strips of fenland left by one generation became the site of activity for the next, and it is even possible that certain areas may have been cut over more than once after an adequate interval for the reforming of the peat. The typical 'turf-ponds' formed by surface digging were generally less than four feet deep, though the areas covered by many of them were often as large as those of the deep excavations forming the broads themselves, as, for example, the huge, shallow cutting known as 'Broad Waters' which formerly covered much of Woodbastwick Fen (Appendix, map 9). In many cases, moreover, the superficial cuttings extended directly from the edges of the deeper basins, enlarging the area of their water surface, as in parts of Hoveton Little Broad (Appendix, map 8).

In contrast with the deep basins of the broads, which can only become colonised afresh by fenland vegetation when the mud deposits have accumulated to within four or five feet of the water surface, the shallow 'turf-ponds' become rapidly overgrown, and form relatively impermanent features of the landscape. This contrast is well seen in the series of maps of Woodbastwick Fen referred to in the previous paragraph. On the western side of the fen lies the deep basin of Decoy Broad, which has persisted with little change of outline from the time when it was made; but the large, shallow turf-pond of Broad Waters, lying in the fen to the east of the broad, and probably much more recent in origin, has been completely eliminated, except for dykes and occasional pools, within the course of the last century.

In certain broadland areas with thick and extensive clay deposits, the latter has been removed in bulk as well as peat. For instance, in the Thurne valley, where clay covers much of the valley width, the chief broads extend beyond the peaty areas into the clay flange itself. The shallow basins of Horsey Mere, Martham Broad and the Hickling-Whiteslea-Heigham series, all partly circumscribed and underlain by clay, are very different in nature from the deep peat-walled basins of the majority of the broads. The presence of steep clay edges to the downstream parts of these broads shows that here clay was removed in some quantity, and leads one to suspect that digging of peat for fuel may not have been the sole, or even the primary, reason for the making of these particular basins. The clay which was extracted appears to have been fairly pure and reasonably free from reed, and many uses can be conjectured for it.

Although the facts so far established are overwhelming in their insistence on an artificial origin for the broads, any conclusion which involves the past activity of man on such a scale cannot be regarded as complete without some measure of support from documentary and other human sources. For any historical inquiry into the origin of the broads the existing histories of the area are singularly unhelpful, and there are few hints that the broads might not have existed at any time in the historical past, or that turf-cutting ever played an important role in the economy of broadland. Even Walter Rye, that most industrious of Norfolk antiquarians and local historians, or Francis Blomefield, his illustrious predecessor, failed to unearth material which might have led them to speculate on the origin of the broads. Indeed, most local historians have simply *assumed* that the broads were natural features existing through historical time as part of the local background. As such an assumption, for example, may be cited Dr. Augustus Jessopp's imaginative picture of the region at the time of the Black Death in 1349: but little weight can be placed on such descriptions unsupported by primary documentary evidence, suggesting the actual presence of the broads.

It is necessary, first of all, then, to ask how old the broads are? The work of the early cartographers is inadequate for our purposes. The county surveys of the sixteenth and seventeenth centuries are on too small a scale and their methods of survey are essentially too approximate for any *negative* evidence they offer to be reliable. The presence of a broad on the early maps is certainly positive evidence of its existence, even though its exact shape need not be taken too seriously; but the absence of many of the broads on maps made as late as the middle of the eighteenth century cannot be regarded as evidence that they did not exist. Saxton showed Fritton Lake and Ormesby-Rollesby-Filby Broads on his map of 1574; Morden added Oulton Broad and two others in the seventeenth century. But an estate map of South Walsham shows the existence of the broad there with much the same outline that it now has, as early as 1668, and a plan of the Island of Lothingland made in 1584 shows that Oulton Broad, Fritton Lake and Flixton Broad not only existed, but also had very similar outlines to those which they still have.

In the absence of cartographical evidence one turns to the use of the word '*broad*'. Its first general use is usually ascribed to Sir Thomas Browne in his writings on the natural history of Norfolk (*c.* 1670), but it was already well established by then and had been in current use for over a hundred years in legal documents and the like. Barton Broad is referred to in an Elizabethan rental, when Simon Tobye paid 12d. rent for 'three acres of fishing in Barton Brode'. A 'broading pasture' and parcels of 'turffe and water-ground' abutting on the 'Broden' are noted in a survey book of South Walsham made in 1566, and from internal evidence in the survey they must have been immediately south of South Walsham Broad and Ranworth Little Broad. Although the word was sufficiently familiar by the sixteenth century to find its way into legal documents, it is very occasionally found at an earlier date. Thus an extent of a manor in South Walsham made in 1315 refers to the existence of a pasture at *Brodingge*, and towards the end of the century there is an interesting reference to the 'Flasshes' in South Walsham, suggesting the existence of a fairly large body of standing water.

References to valuable fisheries are of interest in suggesting the

Plate I Wheatfen Broad. *Glyceria maxima* fringing Fen Channel

Plate II *Above*, oblique air photograph of part of the middle Yare valley, looking south-south-west. Surlingham Broad — foreground; Rockland Broad — distance *Below*, oblique air photograph of part of the middle Bure valley, looking east-south-east. Wroxham Broad — left foreground; Hoveton Great Broad — centre; Salhouse Broad — right mid-distance

existence of lakes before the word 'broad' became current, but very often the location of the fisheries is difficult to pin down. In Barton Turf, the manor of Bartonbury Hall contained three valuable fisheries according to a survey of the manor of 1572. One was in the stream coming from Stalham towards Barton, but the other two were called Buryallewater and Seyveswater. They were 'below the town of Barton'. Barton Broad was then divided into parcels of fishing rights, as we know from Simon Tobye's three acres of fishing, and it is clear that Buryallewater and Seyveswater represented such parcels. The only possible alternative would have been the stream which enters Barton from the east and forms the parish boundary between it and Neatishead, but this can be identified as a fishery called Burwodeswer which is mentioned in the fifteenth century accounts of Bartonbury Hall. But both Buryallewater and Seyveswater were being rented out for their fishing at 8 shillings a year as early as 1415–35, so that Barton Broad was pretty certainly in existence even then. Similarly, a lease made of the manor of Lathes in Hoveton St. Peter in 1536 included 'all that water and fishing in Hoveton and Neatishead called Bronfenn', and the fact that the present Burntfen Broad is still shared by these parishes suggests a common identity of site. There is also an earlier mention of this fishery in a fifteenth-century account roll of St. Benet's of Holme, so that there is a definite indication that Burntfen Broad existed in the sixteenth century.

In documents of the seventeenth and eighteenth centuries the broads, or parts of them, are often described as 'waterground' 'fen and waterground' or 'water and marsh' and such terms are, indeed, still current. Thus, although Surlingham Broad was referred to as such as early as 1608, men continued to refer to it as Surlingham Fen (1675) or as 'fen and waterground' in glebe terriers of the early eighteenth century. Formulæ of the same kind were, however, used much earlier, and appear to suggest the existence of a relatively permanent water-body rather than the shallow, temporary ponds resulting from superficial turf-cutting. Evidence of this kind suggests the existence of Wroxham Broad or part of it in 1483, Snape's Water in 1551 (mentioned again in 1628) and Brimbelow Water east of Wroxham Bridge in 1501. A pool in Bodham Carr in Hoveton St. John and another to the south have had a continuous existence from at least the sixteenth century to 1841 in the latter case. There are also earlier references to 'water and Marsh' which it is impossible to identify precisely on the ground, e.g. in Hoveton St. John in 1413 and 1464, or in Wroxham in 1484.

In sum, the maps, the use of the word 'broad', references to fisheries, and references to 'waterground' or 'water and marsh', make it possible to identify a number of broads for the first time in the fifteenth century. Barton Broad, Wroxham Broad, Ormesby-Rollesby-Filby Broads, Burntfen Broad, South Walsham Broad, probably Heigham Sound and a number of small broads in Hoveton St. John can be identified in this way. Part of South Walsham Broad can be identified even earlier in 1315.

It is of importance, therefore, that there is no concrete evidence of the existence of any broads at all before the fourteenth century. There are no certain documentary references; there are no large Domesday fisheries in the area, and where they can be identified, fisheries of the twelfth and thirteenth centuries have proved to be river fisheries and eel-sets. Nor is there any archæological evidence to prove the early existence of the broads, and the place names of broadland yield only slight evidence, mostly of a negative kind. It has already been pointed out in chapter 2 that many broadland names, quoted by nineteenth-century writers as showing early evidence of open water, have no such significance when sound philology is applied. In fact, no broadland village bears a name which would definitely indicate the presence of a nearby sheet of water when the area was settled by Danish or Anglian farmers; in contrast, the individual broads are often named after the parish in which they lie, or have late names, and this is an interesting feature in itself.

To set against this curious absence of medieval references to the broads before the late fourteenth and fifteenth centuries, there is abundant reference to an important turf industry in the twelfth, thirteenth and fourteenth centuries: the medieval description of Barton as Barton *Turf*, for instance, signifies at least a local reputation for that commodity. Moreover, though it is difficult to locate exactly the location of medieval turf-land or turbary within the boundaries of the parishes and manors where it existed, there is no doubt that the extraction of turf constituted an important activity in all the broadland parishes for which there are records of the period. There was, of course, some turbary in places where there are no broads now, representing either the extraction of peat on a smaller scale, or the acquisition of turbary in broads parishes by places which did not possess alluvial deposits of peat within their own neighbourhood. At Ormesby, for example, there were tenancies in the early fourteenth century which included parcels of turbary which lay in Rollesby. Sometimes the references to turbary occur in places where broads are suspected to have existed in the past, e.g. at Thurne.

In all, evidence drawn from account rolls, court rolls, deeds, leases, surveys and extents, indicates the existence of turbary or of turf production at some twenty places in the thirteenth century and twenty-nine in the fourteenth. Of the twenty mentioned in broadland as a whole in the thirteenth century, fifteen are in parishes which now contain broads; of the twenty-nine mentioned in the fourteenth century, twenty-five now contain broads. Obviously a list of this kind cannot be exhaustive, but the concentration of medieval turbary in the broads parishes is significant, particularly when one notes also the absence of turbaries or turf production from the lower valleys of the Bure, Yare and Waveney, where the clay flange of the most recent marine transgression widens out to cover the whole width of the valley floor.

The earliest references to turbary are of the twelfth century and are contained in the Register of the Abbey of St. Benet's of Holme. For the most part they consist of the granting of rights in turbary, meadow, pasture, wood and the like which accompanied the grant of arable land to the abbey, but this was not always so. There are twelfth-century records of disputes relating to turbary in Hoveton parish, and there are indications that the turbaries, even in the twelfth century, were well-defined and specialised areas devoted entirely to the production of turf, rather than merely rights to cut turf over land which was also used as pasture or mowing meadow. In this the medieval turbaries of broadland differed from their fenland counterparts where superficial cutting on a large scale over a wide area was accompanied by alternative use of the same land as pasture. In broadland, the areas from which the best quality brushwood peat could be dug at depth were smaller, and this must have encouraged the digging of deep pits from a very early date. It is obvious that no other form of land-use would have been possible under these conditions. Turf-pits are, indeed, mentioned in a variety of places. At Neatishead, for example, the mention of Alderfen Pyttes in 1209 not only confirms the early existence of deep cutting but also suggests most strongly the origin of Alderfen Broad. Turf-pits are mentioned at South Walsham in the thirteenth century and at Burgh. The sale of tree-trunks from the turbary in the Southfen at Martham in 1320–1 tells us that the cutting of turf there had certainly reached down to the brushwood peat. Since the only fen which lay to the south of the village of Martham and Martham Hall was at the northern end of

Ormesby Broad it is reasonably certain that here, at least, turf was being extracted from turf-pits which are now covered by the waters of Ormesby Broad.

In order to have created the basins of the broads, covering altogether an area of some 2600 acres, the extraction of turf must have continued intensively over a long period of time. It is not difficult to conceive of a substantial demand for peat in medieval Norfolk. Even by Domesday the woodland of east Norfolk had been cleared to a great extent. Norfolk and Suffolk were the most densely populated counties of England at the time of the Domesday survey, and the Flegg Hundreds and Happing Hundred, in which the deepest broads are now to be found, were the most densely peopled parts of these counties. In the fourteenth century the tax assessment of 1334 and the poll tax returns of 1377 indicate that Norfolk still maintained a strong lead in population and wealth, and the details of the 1334 tax assessment confirm that Flegg and Happing Hundreds in the east of Norfolk were still well above the average for the county as a whole. Norwich was among the largest towns in the country from the eleventh to the fourteenth centuries and Yarmouth had a tax assessment in 1334 which was comparable with that of Norwich. Moreover, Domesday reveals a remarkable concentration of salt-pans in east Norfolk along the coast, in the lower valleys of the Bure and Yare and Waveney, and in the neighbourhood of what are now Ormesby-Rollesby-Filby Broads. Even though the salt industry yielded prime place to that of Lincolnshire in the later Middle Ages, salt-boiling must have used fuel on a large scale, and the only fuel available in large quantities was the turf of the broadland valleys. Turf was preferred for the evaporation of salt in the medieval Low Countries, and in Lincolnshire the produce of some turbaries was reserved for use in the salt-pans, so that although there is no direct evidence of the use of peat in east Norfolk, there is a strong presumption that it was the fuel most used.

Broadland turf was transported both to Yarmouth and Norwich, and possibly farther afield. Lists of tolls levied at both of these places in the fourteenth century include payments for the carriage of turf by water or by cart into the towns. Norwich Cathedral Priory used turf on a large scale, particularly in the kitchens, where as many as 400,000 turves were used in a single year in the early fourteenth century. The demand for fuel, either by a dense local population or for a salt industry of considerably more than local importance, or for large nearby urban populations, must have weighed heavily on the very limited timber supplies and on local resources of turf.

There is scattered evidence of large-scale production of turf from a number of places. At South Walsham, for example, a series of account rolls of the second half of the fourteenth century reveal that the average annual sale of 200,000 turves a year yielded an income of £7 a year. The St. Benet's turbaries at South Walsham also yielded a useful income of 14s. 2d. in 1240. In one year in the fourteenth century the Hoveton turbaries belonging to the abbot of St. Benet's produced twenty-six lasts of turf or 260,000 turves and towards the end of the century six of the lord's tenants in the manor of Moorhouse in Hoveton St. John were fined for taking thirty-nine loads of turf from the lord's fen without licence. Hoveton turf was being taken by water to Ludham in large quantities, even though the costs of transport over some eight or nine miles raised the price of turf by about a third.

Figures quoted above represent mainly the sale of surplus turf over and above that which was required for domestic purposes within the villages themselves, but in a few places, figures are available of the amounts or values of the tithe turves. On the assumption that the tithes represented a literal tenth of all that was produced it is possible to assess roughly the amount of turf produced. On this basis it is clear that at Martham production was approximately 105,000 turves a year in the early fourteenth century; at Hemsby, which also includes part of Ormesby Broad within its boundaries, tithes were worth an average of fifteen shillings a year in the late thirteenth and early fourteenth centuries, with a maximum of twenty-three shillings in 1294–5. Prices prevailing at Hemsby over the period were a shilling a 1000, so that these revenues would represent an annual production in the whole parish of 150,000 turves a year. In Suffolk, the values of the tithes of turf are known for occasional places in 1341. Here too, production was on a large scale, representing a probable annual output of as much as 300,000 turves a year at Oulton, for example.

Figures of this kind make it clear that the digging out of sufficient turf to create the basins of the broads was by no means an impossible task at the rate of production of the order prevailing in those places discussed above. Allowing a little for the waste of turf and the normal practice of leaving balks of turf, and assuming that one turf was equivalent to a quarter of a cubic foot, the basins of the broads concerned could have been dug out in a matter of three centuries. Such calculations are, of course, hypothetical, but they make it clear that the creation of the broads, large as they are, was by no means an impossible task for the hands of medieval men to have accomplished.

Medieval account rolls and tithe records testify to the significance of turf in the economy of medieval broadland, and deeds, leases and surveys have much to tell us of its importance as one aspect of a varied land-use. It is clear that in some places for which the documents have survived the turbary land was of considerable extent even in relation to the arable holdings. Thus, at Burgh and Rollesby in the late thirteenth and early fourteenth centuries, the proportion of turbary to arable holding was of the order of twenty per cent. At Hoveton St. John a holding of some seventy-two acres of arable was accompanied by rather more than thirty-six acres of turbary in 1305. At Martham, at roughly the same date, the proportion of turbary to arable was forty per cent and most of this was in the Southfen. It is clear from the abuttals by which the location of turbary was described in many places that it was normally held in strips similar to those of the arable fields in shape, and similar also to the strip holdings of ' waterground ' noted in eighteenth-century terriers, or to the strip holdings marked on some of the tithe award maps of the mid-nineteenth century.

The transition from turbary to broad appears to have been a long and slow one. Where there are continuous records of turf production during the fourteenth century, as there are, for example, at Martham and Hemsby, production declined, particularly after 1305, and at Martham the end of large-scale production of turf came in the early 1340's. From 1342 onwards turf production was in small quantities and spasmodic; the cathedral priory's share of the tithe turves of the parish was worth nothing except in very occasional years of the second half of the fourteenth century. By the end of the century turf was being bought outside the manor, though some turf deposits at a place called Medwesykes, probably now represented by the fen to the north-west of Ormesby Broad, were being exploited for domestic fuel. Even before the 1340's, turf had become more difficult to extract and more expensive in labour, and in occasional years money was expended in the scouring of the turbary. There is a very similar increase in the cost of producing turves at Hemsby from 1305 to 1341, and there is a hint that here too, turf production was being maintained in the face of a growing threat from standing water in the old turbaries. At Martham, in fact, a fishery is mentioned for the first time in the Southfen in 1340, and reappears regularly in the accounts to the end of the century.

The suggestion of a growing menace from flooding is also apparent at South Walsham. Towards the end of the thirteenth century there was a substantial decline in the yield of the turf-pits which has no counterpart in declining yields in other facets of the manorial economy and therefore appears to reflect a real change in the conditions under which the turbaries were being worked. At South Walsham the first suggestion of the existence of a broad comes in 1315, by which time the turbaries had declined in value considerably from their heyday in the third quarter of the thirteenth century. By the end of the fourteenth century, turf production had ceased entirely, the reed-beds of the abbot of St. Benet's in South Walsham could not be cut because they were flooded with water, and the 'Flasshes' had appeared in a place which must represent roughly the south-east corner of South Walsham Broad. It is clear that in these scattered references we are witnessing the birth of one of the Norfolk Broads.

Normal methods of cutting turf involved simply the cutting of peat to suitable blocks with specialised spades from an open face or from a trench. But at several places there is some evidence at the end of the Middle Ages that peat was extracted from the floors of shallow lakes and was loaded into boats or rafts. The instrument used was the *dydle*, a rake or metal ring with a bag net attached, at the end of a long pole. It is still used for cleaning out ditches and watercourses. The dydle was certainly being used in Hoveton from the middle of the fourteenth century, for the costs of their repair were being included in grange accounts of St. Benet's; and they were being confiscated from peasants who had illegally dug their peat from the lord's marsh. And there is no doubt that it was being used at Barton in the fifteenth century as a scoop to extract peat from the floor of Barton Broad, which was certainly in existence by then. Turf production with the dydle continued there until at least the middle of the fifteenth century.

In the parishes around the Ormesby-Rollesby-Filby Broads, the cutting of peats from a clean dry face seems to have been succeeded in the first half of the fourteenth century by a stage in which the dydle was used in combination with rafts or boats, but turf production ended far earlier than at Barton Broad or at Hoveton, probably because the depth of the basins, and therefore the depth of flooding, was much greater. If this interpretation is correct, the menace of flooding must have been apparent during the fourteenth century, if not before. A long and losing struggle was fought against the difficulties produced by standing water in the turf pits during which new techniques, notably the use of the dydle, were adopted. By this means production could continue until the levels of flooding made the floors of the turf-pits inaccessible, so that turf production went on longer in shallow basins like that of Barton Broad than in the deep basins, such as those of the Ormesby-Rollesby-Filby Broads, where the floors were now too deep to reach by the dydle and where much of the turf had been entirely removed from the sides of the basins as well.

Contemporary chroniclers and hints from other sources indicate that occasional floods had swept the area in the late thirteenth century and early fourteenth. In 1287 flooding affected Yarmouth, Hickling and St. Benet's Abbey and must have been serious farther upstream. Perhaps it was this sea flood that created difficulties which are expressed in a decline of turf production at South Walsham. Flooding in the decade 1300–10 and again in the early 1340's created new problems, probably bringing to an end the large-scale production of turf at Martham and Hemsby.

By then many of the broads were certainly in existence, and the turbary which played so significant a part in the life of medieval broadland was rarely mentioned. Indeed, in a few places the documents permit one to reconstruct the change from turbary to broad. The individual parcels of a small broad in Hoveton parish called Snape's Water can be identified in detail in the early seventeenth century. The ownership of these parcels can be traced back to the sixteenth century, when they are described as ' water and marsh '. In 1524 one of them is designated ' turbary or marsh ' recalling a use of the land which even then had almost been forgotten. But at the end of the thirteenth century when the documents relating to this piece of property begin, it had all been described as turbary. The once productive turbaries of St. Benet's Abbey were broads, or parts of broads, described as fisheries, or ' water and marsh ', when they passed into the hands of the Bishop of Norwich in the sixteenth century.

The evidence of the documents confirms and extends the field evidence from stratigraphy. The picture so far pieced together appears to fit the established facts too well for the essential truth of the outline to be open to serious question. Vertical edges, steep-sided islands, parallel balks, pockets of clay out of place; irregularities in general pattern, anomalous areas; relict parcelling of present-day sheets of water, with medieval counterparts in a similar parcelling of turbary; the regression of the sea in Saxo-Norman times and the influx of a substantial population including the Danish invaders; absence of early medieval references to the broads; the existence of medieval turf-pits and of turbary in a large number of places with broads now in them; the former production of turf on a large scale; the flooding

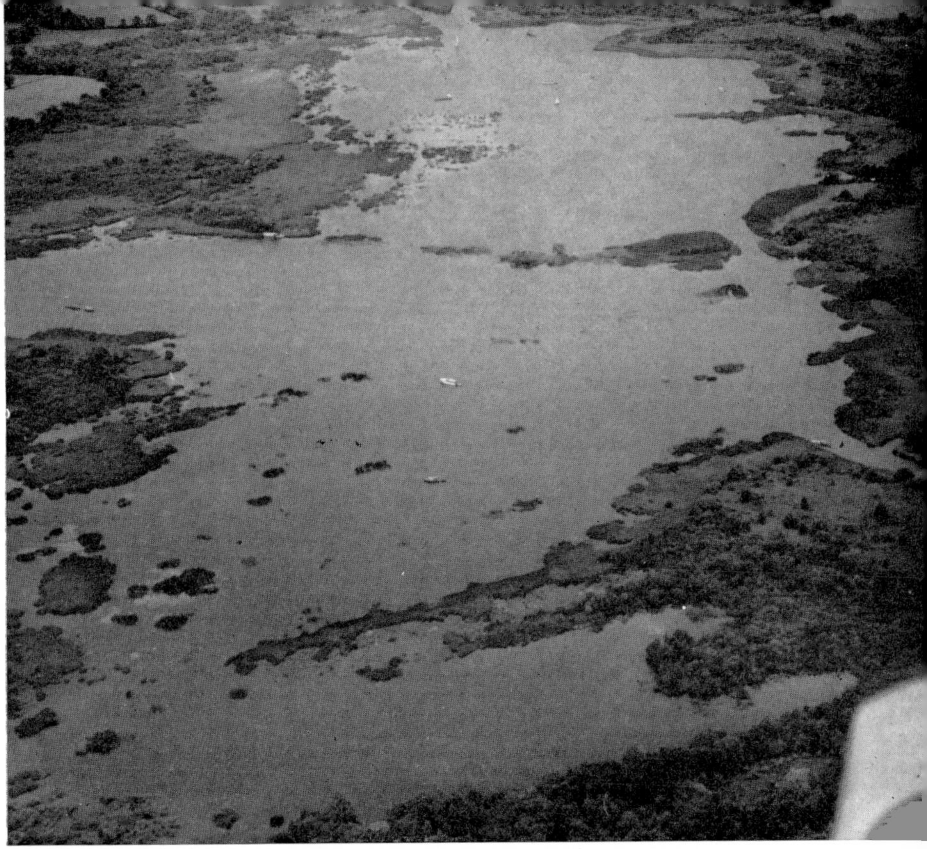

Plate III *Above*, oblique air photograph of Barton Broad, looking north, and showing broken lines of reedswamp and fen marking the positions of old parallel peat baulks across the broad: the lines run in a slightly different direction on either side of the Barton-Irstead parish boundary

Below, embanked and drained grazing levels near St. Benet's Holm, Bure Valley

Plate IV Young alder colonizing tussock-fen (Barton Broad)

of turbaries; and the evidence from certain land-parcels of actual transition from turbary to broad: all fit together and fall into place as contributions to the general conclusion that the Norfolk Broads, the most used and best-known of the British lakes, are literally the handiwork of our ancestors. On the evidence now available they are, beyond reasonable doubt, the flooded sites of former great peat pits, made in the natural fenland in medieval times. At first they must have been sheets of relatively deep water, bounded by sharp margins of undisturbed deposits: but progressive shallowing of the open water by accumulation of mud within their basins, and overgrowth of their margins by encroaching vegetation, have combined to soften their contours and produce the generally more natural appearance of the broads we know today.

Vegetation

CHAPTER 4

THE VEGETATION OF BROADLAND

by J. M. Lambert

One of the chief charms of broadland undoubtedly lies in the variety of scenery and diversity of vegetation to be seen along its water courses. Stretches of wild and tangled fen, with dense thickets of sallow and alder, occur in the middle reaches of the Bure, the Yare and the Ant, and form a background to the open waters of their broads. Flat expanses of grazing marsh, with vast, changing skyscapes, lie over the embankments farther down these rivers, and are particularly characteristic of the valleys of the Thurne and Waveney. Patches of salt-marsh, dissected by creeks and backed by the long line of Breydon Wall, border the great estuary of Breydon Water. All have a character of their own, yet fit together to form an integrated pattern. They give visible expression to the underlying physiographical structure of the region; they bear witness to the past and present economic use of the natural resources of the area; and they reflect the variation in the present physical conditions in the valleys, such as differences in tidal range between the successive reaches of the rivers and between the individual waterways themselves.

Within the boundaries of the broadland region, the rivers fall with only a slight gradient to the sea, and are strongly tidal in their lower parts. The daily rise and fall is much greater in the Yare and Waveney, which enter Breydon Water in direct line with the tidal current, than in the corresponding reaches of the Bure, whose mouth is by-passed by the main flow of water. The tidal effects diminish gradually upstream in the various valleys, until they either die away, as in the Bure and its tributary Ant and Thurne, or are stopped by mills or locks in the upstream parts of the channels, as at Norwich on the Yare and at Geldeston on the Waveney.[1] The salinity effects of the tides, however, do not extend so far up the rivers as the mechanical rise and fall, since the fresh water coming down from the upland holds

[1] The broken and derelict condition of Geldeston Lock now allows tidal water to pass upstream of it, though it forms a barrier to navigation.

back the salt water of the flood tides. The patches of general saltmarsh bordering the lower reaches are correspondingly restricted, though a few salt and brackish water plants may persist some distance upstream along the river banks. Acle Bridge, Cantley and Oulton Dyke have been given as the limits of significant salinity with normal tides on the Bure, Yare and Waveney respectively, though tidal rise and fall is still found in the Bure some distance beyond Wroxham Bridge, with a range of about six inches at the bridge itself, and is appreciable, with a range of one and a half to two feet, at Norwich on the Yare and at Geldeston Lock on the Waveney.

If we except the small, restricted areas of saltmarsh, the most fundamental vegetational differences in the valleys are obviously those which exist between the drained and undrained regions of the alluvium. The former (Pl. III), with their close-cropped level swards of pasture plants, broken only by planted trees along the roads and tracks, and reeds or sedges marking the line of dykes, form a most marked and striking scenic contrast to the wet wildernesses of fen and carr of the areas round the broads. The history of embanking and draining is obscure, and there is little evidence for the twelfth-century dating often ascribed to the river banks: but, whatever the period when drainage was initially begun, there is little doubt that the development of the economic pattern through the centuries has been governed primarily by restrictions imposed by the natural physiographical features of the region. From the agricultural standpoint, drainage has obviously been most successful in the lower reaches of the valleys, where deposits of mineral alluvium—the estuarine clay of the former marine invasion—are spread over their whole width (chap. 2, p. 13). Not only does the clay form a relatively impervious layer, preventing lateral seepage from the rivers, but it also provides a good mineral substratum for the better pasture grasses. Moreover, the areas based on an uninterrupted layer of clay, however thin, are not subject to excessive wastage on drainage such as that which occurs in regions with an entirely peaty substratum.

The middle reaches of the valleys, where the clay forms only a partial cover, are less amenable to drainage. Apart from the greater liability to wastage, the pervious nature of the peat, which here forms the main alluvial fill, allows more lateral seepage of water; the water-logging is moreover aggravated by the presence of the broads, with relatively deep basins, in continuity with the general river system. Various attempts to drain parts of this region have generally failed as a long-term measure, and such land has reverted to rough fen.

The Bargate Nature Reserve in the Yare valley is an example of a previously drained area of this type, and another occurs adjacent to Hoveton Little Broad. A similar fate has befallen areas lying respectively north-west and east of Ranworth Broad, and in the latter, a portion of the derelict marsh has now been purposely flooded by opening the sluices to provide suitable shallow reedswamps for breeding duck.

The derivation of the good downstream grazing levels from a former estuarine condition is still seen in the pattern of some of the drainage dykes. In the most seaward parts of the valleys, a proportion of the dykes are irregular and tortuous in plan, and appear to represent the remains of former saltmarsh creeks incorporated into the general drainage scheme: such areas probably never had a cover of peat before they were embanked. Farther upstream, however, the arrangement of the drains is almost entirely rectilinear, and, although the surface of the estuarine clay is now exposed, a former layer of surface peat was almost certainly present above the clay. The surface levels of these marshes are lower than those of their more seaward counterparts, and this again suggests a loss of an upper peat by wastage down to the clay layer itself.

Mainly as the result of such peat wastage, but also possibly partly through a continued, slow, long-term lowering of the land surface relative to the level of the sea (chapter 2), most of the drained grazing marshes now lie somewhat below the mean water-level of the rivers. The drains which intersect these pastures are sealed off from the rivers to form a ' low-level ' system entirely independent of the ' high-level ' waters of the rivers and their associated broads. Water is lifted from the low-level system into the rivers by electric pumps, which have now largely replaced the former steam-engines and still earlier windmills. The picturesque hulks of former drainage mills, so beloved of the Norwich School of painters, are still seen scattered over the broadland area, but none is now still working regularly.

Apart from areas which have periodically been ploughed up and re-seeded, or have recently been brought under drainage during the last war, most of the embanked levels have been drained and grazed for a long enough period in the past for their vegetation to have become relatively stabilised. Local changes, however, still take place in response to improvements in drainage or variations in intensity of grazing, while the general state of relative stability is from time to time disrupted in certain areas by catastrophic floods. Although the low-lying drained alluvium is protected both by natural coastal features of sand-hills and shore deposits and by the artificial 'walls' which separate it from the tidal channels of the rivers, major inundations have from time to time occurred. The last great break-through from the sea itself took place in 1938, when 700 yards of the sand-hills between Winterton and Horsey were washed away, and sea-water flooded some 7000 acres of the low-lying hinterland; and many of the grazing levels were flooded by salt or brackish water when banks at various places along the rivers gave way under the great tidal surge of 1953. The extent and duration of changes in the vegetation of the flooded areas depend on the length of inundation as well as on the salinity of the flooding water itself, and the temporary or permanent effects of such floods on the general composition of the vegetation have not yet been fully estimated.

Although the ecology of the grazing levels has a very real and intrinsic interest in itself, the attention of the biologist has naturally been centred more particularly on the wilder and more varied vegetation of the undrained regions round the broads. The fascinating patchwork of open water, reedswamp, fen and carr is obviously subject to a far greater range of habitat factors than the more uniform stretches of the grazing levels, and offers a richer set of plant communities. It is with these regions, therefore, that the greater part of this chapter is primarily concerned.

Whereas the rather general sameness of the drained levels arises largely from the consistent use of these areas for pasturage, the undrained fenland has had a much more chequered economic history. In the first place, we have the great peat excavations which produced the basins of the broads themselves, later providing truly aquatic habitats quite distinct from those of the solid fenland round the broads. Secondly, there is the more recent digging of the surface peat to form the relatively impermanent 'turf-ponds' formerly scattered over the whole surface of the fen. And thirdly, we have the direct harvesting of the fenland plants themselves—for litter, fodder, thatch, and a variety of other purposes.

Besides the direct effect of man on the surface pattern of the fens by removal of peat and cutting of the fenland plants, his economic activities have also had a far-reaching effect on the present hydrological conditions. The dyking system of the undrained fenland provides a significant contrast to that of the grazing levels. In the latter, the low-level drains serve primarily as sumps: they are cut off from the river, and are not affected by tidal or other water movements from outside. But in the undrained fenland, the dykes which intersect

Plate V Water soldier and yellow water-lily. Hickling Broad, Norfolk

Plate VI *Above: left,* pondweed (*Naias marina*) which in Britain appears only in the Broads; *right,* great reedmace (*Typha latifolia*). Popularly but wrongly called bull-rush. Bursting in the wind to release the seeds
Below: left, yellow iris or flag (*Iris pseudacorus*); *right,* bog myrtle or sweet gale (*Myrica gale*), male catkins

it have been cut primarily for access, transport and water circulation, and are part of the high-level system in direct communication with the river waters themselves.

The actual number, distribution and character of the dykes in the unembanked areas have obviously gradually evolved in accordance with changing economic needs. It can probably be safely assumed that at the time when the great peat excavations were made, the dykes were absent or relatively few; but as the excavations subsequently became flooded, the broads thus formed were opened up to the river for navigation and trading purposes. Water became the chief means of communication in the region, and additional dykes were made in the solid peat to provide access from the river to the village ‘ staithes ’ and to give free passage to areas where litter, reed, or surface peat were being cut. The whole of the unembanked fenland thus became gradually intersected with a network of open dykes, allowing free circulation of fresh river water throughout.

Though most of the broads and their surrounding fens are still in open communication with the rivers in this way, the free connection has not always been retained. Those broads which have been cut out from the hinterland of peat beyond the clay, in big side-valleys or in embayments of the upland, are often separated from the river by stretches of intervening land which have been drained. In such cases, the former navigable channels and dykes between the broads and rivers are now often closed at the riverward end by sluices, to keep out the tide and diminish the risk of lateral flooding. The best examples of this are seen in the big downstream side-valley broads—the Ormesby-Rollesby-Filby system and Fritton Decoy—of the Bure and Waveney; Hassingham and Buckenham Broads in the Yare similarly have their common exit closed at the lower end; and in Upton Broad, lying well back from the Bure in an embayment of the upland, the entire former connection with the river has now been incorporated into the low-level drainage system of the marshes which separate it completely from the river channel. Such broads are therefore to all intents and purposes now land-locked sheets of water, and provide a rather different set of ecological conditions from those in which water circulation is more free.

In areas where tidal water is not impeded by sluices, the amount of water movement which takes place in the various broads and through the surrounding fens is far from uniform. Differences in range of tidal movement in the different valleys, and in successive reaches of the individual valleys themselves; distances of the various areas from the main tidal channels; number, arrangement, size and state of overgrowth of the dykes; the presence or absence of small subsidiary streams or flushes entering the system from the upland; all combine to give a wide variety of hydrological conditions which is reflected in the range of plant communities found. The position is further complicated by the fact that, although the broads lie above the limits of significant salinity in the rivers and are normally quite fresh, those of the Thurne lying just behind the Horsey sand-hills are slightly brackish in character, through the effect of direct salt-water seepage underground from the sea.

It is obvious that in any general consideration of the present vegetation of the undrained fenland, a primary distinction must be made between the aquatic and marginal communities which have invaded the basins of the broads themselves, and those which grow on the solid alluvium around. In the first case, there is primary vegetation actively colonising open water over a substratum of loose, unconsolidated mud; while in the second, the plants occupy areas of fairly compact peat, or peat and clay, with the surface usually at least a few inches above the average water level.

The muds which have accumulated in the basins of the broads are predominantly organic or calcareous in nature, formed mainly from the remains of aquatic plants and animals, though chemical precipitation of ' lake chalk ' from the richly calcareous water may also play its part. Many of the organisms contributing to the deposition of the mud are microscopic in size, but the shells of fresh-water molluscs, the calcareous sheaths of stoneworts (*Chara* spp.), and other remains of large aquatic plants can be recognised as forming a significant proportion of the constituents of the mud. In some of the broads, particularly those which are strongly tidal such as the broads connected with the Yare, a good proportion of river silt is mixed with the upper layers of the mud, and these are usually black and somewhat denser than the rest. But generally there is only an insignificant silt content, and the muds range in colour from a dark greenish fawn to a light creamy yellow, depending on the proportions of organic and calcareous matter present.

The free water lying over the mud is usually very turbid, owing to the multitude of small microscopic organisms and great amount of fine material suspended in it. Sometimes, in the deeper broads such as Rollesby and Filby Broads and Fritton Lake, these are sufficient to give a very definite greenish tinge to the waters. The actual degree of turbidity varies greatly from broad to broad, depending on their size, depth, and amount of water movement as well as on other factors. Tidal movement, other water currents, wave action, and passage of boats, all help to prevent the suspended matter from settling, or stir up the loose surface of the mud to add to the general opaqueness of the water. It is therefore only in relatively shallow broads, or those with exceptionally still water, that submerged aquatic plants have sufficient light and a firm enough anchorage to grow in quantity. Many of the deep broads, such as Rollesby, Filby and Fritton, have a very poor aquatic flora, and such water plants as are present are limited to a few shallow marginal areas. The open stretches of Ranworth, Decoy, Wroxham, and Hoveton Little Broads, with continuous water movement, are also almost devoid of water plants, though they occur in abundance in the sheltered neck of Hoveton Great Broad, in the still waters at the south end of Barton Broad, and in the deep but protected bays of Martham Broad. The small, undisturbed broads of Upton and Hassingham are likewise densely filled, and in parts of the shallow Hickling-Whiteslea-Heigham series, a veritable forest of stoneworts, pondweeds and blanket-weed can be seen covering the bottom of the broad.

Entirely free-floating water plants, such as the frog-bit (*Hydrocharis morsus-ranae*), the duckweeds (*Lemna* spp.) and the bladderwort (*Utricularia vulgaris*), are naturally restricted to open water areas where there is little current or wind action to sweep them away, and tend to accumulate round the margins of the broads or in sheltered bays or inlets. Rooted plants with floating leaves, such as the water-lilies (*Nuphar* and *Nymphaea*) and amphibious bistort (*Polygonum amphibium*) are also found mainly in the shallower marginal regions, though some may occur in deeper waters in an entirely submerged condition. Many of the aquatic plants are rooted in the mud in the early stages of their growth, but are gradually torn away from their unstable roothold and end the season in an entirely free-floating state. For instance, the great floating masses of hornwort (*Ceratophyllum demersum*) which used to cover the surface of Surlingham, Strumpshaw and Rockland Broads [1] in late summer and effectively excluded all other plants below them, began the season as rooted plants, developing from dormant winter buds at the bottom of the broads; the water soldier (*Stratiotes aloides*) (Pl. v) also rises and falls in the water at different times of the year, so that sometimes its rosettes of spiky

[1] The hornwort, together with certain other aquatics, seems virtually to have disappeared from these tidal Yare Broads during the last few years. The cause of this has not yet been established, but may be related to changes in the nature of effluents from Norwich.

leaves lie on the floor of the broads, while at others they pierce the surface of the water.

The complexity of factors determining the presence, relative abundance and distribution of aquatic plants in the different broads is further complicated by the indirect effects of water circulation, possibly in relation to differences in the mineral status and aeration of the water itself. Whereas certain plants, such as the yellow water-lily (*Nuphar lutea*; Pl. v), the frog-bit (*Hydrocharis*) and the lesser duckweed (*Lemna minor*), are found in a wide range of broads, others are limited to those with greatest tidal movement, or to parts where there is a small inflowing stream. The hornwort, formerly abundant in the strongly tidal broads of the Yare, is absent or only inconspicuous in land-locked or still waters. The water starwort (*Callitriche stagnalis*) and the Canadian waterweed (*Elodea canadensis*) are other examples of water plants which appear only to be common in areas where the water is constantly renewed: at Hassingham, for instance, where tidal circulation in the broads as a whole is eliminated by a sluice, the latter is scarcely represented among the submerged aquatic plants in the main basin of the broad, though it clogs the dykes where there is a small inflow from the upland. Conversely, many aquatic species appear to be restricted to relatively stagnant broads. The best development of the water milfoil (*Myriophyllum verticillatum*), for instance, is seen in the land-locked Upton Broad, and the bladderwort (*Utricularia vulgaris*) also comes into this category. The various species of stonewort (*Chara* spp.) are only found in quantity in broads with not much water movement, such as Upton, Martham and the Hickling-Heigham series; and the same applies to the rare pondweed (*Naias marina*; Pl. vi), which has so far only been recorded from the Thurne Broads, Upton Broad, the pinched-off western end of Hoveton Little Broad, and the south end of Barton Broad.

A further point of interest in this connection is that the calcareous remains of *Chara* have been found in abundance, in juxtaposition with fresh-water mollusc shells, in the deeper layers of mud in a great many broads where the living plant is no longer present. This suggests that somewhat different ecological conditions existed in such broads in the past, and it is tempting to think that the disappearance of the stoneworts from them may be connected in some way with the original opening up of the flooded basins to circulating tidal water.

There is little evidence so far available as to whether the slight brackishness of the Thurne Broads has any significant effect on the floristic composition of the communities in their waters. Certainly some plants, such as the *Charas*, are far more abundant now in these broads than elsewhere, and *Naias marina*, as its name implies, has been regarded by some to be favoured by brackish water. But since these plants have also been found in quantity in completely freshwater broads like Upton, it seems improbable that salinity in itself is a significant determining factor in their distribution, at least the concentrations in which it occurs in these broads.

The aquatic communities are often subject to great fluctuations from year to year, both in total quantity and the relative abundance of different species. In a hot, sunny summer, the mats of hornwort which clogged the broads of the Yare were far thicker and much more resistant to the passage of boats than in a cool, dull season. The small introduced water fern (*Azolla filiculoides*), has been very intermittent in its appearance, sometimes forming continuous, red, floating mats, while in other years it cannot be found. The water soldier (*Stratiotes*) was dominant in Hoveton Great Broad in 1947, but appeared to be completely absent in 1953. Moreover, the occasional dredging of broads and removal of aquatic plants may completely upset the balance of the various species; for instance, when much of the hornwort was dredged out from Rockland Broad some years ago, the water was immediately filled in the same season by great masses of Canadian waterweed, normally excluded by the dense floating hornwort mats.

Although the true water plants play a most important role in filling up the basins of the broads by adding their remains to the layers of accumulating muds, their communities are generally too discontinuous and often too impermanent for them to be regarded as the real pioneers of the continuous series of plants encroaching on open water from its edge. The marginal vegetation invading open water typically passes through three phases—reedswamp, fen and carr—with different species forming the dominant plants at each successive stage. The advancing front is formed by the reedswamp plants, encroaching on areas where the surface of the mud is still well below the general water level. By accumulation of more mud trapped by the submerged parts of the reedswamp plants, and by the growth of peat from dead plant remains *in situ*, the substratum is gradually stabilised and raised, so that other species can invade. When the surface has been built up to a height just above the average water level, it is still occupied by mainly herbaceous plants, which form the primary fen phase. With further consolidation of the substratum by continued peat accumulation, accompanied by the establishment of a thick fen mat by rhizome-forming species, or by the entry of tussock-forming plants, conditions sooner or later became suitable for colonisation by bushes and trees. This culminates in the eventual formation of the closed-canopy, rather shrubby woodland known as carr.

As in the case of the plants of the open water, the actual species involved in the various phases of the primary succession vary from broad to broad in relation to the particular ecological conditions existing in their basins. Quite different marginal plants are found, for instance, in the strongly tidal Yare valley broads from those where tidal movement is restricted or absent, as in the broads of the Ant and Thurne, or in the entirely land-locked broads.

The actual details of the different successions have not always been easy to work out. In the first place, the marginal communities which have grown up over the muds are superficially continuous with the adjacent communities of the solid fenland around the broads: so, as a preliminary step, the actual limits of the basins have had to be established, and the true primary communities distinguished from the rest, which have a rather different history. Then the different primary communities themselves have had to be sorted out to see which of them represent phases of the same succession and which form parts of parallel series. In broads which have been allowed to grow up more or less undisturbed, it is often possible to see the whole range of communities belonging to one series neatly arranged in concentric zones: the pioneer plants border the open water, while progressively older communities lie behind them. Usually, however, the marginal vegetation is much more patchily arranged. Parts of the reedswamp may have been cut away by deliberate clearing or eroded by the wash of power craft, so that the older communities are exposed in places at the edge of the open water; or the growth of reedswamp may have been uneven, so that bays have been pinched off from the main body of water and grow up more slowly or remain as 'pulk-holes', while the rest of the vegetation round them progresses to an older stage; or the presence of shallowly-submerged balks of peat running out into the broads may affect the vegetation in their immediate vicinity; or the cutting of reed and sedge may alter the composition of the fen and prevent colonisation by bushes at the appropriate stage. But by piecing together the evidence from the living communities of the various areas, and by digging up the fresh peat immediately below them and examining its composition and thickness, it has usually been possible to reconstruct the general sequence of events.

Most of the detailed work on the composition of broadland vegetation was carried out between 1947 and 1953, at a time when interference with the marginal vegetation was at a minimum and many of the broads were becoming rapidly overgrown. Within the last few years, however, the general vegetational picture has been much modified and upset by the extensive depredations of a new arrival on the broadland scene, namely, the coypu (*Myocastor coypus*). These South American rodents, bred in Britain since about 1929 for their valuable pelts, rapidly became naturalised over the whole of broadland following escapes from former fur farms on the Yare. Their effect on the vegetation was relatively insignificant until a few years ago, but they ultimately established themselves in such vast numbers in the east Norfolk river valleys that they virtually destroyed the pioneer communities round many of the broads. Not only did they damage the vegetation directly by their actual consumption of living plant material but, since they are especially partial to the juicy underground parts of reedswamp and fen plants, they often indirectly caused the break-up and disappearance of great stretches of semi-floating, marginal vegetation by mechanical destruction of its rhizome mat and roothold. Although the coypu population was drastically reduced by the severe winter of 1962-63 combined with intensive trapping, its effects are still seen everywhere in the broadland area.

The full significance of this massive coypu occupation can only be properly understood in the light of the more orthodox vegetational picture shown by the broads at the time of their maximum overgrowth some ten to fifteen years ago. The following account therefore attempts to indicate the general successional relationships between the main communities before the period of large-scale coypu damage, from which basis it should then be possible to assess the present ecological status of the remaining marginal vegetation round the broads.

In those broads with a moderate overall water movement—and the majority of broads come into this category—the reedswamp phase is normally dominated by a more or less continuous zone of the lesser reedmace (*Typha angustifolia*), with patches of bur-reed (*Sparganium ramosum*) and true bulrush (*Schoenoplectus lacustris*). The bulrush can occupy rather deeper water than the reedmace and sometimes forms a definite pioneer zone in front of the latter; it is a particularly characteristic plant of the broads of the Ant, and in Barton Broad, for instance, it used to form great open beds in which white and yellow water-lilies were intimately intermingled.

As the bulrush and reedmace advance into open water, they are invaded from behind by the common reed (*Phragmites communis*), which forms the dominant plant at the early stage of the fen. This rapidly builds up a matted, semi-floating raft of roots and rhizomes above the loose and spongy reedswamp peat, and other subsidiary plants soon enter to join the reed. The water hemlock (*Cicuta virosa*), the great broad-leaved water dock (*Rumex hydrolapathum*), and the yellow-green cyperus sedge (*Carex pseudo-cyperus*) are among the first of these, and often occur in the transition zone between the reedswamp and fen. But they are soon joined by the hemp agrimony (*Eupatorium cannabinum*) and the great willow-herb (*Epilobium hirsutum*), with their showy pink and red-purple flowers; the water mint (*Mentha aquatica*) and the yellow flag (*Iris pseudacorus*) also come in here, and, more rarely, the great spearwort (*Ranunculus lingua*) adds to the assemblage. At a slightly later stage, the sweet-smelling meadowsweet (*Filipendula ulmaria*) and the purple and yellow loosestrifes (*Lythrum salicaria* and *Lysimachia vulgaris*) enter to form conspicuous patches among the grey-green reed, together with the feathery leaves and delicate white umbels of the marsh parsley (*Peucedanum palustre*), the well-known food-plant of the swallow-tail butterfly. The plants are often bound together by the twining stems of the great bindweed (*Calystegia sepium*), with large white trumpet flowers, and the rare marsh pea (*Lathyrus palustris*) also sometimes climbs among them. Other smaller plants, such as the marsh horsetail (*Equisetum palustre*), the water parsnip (*Berula erecta*), the skull-cap (*Scutellaria galericulata*), and the straggling marsh bedstraw (*Galium palustre*), form an understorey to the tall reed haulms, and occasionally small patches of the little adder's tongue (*Ophioglossum vulgatum*) and the creeping loosestrife (*Lysimachia nummularia*) occupy bare patches between the reedstools.

Before the reed has had time to build up a very thick and stable mat, it is generally supplanted by one or other of the big sedges—the tussock sedge (*Carex paniculata*), the fen sedge (*Carex acutiformis*), or the saw sedge (*Cladium mariscus*). In broads where water movement is fairly free, the commonest of these is the tussock sedge, which eventually forms huge, close-set stools three or four feet high, and crowds out the reed which only persists in a subsidiary role between the tussocks. The breaking up of the dense reed cover allows the entry of additional smaller plants, and many of these, such as the marsh fern (*Thelypteris palustris*) and the introduced orange balsam (*Impatiens capensis*), gain a foothold on the tops and sides of the tussocks themselves. Moreover, the increasing weight of the *Carex* tussocks begins to depress the

Plate VII *Above*, River Yare entering Breydon Water
Below, sweet flag and great hairy willowherb

Plate VIII Scurvy-grass flowering in May

relatively thin mat which underlies them, so that pools of water appear between, allowing the re-entry of various water plants, such as the frog-bit and the lesser duckweed. The mixed tussock-fen community which eventually develops is therefore relatively rich in species, and this, together with its characteristic physiognomy of alternating stool and pool, make it one of the most striking and interesting communities found round the margins of the broads.

The upstanding *Carex* tussocks, with their tops well above the water level, form an excellent base for the establishment of seedlings of sallow (*Salix atrocinerea* and/or *S. cinerea*) and alder (*Alnus glutinosa*). The initial stages of bush colonisation here are therefore not dependent on a gradual building up and stabilisation of the whole fen surface, and take place relatively quickly. The *Carex* tussocks, which are fairly tolerant of shade, continue to increase in size despite their exploitation as a foothold by the trees, but the increasing weight of the latter causes still further sinking of the basic raft of thin fen peat on which the succession is built up; the pools between the tussocks therefore become gradually more pronounced, and the subsidiary species more and more restricted to the tops and sides of the tussocks themselves. As the trees become larger and their canopy closes, many of the herbaceous plants of the fen die out or are limited to the open patches between the trees, though a few, like the hemp agrimony, the yellow flag (in a non-flowering condition) and the marsh fern remain in the deeper shade.

With the progressive break-down of the fen mat, the sedge stools become rolling and unstable, and no longer able to bear the trees erect; moreover, the slight but continuous subsidence of the community as a whole carries the roots of the larger trees well below the general water-level, so that they become moribund or dead. The resulting carr is therefore characterised by frequent leaning and dying trees and prostrate trunks intermingled with younger bushy growth, all underlain by an excessively soft and quaking floor of alternating tussocks and black, fœtid pools. It fully merits the name of 'swamp carr' which has been applied to it, and is so treacherous that parts are almost impossible to penetrate on foot.

The true swamp carr is only a relatively transient phase, since its floor is gradually stabilised and raised by accumulation of brushwood debris and compaction of muds beneath. The spread of shade-tolerant rhizome-forming species, such as *Carex acutiformis*, moreover helps to re-establish a firm mat between the stools, and the tussocks themselves begin to degenerate where the shade is most intense, so that the ground becomes more level. Shrubby plants, such as the wild black and red currants (*Ribes nigrum* and *R. rubrum*) and thickets of wild raspberry (*Rubus idaeus*), dewberry (*R. caesius*) and bramble (*R. fruticosus*) begin to occupy the ground; and a number of larger ferns—the broad buckler-fern (*Dryopteris austriaca*), the lady fern (*Athyrium filix-foemina*), and sometimes the handsome royal fern (*Osmunda regalis*; Pl. x)—may be found in these later stages of the carr. Alder and sallow remain the dominant trees, interspersed with occasional buckthorns (*Rhamnus cathartica* and *Frangula alnus*) and are often wreathed with skeins of honeysuckle (*Lonicera periclymenum*); but birch (*Betula pubescens*) and ash (*Fraxinus excelsior*) and even occasionally oak (*Quercus robur*), begin to come in among them in the less wet patches. This more mixed carr has a greater stability and permanence than the swamp carr which precedes it, but whether it forms the real climax of the succession, or whether it progresses to a still drier type of woodland, is not clear: most of the carr communities developed over the muds of the broads are still too young for this point to be established with any certainty.

In broads with slightly less water movement than those which support the characteristic tussock-fen, the rhizomatous fen sedge (*Carex acutiformis*), instead of the tussock sedge, may follow the reed mat directly and form the dominant plant at the succeeding late fen stage. In contrast to the uneven surface of the mixed tussock-fen, a more continuous level fen mat is therefore maintained, which offers no convenient, upstanding, dry foothold for seedling trees. Premature bush colonisation is thus prevented, and a greater general thickness of fen peat, bound together by living sedge rhizomes, is accordingly built up to give a more stable base for the carr which is eventually formed; the persistence of the shade-tolerant fen sedge under the trees moreover prevents the surface mat from breaking up as the shade becomes more dense. Although some general subsidence of the whole carr community naturally takes place, the continuous ground mat gives sufficient support for the trees to be able to develop fairly well and remain more or less erect. The resulting carr is therefore more of a semi-swamp type.

When the dominant plant of the fen is the great saw sedge (*Cladium mariscus*), which is characteristic of areas with still more restricted water circulation, the entry of trees is delayed even longer. The saw sedge may either follow a sparse reed mat or colonise the preceding reedswamp direct: but once it is established under optimum conditions, it dominates the fen most thoroughly, and relatively few subsidiary species can compete with it. Not only do its large, long-lived leaves form a dense living stratum, but the dead remains are so coarse and resistant to decay that a thick dead-leaf mattress is formed as a massive understorey. The whole surface of the ground is so effectively covered that seedling trees can only become established with great difficulty, and a good depth of fen peat is therefore formed before the trees come in. Shrubby plants, such as the bog myrtle (*Myrica gale*; Pl. VI) and creeping willow (*Salix repens*) often precede them, and the carr which eventually develops—fen carr—is borne on such a thick and massive mat that not much subsidence takes place, and the ground is relatively firm and dry. Birch, ash and oak, as well as the earlier alder, sallow and buckthorn, soon become established, and form large trees which give the carr a rather different appearance from the more bushy swamp and semi-swamp carrs.

Although one or more of the three types of succession just described are found in the majority of the broads, other communities occur in those where water movement is very great or—at the other extreme—where it is almost non-existent.

Under the rather exceptional conditions in the most strongly tidal broads—Surlingham, Strumpshaw and Rockland, in the Yare valley—it is difficult to distinguish between the primary reedswamp and fen phases, since both are dominated by the broad-leaved sweet-grass (*Glyceria maxima*), which forms great floating rafts, often completely free from the mud below, and rising and falling freely with the tide. Where current scour is greatest, as at the entrances of the dykes connecting the broads to the river, or along the narrow central channel of the overgrown part of Surlingham Broad (Appendix, map 12), the outer edge of this floating raft is often protected by a narrow fringe of reed anchored deeply in the mud; patches of vigorous reed have also been found to occupy small submerged islands in the centre of Surlingham and Rockland Broads, where, because of their deeply-seated rhizomes, they are able to maintain themselves against the movement of the water round them. But, since these marginal and open water beds of reed are quickly overwhelmed by the sweet-grass wherever mechanical conditions allow the establishment of the latter plant, it looks as though the general ecological conditions in these broads definitely favour the sweet-grass rather than the reed in at least the early stages of the succession.

The sweet-grass raft consists of interwoven rhizomes and roots, covered by a mass of long, semi-erect or almost prostrate, bright green leafy shoots. As in the case of the saw sedge fen, the dominant plant forms such a dense vegetative mass that only a few subsidiary species can be found among it. The long, trailing shoots of the woody nightshade (*Solanum dulcamara*) are fairly consistently present, and occasional haulms of persistent reed and the erect spear-like leaves of the great reedmace (*Typha latifolia*) (Pl. VI) in places overtop the general level of the fen: but apart from these, and a few isolated plants of marsh marigold (*Caltha palustris*), purple loosestrife (*Lythrum salicaria*), marsh woundwort (*Stachys palustris*), meadow rue (*Thalictrum flavum*) and the stinging nettle (*Urtica dioica*), the great stretches dominated by the sweet-grass have a remarkably uniform appearance.

By gradual accumulation of debris beneath the floating raft, water circulation is cut down and the sweet-grass becomes less vigorous and more liable to invasion by other fenland plants. The common reed (*Phragmites*), and, more rarely, the reed-grass (*Phalaris arundinacea*) are now able to compete successfully with the sweet-grass, and rapidly either eliminate it or reduce it to a subordinate position. Their more upstanding habit at the same time allows the entry of other subsidiary plants, and the reed fen which is eventually developed is very similar in composition to that which was described earlier.

When the substratum is sufficiently stabilised, isolated bushes of sallow, or sometimes of alder or guelder-rose (*Viburnum opulus*) eventually establish themselves to give patches of shade. Since both the sweet-grass and the reed are fairly quickly eliminated by this, the young carr is at first characterised by much more bare ground than that which follows the fens dominated by the shade-tolerant tussock sedge or fen sedge. The peat mat beneath the carr is moderately thick, so that the carr itself is of a semi-swamp type, though it is rather unlike that of the less strongly tidal broads in several respects. Although a number of plants, such as the yellow flag (Pl. VI), are common to both, the ground flora in general has a rather different appearance. The reed and reed-grass may continue to occupy the lighter patches between the trees, together with other plants persisting from the fen, but elsewhere, instead of a dense mat of fen sedge with a variety of ferns, the bare, black peat beneath the trees becomes more sparsely covered with rough-stalked meadow-grass (*Poa trivialis*) and patches of forget-me-not (*Myosotis palustris*) and bittercress (*Cardamine amara*). The chief sedge present is usually the tufted sedge (*Carex elata*), which forms isolated clumps rather than a continuous cover; the tussock sedge occasionally comes in, but only in those parts well away from the main tidal movement. The chief plant of the shrub layer is usually the wild privet (*Ligustrum vulgare*), and black and red currant bushes

Plate IX *Angelica sylvestris* growing on fen

Plate X *Above*, royal fern (*Osmunda regalis*)
Below, crested buckler fern (*Dryopteris cristata*)

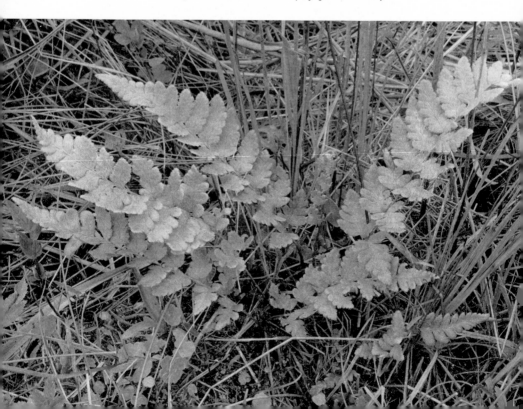

are fairly abundant; the wild raspberry, however, is generally sparse or absent. The low-growing sallow (*Salix cinerea*) is commoner than the alder among the trees, and is often accompanied by guelder-rose and later by ash. The true buckthorn (*Rhamnus*) is also often present, but the alder buckthorn (*Frangula*) is only rarely found.

The strongly or moderately tidal broads, together with the land-locked broads which have a definite inflow from the upland, are all characterised by very vigorous reedswamp and fen communities, generally dominated by a single strong-growing species. But in those broads where water movement is at a minimum, such as the blind ends of Sutton Broad and the Hickling-Whiteslea-Heigham series, leading off respectively from the scarcely tidal Ant and Thurne, the fen phase is usually characterised by plants of lower habit. The sweet-grass and the tussock sedge are completely absent, and though the reed, the fen sedge and the saw sedge are common in places, they tend to be reduced in stature and are often replaced by the fen rush (*Juncus subnodulosus*), with patches of cotton-grass (*Eriophorum angustifolium*), bog-rush (*Schoenus nigricans*), purple moor-grass (*Molinia caerulea*), and smaller sedges (*Carex appropinquata*, *C. nigra*, *C. lasiocarpa*, *C. rostrata* and *C. panicea*). The low-growing fen is often very mixed in composition, since the absence of a large single dominant gives the lesser species a better chance of survival. Here can be found the marsh pennywort (*Hydrocotyle vulgaris*), the bog bedstraw (*Galium uliginosum*), the large birdsfoot trefoil (*Lotus uliginosus*), the tufted vetch (*Vicia cracca*), the bog-bean (*Menyanthes trifoliata*), the marsh orchids (*Orchis fuchsii* and *O. praetermissa*) and their hybrids, the narrow buckler-fern (*Dryopteris spinulosa*), and sometimes the rare crested fern (*Dryopteris cristata*) (Pl. x). Many of the other plants which occur in a subsidiary role elsewhere also come in here as well, so that such fens are often bright with flowers and are some of the plant collector's best hunting grounds. The fen mat grows slowly and forms at first a very swinging raft, but the *Juncus* rhizomes hold it together so firmly that it is generally quite safe to walk upon, provided care is taken. Many of these fens have been cut for litter in the past, so that bush colonisation is often absent or sparse. When carr is allowed to develop, however, it is normally of the semi-swamp type.

When periodic flooding by tidal alkaline water is absent or negligible, patches of bog-moss (*Sphagnum* spp.) are often found within the fen, suggesting a transition to more acid conditions. The bog-moss is usually clumped just above the general water level round the stools of larger plants, though it may form a more continuous cover in slightly less wet patches; hummocks or carpets of bog-moss occur, for instance, in the reed-fens and carrs surrounding Barton Broad, and larger stretches are found around parts of Hickling Broad and Horsey Mere. Associated with the bog-moss may be other more acid-loving plants, such as the sundew (*Drosera rotundifolia*) and the hair-moss (*Polytrichum commune*), though these are very far from common.

Perhaps one of the most interesting features of the vegetation which has encroached on the broads is that most of the communities are comparatively young, and that by far the greater part of the overgrowth seems to have taken place within the last hundred years. This has been ascertained by comparing the original limits of the basins, revealed by boring, with the outline of open water shown on the old tithe maps, made between 1838 and 1842, a little more than a century ago; in many cases, an almost exact coincidence has been found between them. Further comparison of the area of open water shown on the tithe maps with the first edition six-inch Ordnance Survey maps of 1880–5, and with the Air Ministry vertical air photographs of 1946 (see Appendix), moreover shows that the rate of overgrowth has progressively increased, since, on the whole, most of the closure has taken place in the latter period.

This serious diminution in the area of free water prior to coypu effects was only too well realised by local people, who could remember open broads later virtually extinct, and big stretches of water replaced by reedswamp and fen. It is usual to attribute it mainly to increasing neglect, aggravated by two World Wars and rising labour costs. But greater significance should be attached to the interplay of natural phenomena. The basins of most of the broads, when they were first flooded, were obviously far too deep for any reedswamp vegetation to invade. These peat-walled basins, have, however, gradually accumulated organic muds within them through probably several centuries, and the time eventually arrived when many of the muds reached fairly uniformly to within four or five feet of the water surface in the majority of cases. Conditions thus rapidly and progressively became more favourable for the encroachment of rooted reedswamp plants, which need the mud for anchorage and can rarely colonise water more than four feet deep. Many of the broads have reached a very critical stage in their infilling, where the accumulation of an extra foot of mud in any part may give conditions suitable for the rapid spread of reedswamp vegetation and the fen and carr which follow it. In some of the shallower basins, such as Dilham, Sutton and Calthorpe, the original broads are now nearly extinct; parts of the Hickling-Whiteslea-

Heigham series are also very much reduced from their former vast expanse, and Horsey Mere has only been kept open by frequent reedswamp clearing. On the other hand, in the deep basins, such as Decoy Broad, the Ormesby-Rollesby-Filby series, and Fritton Lake, the surface of the mud is still well below the water level, and there is relatively little primary vegetation to be found.

While the foregoing is probably true for the majority of the broads with a reedswamp rooted in the mud, those Yare valley broads which possess a marginal raft of sweet-grass present a rather different picture. Here, the encroachment of this entirely floating mat is theoretically unlimited, restricted only by tidal scour, and deeper water can therefore be invaded. This is probably the explanation why most of the Yare broads were more overgrown at the beginning of the last century than those of the other valleys, and why the correspondence of lake mud limits and tithe map outlines is less marked here than in other comparable basins. Surlingham and Strumpshaw Broads, where the sweet-grass is especially vigorous, have been on the verge of extinction for some time past, although their original basins correspond closely in size and depth with those of several broads which have never displayed a comparable state of overgrowth, even before the coypu infestation.

The effects of coypu activities in the secondary opening up of overgrown broads and waterways has naturally been most conspicuous in areas where much of the marginal vegetation was still at a comparatively early stage in the succession. Thus, many of the former wide reedswamp fringes round the broads have virtually disappeared, usually leaving mud-banks a few inches below the surface, and the water is bordered instead by vegetation representing later phases in the series. In certain places, these older communities themselves are also in an advanced state of disintegration, and their former floristic composition has frequently changed through the elimination of species selectively favoured as food-plants by the coypu. Furthermore, in badly infested areas, there is some evidence that even established carr has been undermined by the activities of these rodents, as for instance along the swampy margins of Heron's Carr in Barton Broad. In short, the present picture is one of widespread destruction of the primary communities, in which the more vulnerable plants have often largely succumbed.

In addition to coypu damage, moreover, there are other factors at work which may affect encroachment, so that, even before the coypu, the growing up of the broads was by no means an entirely continuous and uninterrupted process. In most of the broads, invading plants are so loosely anchored in the soft, oozy mud that exceptional winds and tides are often sufficient to detach great masses of reedswamp or fen from the edge of the marginal belt. These float away to form 'hover', which drifts about the broads or down the rivers until it eventually disintegrates or becomes lodged in a new position. The floating sweet-grass reedswamp is especially liable to break up in this way, and drifting islands of hover, varying in size from a foot or two to several yards in diameter, are a common sight in the Yare. Again, frosts are sometimes responsible for the removal of marginal material, since ice-sheets binding together flood debris and reedswamp stems tend to collapse outward with tidal fall, and are carried away by the current.

Man himself has also certainly had some effect on the vegetation colonising the open water. Several of the common reedswamp plants have, or had, a definite economic value, and were regularly cut in the past. The true bulrush (*Schoenoplectus lacustris*), locally known as 'bolder', was used largely for rush mats, and limited cutting for this purpose was still carried out in a few places until the beds were destroyed; the lesser reedmace (*Typha angustifolia*) or 'gladden', which used to fringe most of the broads, was formerly used, together with the bolder, for 'frail' baskets and horse-collars; stools of the tussock sedge (*Carex paniculata*) were sometimes removed and trimmed to make fireside seats in local cottages and hassocks in churches; and the Norfolk reed (*Phragmites communis*), which is particularly durable and valuable for thatch, still has a good market at the present day when labour is available for its harvest. It is doubtful, however, whether such cutting of reedswamp and fen plants seriously restricted their growth. The bolder and gladden beds tended to be nursed by carefully regulated harvesting rather than destroyed, and the reed was removed in the winter after the haulms were dead. But the cutting was often accompanied by a certain amount of trimming and clearing of the adjacent vegetation, and it moreover had the long-term effect of maintaining certain communities beyond their normal span in the natural succession.

Whereas the vegetation actually bordering the open water could be easily cut and carried by boat, many of the quaking tracts of primary vegetation behind the reedswamp were probably far too treacherous and inaccessible to have been much exploited. It is in these areas, therefore, that the best examples of entirely natural plant communities, unmodified by man, were formerly to be found and still exist in part.

But when we come to consider the vegetation of the solid undrained fenland round the basins of the broads, we find a rather different picture. Most of this fenland, though waterlogged, has its surface just high enough above the average water level to be capable of bearing trees; and if earlier generations of marshmen had not kept the vegetation open by cutting, burning and clearing, this whole region would long ago have been covered by carr of the fen carr type.

Until quite recent times, most of the fens were regularly cut for hay and litter, of which a considerable bulk was sent as far afield as London for the use of cab-horses; 'mowing-marshes' which had been left uncut for a year or two were often burnt over in the winter to remove the old tangled growth; the firmer parts of the fenland were sometimes used for summer grazing after the hay had been removed; and there was widespread harvesting of reed and sedge for thatching, the reed to cover the fall of the roof, and the sedge to form the ridging at the top.

These practices have inevitably left their mark on the composition and present pattern of the fenland vegetation. Annual summer or autumn mowing of hay or litter removed living vegetative shoots, to which some plants are more tolerant than others; the sweet-grass (*Glyceria maxima*), the fen rush (*Juncus subnodulosus*), the black bog-rush (*Schoenus nigricans*), and the purple moor-grass (*Molinia caerulea*), for example, are favoured by this at the expense of the common reed and sedges. Winter harvesting of reeds for thatch only removes dead stems and does not affect the vigour of the reed itself; but slower-growing plants with long-lived leaves, such as the saw sedge (*Cladium mariscus*), may be incidentally cut down along with the reed and eventually eliminated. Similarly, burning may not seriously affect those plants whose aerial parts die off in the winter, and whose perennating rhizomes lie in the wet peat; but shrubby plants, and plants with winter-green leaves, may be destroyed or retarded. The turning of cattle on to the fenland in the past for even a short period in the summer had both direct and indirect effects; on the one hand, there was selective feeding on the most palatable plants, with fenland grasses generally eaten short in preference to the coarser rush and sedge, while, on the other, the resilient low-growing plants were usually less damaged by trampling hooves than taller and more brittle species.

Although many of the plants which occur in the primary fens can be found again in the reed-beds and former mowing-marshes of the fenland between the broads, the balance between the different species has thus often been upset. Certain plants have been eliminated or reduced to a subordinate position by human management, while others, which are poorly represented round the broads, may be more prominent. The tussock sedge, for instance, was rarely allowed to develop its characteristic stools in fens which were regularly mown, and those which reached any appreciable size were usually grubbed up where they impeded mowing; the fen sedge often plays only a minor role in the secondary fenland except in some areas which have not been cut for many years; and the saw sedge is often partially or completely replaced by the reed, the fen rush, the bog rush, or the purple moor-grass in areas where one would expect it to be dominant in the absence of human interference. Conversely, the purple small-reed (*Calamagrostis canescens*) is often conspicuous in areas which were formerly mown or grazed, whereas it plays very little part in the primary successions; and the reed-grass (*Phalaris arundinacea*) is also more abundant in former mowing-marshes of the Yare than in the primary fens.

The degree of water movement in the secondary fens also, of course, affects the distribution of plants, and the communities generally show a definite pattern in relation to the dykes. In the Yare valley, for instance, the open tidal dykes are outlined by the sweet-grass or the reed, while saw sedge and fen rush communities lie well away from them. Since water movement is less free through the compact peat than in the open broads, the floristic differences which are so marked in the marginal vegetation of the various broads are to some extent 'ironed out' in the fens which lie between, especially when the dykes are relatively few and far apart. Sometimes in the past additional dykes have been specially cut to encourage the growth of certain plants, particularly in the Yare valley mowing-marshes where the sweet-grass formed a valuable fodder crop and was favoured by free water circulation.

The numerous shallow peat cuttings which broke up the surface of the fens have also served to complicate the picture. Though peat is now no longer cut, the outlines of former turf-ponds are often quite distinct. They are frequently marked by lines of bushes, arising either from green living stakes set to delimit one holding from another, or by natural colonisation of the staddles of peat between the ponds. Most of the turf-ponds have now grown up again to fen, indistinguishable from that of the adjacent undug areas; but others, more recent in origin, are marked by great beds of vigorous reed, or even by reedswamp plants. Much of the great cutting in Woodbastwick Fen

(Appendix, map 9), for instance, is now firm ground again and has been used as mowing-marsh, while in contrast swampy morasses still exist in many parts of the later Catfield diggings near Barton Broad (Appendix, map 20).

Although the hand of man has been so prominent in the immediate past history of the Norfolk fens, the present position of the vegetation is very far from stable. Increasing labour costs during the twentieth century, together with the dying out of horse-drawn traffic, have seriously restricted and made unprofitable the widespread exploitation of the fens. Only a few areas of mowing-marsh are still cut for local use, and harvesting of reed and sedge is now limited to a few of the best and most accessible beds. Dykes, no longer plied by the wide reed and litter-boats, have become choked and overgrown so that reduction in water circulation has altered the detail of the fen. Major changes in the structure and composition of the vegetation have taken place well within living memory, with increasingly rapid replacement of one community by another, and unchecked colonisation by bushes and trees. Many of the areas shown as mowing-marsh in maps at the end of the last century have now become bushy wildernesses, and the occasional finding of unexpected overgrown tracks in deserted stretches of fen and carr is often our only indication of the busy activity of earlier generations of Norfolk marshmen.

These areas of secondary fenland on the solid peat outside the basins appear to be less affected by coypu damage than the more vulnerable primary communities of the broads, but much of the vegetation is riddled by old coypu runs and there is considerable indication that the damage has not been negligible. Many of the reedbeds and sedge fens have been partly or entirely destroyed, big patches of rush have disappeared, areas of sweet-grass along the Yare dykes have been denuded, some of the fenland rarities have vanished from localities where they grew, and even osier carrs have been affected.

Except for the grazing levels, therefore, the whole broadland scene is at present at a very critical transitional stage. More rapid and far-reaching changes seem to be taking place today than at any period in its recent history. Not only have most of the broads now reached —or passed—the critical stage in their infilling when vegetation can theoretically invade, but the solid fenland between the broads is rapidly changing in aspect. It is unlikely that the undrained fens will ever regain the economic value of the past. The spread of sailing and pleasure cruising since the turn of the century has placed present-day emphasis on the maintenance of the open water rather than on the management of the fens, and the careful cutting of reedswamp plants for use has given place to mechanical dredging and clearing, aided by coypu damage. But the reedswamps, the fens and the carrs are as much a part of the pattern as the open water itself, and the preservation of a good balance of these should be of vital importance to all who wish to perpetuate the traditional picture of the Norfolk Broads.

CHAPTER 5

SOME FLOWERING PLANTS OF THE BROADS

by E. A. Ellis

One does not have to be a botanist to enjoy the peculiar beauty and diversity of plant life throughout this wilderness of swamps and waterways. Each river and each group of broads has some fresh feature to catch the eye on the shore and in the water itself, and the pattern changes day by day throughout the year. Thus the blue waters of Hickling, bounded by great belts of reed (*Phragmites communis*) reveal in their depths a fantastic water-garden of crisp-leaved stoneworts (*Charophytes*), submerged blankets and curious spheres of an alga (*Cladophora sauteri*) and the toothed and succulent fronds of one of Britain's rarest pondweeds (*Naias marina*). Barton Broad is distinguished at once by its wealth of white water-lilies (*Nymphaea alba*) and bulrushes (*Scirpus lacustris*) and its still, peaty waters provide a perfect habitat for the water-soldier (*Stratiotes aloides*). In Rockland Broad in the strongly tidal Yare valley, the water plants are different again, with hornwort (*Ceratophyllum demersum*) and yellow water-lilies (*Nuphar lutea*) predominating, while white water-lilies are absent.

The fringing vegetation varies much in character according to the nature of the ground, which may be peaty with little mineral matter, predominantly clayey, or well supplied with river silt. The physical impact of tidal ebb and flow and the presence of varying amounts of salt in the water also play an important part in determining the pattern of the marginal flora. In the past, even the very recent past, sea flooding has produced great changes in the plant life of the Horsey-Hickling area for varying lengths of time, as in 1938, when hundreds of acres of marsh and fen were devastated and much of the original vegetation was replaced temporarily by salt-loving species.

The diversity of species in waterside plants is to be found no less in the more consolidated swamps and fens farther away from the water. In general, the land surrounding the Bure and Ant Broads supports a fen-peat flora with occasional pockets of true bog plants in the least well-drained areas. The Yare fens, on the other hand, receive a wash of calcareous river water too frequently to allow the local development of conditions suitable for the growth of *Sphagnum* mosses anywhere, and for the same reason the composition of the flora is varied in favour of species that thrive on well mineralised or silty peats. One very common plant of the Yare and Waveney fens, the meadow rue (*Thalictrum flavum*) is significantly absent from the flood-plain of the Bure and its tributaries.

Under natural circumstances, the fens become colonised in time by trees and bushes which eventually form the scrub-woods known as carrs. Here again, there are noticeable differences in the composition of the major vegetation. Alder (*Alnus glutinosa*) and alder buckthorn (*Frangula alnus*) commonly predominate in the Bure-Ant-Thurne region while grey sallow (*Salix cinerea*) and common buckthorn (*Rhamnus cathartica*) flourish to a greater extent on the more alkaline fens of the Yare valley.

As Dr. Lambert has stressed in chapter 3, Man's exploitation of the area through the centuries has been largely responsible for determining the present distribution of many of the specialised plant communities. Summer and winter mowing, burning, partial grazing, peat-cutting, the deliberate removal of scrub, the making of artificial water-lanes for various purposes and even the treading of pathways have all, in patchwork fashion, altered the course of nature. Regular mowing in July eliminates some of the taller plants such as reed (*Phragmites communis*) and prickly sedge (*Cladium mariscus*) and permits an increase of fen rush (*Juncus subnodulosus*) and many other plants of short stature, such as the marsh orchids, devil's-bit scabious (*Succisa pratensis*), adder's-tongue fern (*Ophioglossum vulgatum*), ragged robin (*Lychnis flos-cuculi*), bog bedstraw (*Galium uliginosum*) and in some places the white-chaliced grass of Parnassus (*Parnassia palustris*). The burning of marshes is sometimes followed by an increase in the delicate little marsh fern (*Thelypteris palustris*), whose spores readily colonise the moist peat newly sterilised by fire. After a conflagration has destroyed the haulms of marsh plants in late winter, greater numbers of seedlings survive in the summer following, because they enjoy fuller access to sunlight. Species whose fruits or seeds are spread by winter floods tend to multiply under these conditions; milk parsley (*Peucedanum palustre*), angelica (*Angelica sylvestris*; Pl. IX) and yellow flag (*Iris pseudacorus*) are notable examples.

Trampling and grazing by horses and cattle on the slightly better drained marginal fens often result in irregular consolidation of peat and an increase of grassy and rush-grown hummocks interspersed with wet hollows which become filled with mosses, marsh pennywort (*Hydrocotyle vulgaris*) and occasionally the elegant little bog pimpernel (*Anagallis tenella*). On Yare valley marshes dominated by rond-grass (*Glyceria maxima*), the impact of livestock gives rise to irregularities in contour and a consequent enrichment of the flora by such plants as marsh marigold (*Caltha palustris*), creeping buttercup (*Ranunculus repens*), meadowsweet (*Filipendula ulmaria*), meadow rue (*Thalictrum flavum*), marsh thistle (*Cirsium palustre*) and marsh bedstraw (*Galium palustre*).

So far, little has been said of the impact of the teeming animal life of broadland upon its plants, nor of the curious features of many of the plants themselves. In the remainder of this chapter some attempt will be made to remedy this by particularisation rather than generalisation. We shall take a look at the flora, section by section, and mention will be made of interesting points as they arise.

THE FLOWERING PLANTS (*Angiospermae*)

The buttercups include several important members of the aquatic and marsh fraternity. Marsh marigolds are conspicuous in spring and commonly produce a few flowers again in autumn. The hairy buttercup (*Ranunculus sardous*) is a feature of the trampled grazing marshes. Great spearwort thrives in the open parts of floating 'reed-swamps' and in recent years, where coypus have destroyed its competitors, it has been able to increase its hold locally, because its acrid leaves save it from being eaten by these invaders. Celery-leaved crowfoot (*Ranunculus sceleratus*) is common in dykes on the grazing levels and although it is poisonous to cattle, it rarely gives rise to trouble except in severe droughts, when young beasts have been known to eat enough of it in the flowering condition to bring about their deaths. The water buttercups are represented in the broads mainly by *Ranunculus circinatus*. Lesser celandine (*Ranunculus ficaria*) comes down into some very wet habitats, where it tends to propagate itself by bulbils rather than fruits. Meadow rue exhibits a wide range of leaf forms and the condition of the plants is variously affected by gall midges developing in their flowers, a systemic rust fungus, degrees of shading and the position of the rootstocks in relation to calcareous flooding. Some of the plants turn purple and white, which suggests that they may be attacked by a virus.

Of the two water-lilies found in the broads, the yellow is the more widely distributed and in small waters it may become a nuisance because its enormous rootstocks are difficult to remove. These roots grow horizontally on the surface of the mud and may be as much as nine feet long and two inches thick. The rootstocks of the white water-lily are just as firmly rooted and tend to be more deeply embedded in the mud; they are black and do not run and branch so extensively as the others. The two species, when not in flower, are easy to identify by their leaves. In the white lily the leaf stalk is round and the veins of the leaves are relatively few and radiate widely from one basal point. In leaves of the yellow lily the veins are numerous and run in parallel lines close together along the midrib, branching only near the edge of the leaf; the leaf stalk is triangular in section. The yellow lily has soft, flexible leaves underwater in addition to harder floating leaves, while the white lily has only floating leaves. Both species have peculiar crystals of oxalate of lime in their tissues and these crystals are common in mud where they are growing. The bottle-shaped seed heads of the white lily are withdrawn under water when the flower has faded and there they decay and liberate their seeds. Those of the yellow lily stay above water until they open and release white mucilaginous bags of black seeds which float for a short time before they decay and the seeds sink. Each of these bags contains about twelve seeds and there may be fifteen bags in one seed head. The seeds of the white lily are small and pink and are eaten by moorhens; those of the other species are large and black and are said not to be touched by moorhens, although it has been recorded that they were a food of prehistoric man.

Hornwort (*Ceratophyllum demersum*) is chiefly abundant in the Yare Broads, where in the heat of summer its massed fronds give rise to a local phenomenon known as the ' singing ' of the water weeds. On a still evening after a sunny day of active photosynthesis, the hornwort is fizzing with little bubbles of oxygen, which produce a jiffling movement of the fronds and cause them to grate crisply against one another and so ' sing '. The beds of hornwort decay very rapidly at the end of summer, leaving the waters clear, while fragments remain in the muds, together with anchor-like fruits, until the following spring encourages renewed growth.

The dainty white climbing fumitory (*Corydalis claviculata*) is a plant apt to surprise visitors to Horsey Mere, where it grows in great quantities on the sites of plantations killed in the 1938 sea floods and along the banks of the mere where there is an accumulation of reedy flood litter. It is present also in a few other parts of the Bure-Ant-Thurne valley carrs.

In early spring, what may be called the sub-maritime reaches of the broadland waterways are to be seen flanked by beds of snow white blossoms of the scurvy-grasses (*Cochlearia officinalis* [Pl. VIII] and *C. anglica*) which appear also on the estuary salt-marshes of Breydon Water. Cuckoo-flowers (*Cardamine pratensis* and its variety *dentata*) grow chiefly in the mowing-marshes, but odd plants sometimes appear in reed grounds. They are commonly self-propagated by their green leaflets which break off and grow into new plants. Colonies of attractive 'double' flowered plants occur, especially in the neighbourhood of Barton Broad. The large bittercress (*Cardamine amara*) which much resembles the cuckoo-flower, but has whitish petals instead of pale lavender, is common in many of the carrs, especially amongst alders.

The marsh violet (*Viola palustris*), with its rounded leaves and lilac-coloured flowers, grows in many of the mossy fens of the Bure region and along the lower Waveney, but not near any of the Yare Broads. It is a local food plant of the pearl-bordered fritillary butterfly here.

The red campion (*Silene dioica*) has not yet been hybridised out of existence by the white campion in broadland, where it flourishes in many of the waterside clearings of the valley woodlands. Ragged robin (*Lychnis flos-cuculi*) is one of the plants favoured by the summer mowing of marshes and it is less common near the broads than it was fifty years ago. Its magenta flowers have a great attraction for swallowtail butterflies when these emerge in May and June.

Plants of the goosefoot family are present mainly on river banks in this area, except after sea floods have swept over the marshes, when the common and hastate oraches (*Atriplex patula* and *A. hastata*) grow from the flood refuse and exhibit a curious gigantism for one or two successive years, some of them developing prostrate rosettes as much as ten feet in diameter.

Tall marsh mallows (*Althaea officinalis*) with downy foliage and pale rose-pink flowers, flourish on clay banks and in odd corners of the grazing levels, but do not appear in the more peaty fens.

In recent years, river valleys in many parts of Britain have been invaded by the robust purple balsam (*Impatiens glandulifera*), a plant of the Himalayas, which has ousted the native flora in a devastating manner. Although small colonies of this species have existed alongside the rivers of broadland at a few points for the past quarter of a century, they have kept within bounds. A less domineering plant, the orange balsam (*Impatiens capensis*), a native of north America, has become widespread in the valley of the river Bure and has recently invaded the Ant, Thurne, and Yare, where it has found a niche in swampy marginal land without greatly altering the general composition of the flora. It is known that seeds of this balsam were taken from a naturalised colony along the river Test and thrown into a pool forming part of an upper tributary of the river Bure in 1927. From that centre it spread rapidly downstream and it is now familiar to visitors on the broads in summer.

Spindle (*Euonymus europaeus*) and buckthorn (*Rhamnus catharticus*) are characteristic trees of the Yare valley carrs but are not prevalent in the alder carrs of the rest of broadland, while the reverse holds for the alder buckthorn (*Frangula alnus*). Alder buckthorn was cut to supply a high-grade charcoal from this area during the last World War.

Some members of the pea family contribute brilliant flower colours to the mowing-marshes in summer, in particular the yellow marsh birdsfoot-trefoil (*Lotus uliginosus*) and the violet-blue tufted vetch (*Vicia cracca*). The marsh pea (*Lathyrus palustris*) is fairly widespread amongst the taller vegetation of the fens. Strawberry clover is a common plant of the grazing levels on the old estuary clay, where it has shown itself to be highly resistant to sea flooding on various occasions.

Meadow-sweet (*Filipendula ulmaria*) flourishes on neglected mowing-marshes, very noticeably in the Yare valley. The wetter ground of the broads is free from all kinds of blackberries, which appear only on banks and the stools of dead trees. The field rose (*Rosa arvensis*) grows freely in some of the carrs, while the dog rose (*Rosa canina*) is present mainly on rather higher ground, although its trailing branches may be seen dipping into the waters of the broads and rivers in many places. Marsh cinquefoil (*Potentilla palustris*) occurs in wet peaty hollows in the fens. Silverweed (*Potentilla anserina*) is one of the plants which exploits the clay lands immediately after sea flooding has reduced competition. Hawthorn (only one species, *Crataegus monogyna*) and sloe (*Prunus spinosa*) grow in the carrs, but not in the parts which are perpetually flooded.

The ivory-white chalice-like flowers of the grass of Parnassus (*Parnassia palustris*) appear with the devil's-bit scabious (*Succisa pratensis*) on the broadland fens in early autumn; but with the increasing neglect of summer mowing in recent years, the plants appear to have been shaded out of existence in many of their former habitats here.

Wild blackcurrants (*Ribes nigrum*) are locally plentiful in the wetter carrs; red currants are also common and in some years both species produce immense quantities of fruit, which attract birds. It is worth recording that in the summer of 1947, following a notoriously hard winter which decimated the population of woodland and garden birds in East Anglia, it was found possible to gather large quantities of excellent black, red and white currants from the wild bushes round some of the broads. It is interesting that although many of the wild black currants are affected by big-bud mites, some bushes estimated to be as much as seven years old have been found free from reversion virus disease, in the neighbourhood of Surlingham Broad. There is much variation amongst the bushes and examples of both red and black currants of high quality have been found from time to time in the wild, bird-sown populations. Curiously enough, currants in the carrs are not much troubled by the sawflies which so often defoliate them in gardens. This may be because the sawfly larvae go to ground to pupate and would often find themselves in water under the wild bushes.

The sundews (*Drosera rotundifolia* and *D. longifolia*) used to be much more common on some of the ill-drained fens adjacent to the Ant than they are now. On one occasion, F. W. Oliver recorded that he saw vast numbers of white butterflies, thought to have formed part of a migratory swarm, captured by sundews near one of the broads.

The most showy flower of the waterside is purple loosestrife (*Lythrum salicaria*), with its tall magenta spikes, which flowers in July. Many of the plants are rooted on old rotten posts; others thrive in neglected mowing-marshes, with hemp agrimony and meadowsweet. It is worth while examining the loosestrife flowers under a magnifying-glass, comparing those of several different spikes. As Darwin noticed long ago, a series of three distinct structural arrangements has been evolved to promote cross-pollination by visiting insects.

Of the several willowherbs occurring in the marshes, the great hairy willowherb (*Epilobium hirsutum*, Pl. VII) is the most conspicuous, chiefly in places where spoil has been thrown out of dykes and rivers. It is safe to walk where there is a bed of this plant in a marsh, just as one can be sure of a firm footing wherever the stinging nettle flourishes. The rose-bay (*Chamaenerion angustifolium*) appears on marsh banks and along some of the trackways from time to time, after there have been local fires. In this respect it behaves like the bracken fern in broadland and the two sometimes turn up together in patches isolated in a waste of reed beds, so that their presence comes as something of a shock to those who are sailing down the rivers.

Both the whorled and spiked water milfoils (*Myriophyllum verti-*

cillatum and *M. spicatum*) abound in the dykes and in the Ant and Thurne Broads, where the mare's-tail (*Hippuris vulgaris*) is another characteristic plant.

Several noble Umbelliferae are well established in and near the broads. Cowbane (*Cicuta virosa*) is to be found afloat or weakly anchored at the broads' margins; when its rhizomes are sliced by marshing implements an oily substance spreads from them to form an iridescent film on the water. Although cowbane is highly poisonous to many mammals, including man, it is often eaten, apparently with impunity, by the coypus which have almost eliminated it from some of the broads in the past few years. The water parsnip (*Sium latifolium*) is now a rare and disappearing species here: like the flowering rush (*Butomus umbellatus*) it has been cleared from many of the old dykes in the grazing levels in recent years. Parsley water-dropwort (*Oenanthe lachenalii*) is chiefly a plant of salt marshes and sub-maritime fens; but in broadland its range includes many old mowing-marshes rarely or never reached by any trace of salt water at the present time. Both wild angelica (*Angelica sylvestris*) and milk parsley (*Peucedanum palustre*) are common in the broadland fens and both are food-plants of the swallowtail caterpillars. Their winged fruits float readily and are widely dispersed by winter floods, so that they are able to exploit artificially cleared spaces in the undrained parts of the marshes. After much of the permanent vegetation was laid low by sea flooding in the vicinity of Horsey, Martham and Hickling in 1938, milk parsley was very abundant for a few years as a result of colonisation by seed. A rare albino form of the angelica appears here and there with some regularity at Surlingham, and a tremendous amount of variation is to be found in the floral structures and in the flowering performance of this species under differing conditions within its range of broadland habitats. In the Yare marshes a milky slug (*Agriolimax agrestis*) habitually destroys quantities of angelica flowers and developing fruits by night during August and September, and in some years it serves those of milk parsley in the same way.

Great water dock (*Rumex hydrolapathum*) is a common and conspicuous plant of the waterlogged marshes and watersides. Its growth is typically perennial, but its life is of only short duration in some of the more stagnant fens where little mineral matter penetrates. In the past few years this dock has been killed out over large areas as the result of coypus gnawing the rootstocks in winter. Persicaria (*Polygonum persicaria*) and water pepper (*Polygomum hydropiper*) are

Plate XI *Above*, *Trametes rubescens*, a bracket-fungus common on boughs of grey sallow and alder in the carrs

Below, Tar spot (*Rhytisma salicinum*) on grey sallow leaves

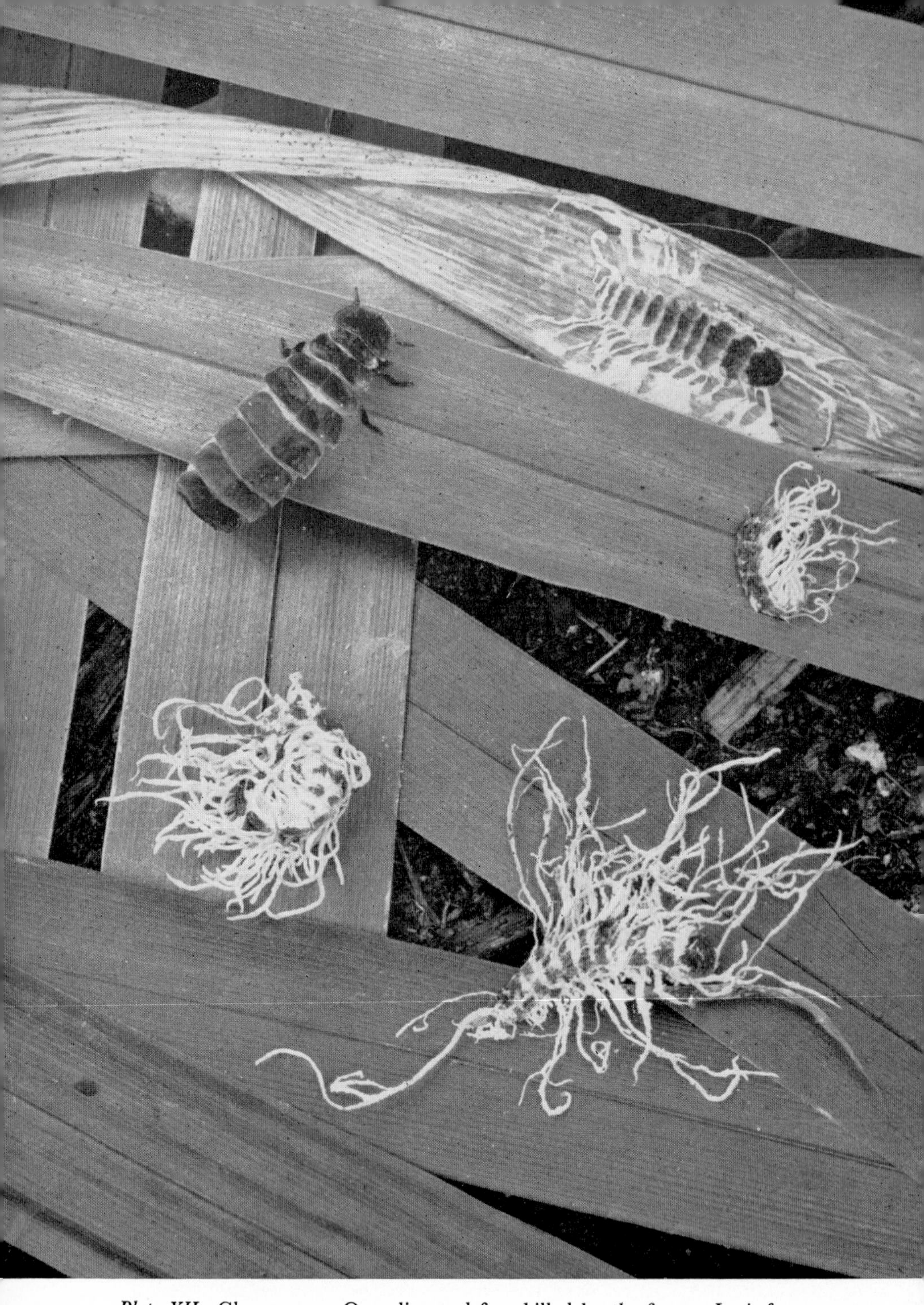

Plate XII Glow-worms. One alive and four killed by the fungus *Isaris fumoso-rosea*

ever-present weeds of disturbed muddy ground near the broadland rivers and broads and in the first year after dredging operations have been carried out they are often the first plants to appear in quantity on the mud.

The stinging nettle (*Urtica dioica*) grows freely along the banks of dykes where rich mud is drawn out from time to time and it occupies some of the higher ground on the carrs, where it resists tidal and winter flooding but does not take hold in true fens and reed-swamps. The hop (*Humulus lupulus*) is a common climber amongst the sallow bushes in carrs and it is often present in areas where the broad-leaved sweet-grass or rond-grass (*Glyceria maxima*) is plentiful near the Yare Broads.

Bog myrtle (*Myrica gale*) is locally plentiful in old sedge marshes about the broads of the Bure, Ant and Thurne and there are a few small colonies in the Yare valley. Under normal circumstances the male and female flowers are borne on separate bushes and it is of interest that one large, spreading, straggly bush, long isolated from others of its kind in an old sallow carr at Surlingham, bears flowers of both sexes on the same branches. In broadland, bog myrtle produces catkins (Pl. VI) in April and again, on a smaller scale, in summer. In this habit, it resembles the almond-leaved willow (*Salix triandra*). In some years the bushes are completely defoliated by the caterpillars of one of the Tortricid moths in early summer.

The alder (*Alnus glutinosa*) and the grey sallow (*Salix cinerea*) are the most thoroughly characteristic indigenous trees of the broads, where they invade uncut marshes and swampy ground and form scrub woodlands known as carrs. In areas where the ground water inclines towards acidity, the alder tends to predominate. The most notable alder carr in the district is known as ' Heron's Carr ' fringing Barton Broad, where many acres of these trees in all stages of growth and decay form a jungle, much of which stands on quaking peat, with many remains of pioneer sedge tussocks as the margin of open water is approached.

Varieties of the white willow (*Salix alba*) are a common feature of the broadland landscape, especially alongside some reaches of the rivers and many of the marsh roads. These trees are almost always grown from cuttings or else from temporary mooring stakes stuck in by yachtsmen. In time, most of the white willows, which are shallow-rooted, get blown down by gales and it is common to see revealed at the centre of the great uprooted base the original sharpened end of the live willow stake which was thrust into the marsh long years before. Wrens commonly and kingfishers occasionally nest in the vertical ‘cliffs’ formed by the soil-caked root masses of wind-felled willows along river banks. The common osier (*Salix viminalis*), almond-leaved willow (*S. triandra*) and purple willow (*S. purpurea*) almost certainly came into broadland by way of cultivation as osiers, and although they are all fairly widespread here, one never gains the impression that they have a place in the natural vegetational succession of this region. A variable population of grey sallows (*Salix cinerea*) includes bushes which exhibit characters suggesting hybrid origin involving some of the planted osiers. Interesting colonies of such forms tend to develop on river dredgings. The sallows bloom in early spring, providing nectar and pollen for bees and nectar for many moths by night. In May, downy ‘seeds’ blow from the boughs in blizzards and spread everywhere over land and water in a spectacular manner. Great drifts of fluff accumulate round the margins of the broads at such times, and exposed mud and peat becomes ‘alive’ with millions of tiny sallow seedlings before the month is out. The seeds must germinate at once or perish; indeed, their quickening is to be seen in the development of bright green pigment even as they float on the water, where they appear much like specks of very small duckweed. They are often picked up and used as mock prey-offerings by male flies of the genus *Hilara* in their nuptial flights over the water.

Ling (*Calluna vulgaris*) and cross-leaved heath (*Erica tetralix*) appear in parts of broadland behind the coast dunes and along the fringes of higher ground inland. The wintergreen (*Pyrola rotundifolia*) is restricted to less than half a dozen sites in bush-grown portions of the fens. Water violet (*Hottonia palustris*) with its pale green combs of aquatic leaves and delicate whorls of light mauve blossoms, is seen at its best in some of the dykes in May and June. Yellow loosestrife (*Lysimachia vulgaris*) is conspicuous on most of the local fens in July, where its flowers attract a special bee (*Macropis labiata*) and its leaves, only in a very few places, harbour one of Britain's rarest weevils (*Tapinotus sellatus*). Sea milkwort (*Glaux maritima*) extends up the rivers as far as salt water goes on average tides; it grows on the little strips of marsh (ronds) lying between the rivers and their raised banks. The brookweed (*Samolus valerandi*) is plentiful in slightly brackish marshes, but it also appears far inland, away from salt water, in the same way as the parsley water-dropwort.

Wild privet (*Ligustrum vulgare*) grows freely in the Yare valley carrs, where its berries attract birds in winter. Ash occurs in carrs which are not too wet and stagnant. Young trees often develop in the marshes, but die out before they have reached maturity.

The large trefoil leaves of bogbean (*Menyanthes trifoliata*) are noticeable in the wetter parts of the peatland in summer, but to see the splendour of their pink-and-white-fringed blossoms one must visit the fens in May. Water forget-me-nots (*Myosotis scorpioides* and *M. caespitosa*) abound round the broads and form great banks of vivid blue along watersides where bushes have been removed in the previous season. The great bindweed (*Calystegia sepium*) is a true native climber of broadland, where it not only entwines itself round the bushes but also sprawls by the acre over tall fen plants such as hairy willowherb, meadowsweet and reed. The true deadly nightshade (*Atropa bella-donna*) has long been known as an inhabitant of the land immediately surrounding Horsey Mere. After the sea flooding there in 1938, it became more widespread and abundant for a few years. It forms large bushes in summer and the dull purple, bell-like flowers are visited by many humble-bees. Bittersweet (*Solanum dulcamara*), with its sprawling woody stems, violet-and-yellow starry flowers and finally red berries, is a common broadland plant, completely tolerant of flooding. Water-betony (*Scrophularia aquatica*) growing by the waterside is commonly attacked by little grey and blackish weevils of the genus *Cionus* and its liver-coloured flowers are visited regularly by wasps. On some of the old turf-fens where quaking pools still exist, it is possible to see great swards of the rosy hooded blossoms of red rattle (*Pedicularis palustris*) in summer.

All four kinds of British bladderworts (*Utricularia vulgaris*, *U. neglecta*, *U. intermedia* and *U. minor*) have been found in the broads district, but only one of them (*U. vulgaris*) is likely to be noticed by anyone not specially searching for them. This is common and may be found sometimes in large quantities, floating amongst reeds, with its bright yellow flowers rising some six inches above the water. There are no roots, and the plant consists of a stem which may be as much as six feet long, with side branches, and clothed densely with dark olive-green leaves which are profusely branched and not unlike those of water-milfoil, except for the numerous bladders. In their natural position under water the bladders, if they have no prey inside, have their sides pressed together, but if the plant is lifted out of the water many of them suddenly expand and take in air with a crackling noise. Each bladder has a mouth closed by a tightly-fitting valve on which are four long hairs projecting outwards. It is supposed that a vacuum is set up in the bladder and that when a small animal touches these 'trigger' hairs, the valve opens and the inrush of water carries the animal in with it. This explanation is attractive, but it may not be correct, for one of the bladders may capture as many as a dozen water-fleas in half an hour and it seems improbable that it could absorb the contained water and re-establish a vacuum so rapidly after each capture. It seems possible that the prey, consisting most commonly of small creeping forms, are attracted to the bladders by some secretion or odour of decay and push their way in. *U. minor* and *U. intermedia* are much rarer and both may be found creeping amongst moss on ill-drained marshes, or in shallow pools. In some years, *U. minor* does not flower, while *U. intermedia* very rarely produces flowers in this country. *U. neglecta* has only made its appearance intermittently; it may arrive through the agency of immigrant water-birds from time to time and become established for a few years in a newly cleaned-out ditch or pool, like the common stonewort (*Chara vulgaris*).

The bladderworts die down in winter, but survive in the form of 'turions' or resting-buds. These are small balls of tightly packed leaves which are formed at the ends of the branches in late summer and germinate in the following spring. They can easily be forced into growth by heat and can be cultivated indoors in winter. When the plants suffer from exceptionally dry weather in summer, they tend to develop broad instead of narrow leaf-segments and turn into land-forms in the same way as water crowfoots.

Water-mint (*Mentha aquatica*) gives a characteristic scent to the marshes wherever it is bruised underfoot. It flowers late and its blossoms attract many insects, including hive bees, in August. Gipsywort (*Lycopus europaeus*) is a very common plant of the waterside and it is tolerant of a lot of shade. Its leaves are devoured by a shining brown-and-bronze beetle (*Chrysomela polita*). Marsh woundwort (*Stachys palustris*) and skull-cap (*Scutellaria galericulata*) are other common plants of the mint family in the old mowing-marshes.

A robust form of the marsh bedstraw (*Galium palustre*) is common in wet places amongst reeds and sedges and in rush-fens the bog bedstraw (*G. uliginosum*) tends to replace it. Guelder rose (*Viburnum opulus*) flourishes in the carrs, especially in those of the Yare valley, where it produces showy white umbels of night-scented blossoms in June and July and quantities of translucent red berries in autumn. The foliage of guelder-rose turns fiery red and crimson at the end of summer and looks very lovely when reflected in the water of broads and channels.

The common and marsh valerians (*Valeriana officinalis* and *V. dioica*) grow in the undrained marshes of almost the whole district, where trees or saw sedge are not dominant. The bur-marigolds (*Bidens cernua* and *B. tripartitas*) both occur on the broads, commonly occupying muddy places disturbed by waterfowl round the margins. Marsh ragwort (*Senecio aquaticus*) is present chiefly on rough grazings, and along the brinks of drainage dykes. The lovely sea-aster (*Aster tripolium*), although properly a plant of the salt marshes, appears alongside the rivers here twelve miles or more inland and isolated plants are seen flowering in the most unlikely situations from time to time. Hemp agrimony (*Eupatorium cannabinum*) is a tall and vigorous species common in the watery marshes, where its old-rose tassel flowers attract large numbers of the gayer butterflies in July and early August. Fibres from the bleached dead stems tend to break free and resemble loose shreds of hemp by the time the reed-cutters are at work just after Christmas.

The most noble plant of the broadland composites is the marsh sowthistle (*Sonchus palustris*), which used to be on the verge of extinction here but is now widely distributed and locally plentiful. It is a perennial and in summer the stems stand ten feet high, their pale yellow flower-heads topping the riverside reed-beds along the lower reaches of the Yare and Waveney, the margin of Horsey Mere, the Bure near Acle and in a few places elsewhere.

Lesser water plantain (*Baldellia ranunculoides*) is to be seen in plenty near some of the Ant and Thurne Broads and in some of the other marshes where there are still rather ill-drained old rough grazings in small waterside strips here and there. It is specially noticeable in dykes beside the coast road at Somerton. Water plantain (*Alisma plantago-aquatica*) is common in the dykes and arrowhead (*Sagittaria sagittifolia*) grows in the upper parts of the rivers and in some of the deeper main drains. Flowering rush (*Butomus umbellatus*) is an attractive tall reedswamp plant with large umbels of pink flowers; it is not nearly so common in broadland as it was at the beginning of this century, when it grew in many of the dykes of the great grazing levels. Frogbit (*Hydrocharis morsus-ranae*) is probably more common in this area than in any other part of the British Isles; it floats in summer on dykes and in the bays of broads, where its rounded leaves are called ' Halfpennies-and-pennies ' by local marshmen. Pretty, three-petalled white flowers appear in summer and they are unisexual. It has not been established that frogbit produces viable fruits in England; survival is assured by resting buds which drop down to the mud when the floating plants die and decay in autumn; these buds rise to the surface and develop into new plants in the following spring.

Water-soldier (*Stratiotes aloides*; Pl. v) is a common plant in many of the broads and may become so abundant as to block dykes completely. In some places they are packed so tightly that they push their leaves out of the water. As a rule, they sink to the bottom in autumn; but some plants never come to the surface at all and these have longer and more flexible leaves than those which float. Normal plants are aloe-like in form, with red-tinged, saw-toothed leaves forming rosettes. Plants flowering in June and July have light green crowns where the leaves emerge slightly from the surface of the water. The comparatively large, three-petalled white flowers are not known to produce fruits in Britain, although both female and hermaphrodite flowers have been found here. It is a curious fact that the water-soldier plants are predominantly male south of Latitude 52° N, predominantly female above Latitude 55° N and functionally male and female in between, where fruits are produced. It is of interest that fossil seeds have been found in the Pleistocene Forest Bed deposits of East Anglia and elsewhere in Europe north of the climatic belt within which they are developed at the present time.

Canadian pondweed or water-thyme (*Elodea canadensis*) has been established in the broads district for about a century. In the early years of its spread, its rampant growth caused wide concern, for it choked fresh-water channels and invaded some of the broads in a spectacular manner. Stevenson, in his *Birds of Norfolk*, vol. 3 (1890), cites instances of mute swans having cleared large quantities of this weed from waters at Hoveton and Surlingham and he observes that its abundance on Hoveton and Wroxham Broads proved a great attraction to coot, wigeon and tufted ducks. *Elodea* is no longer a major nuisance in this area, although it has shown a marked tendency to make a ' come-back ' from time to time, following the local clearance of other weeds. Only female plants are known in East Anglia and seeds are not set; the small pink flowers grow up through the water by an enormous elongation of the floral tube, which may reach a length of twelve inches. In Canada, where both sexes are found, the male flowers become detached and rise to the surface, where their pollen sacs burst and the pollen floats until it comes in contact with the pistils of the female flowers.

The pondweeds (*Potamogeton* species) are well represented in the waterways of broadland. The tench-weed (*P. natans*) is noticeable with its broadly elliptical, bronze-tinted floating leaves, in quiet bays and wide, deep dykes. The closely related *P. coloratus* is present in some of the fen pools and the reddish pondweed (*P. alpinus*) has been found in some of the peaty waters. The long-stalked pondweed (*P. praelongus*) is a broads speciality but the shining and perfoliate pondweeds (*P. lucens* and *P. perfoliatus*) are more widespread and plentiful and occur also in local rivers. Several species with ribbon-like leaves are found in varying abundance and the fennel-leaved pondweed (*P. pectinatus*) shows the greatest tolerance of salt water and is common in all the shallower broads, a great many of the dykes and in places where muddy shelves are formed at the bends of the rivers. *P. pectinatus* produces tuber-like offshoots towards the end of summer and these tend to break away and establish fresh colonies in the following year.

Since 1883, Hickling Broad has been noted as the haunt of *Naias marina* (Pl. VI), a submerged water-weed which has an almost world-wide distribution but in Britain lives only in the broads, where until very recently it has been confined to slightly brackish waters. Its seeds have been found in various Pleistocene and post-glacial lake deposits in England and Wales, showing that it enjoyed a wider distribution here in the past. At the present time it is spreading beyond the confines of the brackish Hickling area and has been found since 1949 in Barton, Alderfen, Upton and Hoveton Inner Broads, the waters of which are not brackish. The plant forms extensive beds, rooted in mud at depths ranging from fifteen inches to seven feet. It has been found only in comparatively clear waters and it has shown itself able to compete successfully with the stoneworts (*Charophytes*) which abound at Hickling and with the water-milfoils (*Myriophyllum spicatum* and *M. verticillatum*) there and elsewhere. It is commonly pulled up by diving ducks and its seeds have been found in their crops.

The rushes are not so much inhabitants of the waterside as they are of the marshes, where the various species are often to be seen growing in a patchwork which reflects the varied character of the ground supporting them. Thus the blunt-flowered or fen rush (*Juncus subnodulosus*) is typical of mowing-marshes, where it is often displaced in the more 'sour' spots by the sharp-flowered rush (*J. acutiflorus*), distinguishable from a distance by the brighter, chestnut colour of its flowers. On rough grazings and what may be called meadowy marshes, the soft rush (*J. effusus*) grows in large clumps, while the hard rush (*J. inflexus*) is also found in such places, but tends to mark the presence of clayey ground; it has thin, wiry, bluish-green stems and leaves. The so-called ' common rush ' (*J. conglomeratus*) is less plentiful than any of the species mentioned so far, in this district; but it is fairly well distributed in the least alkaline parts of the fens and is sometimes plentiful on the fringes where cross-leaved heath and purple moor-grass grow. Salt-flooded marshes towards the coast have the sea-rush (*J. maritimus*), the round-fruited rush (*J. compressus*) and the mud-rush (*J. gerardi*).

The yellow flag (*Iris pseudacorus*, Pl. VI), abounds all over broadland, outside the great grazing levels of the Breydon estuary. Brown seeds spilled from its pods in winter are dispersed by floods and may often be found germinating amongst marsh litter in spring. Old plants survive shading by trees and bushes when carrs develop on the fens, but in shade it has been found that fewer flowers appear and that less growth is made year by year. A record of each summer's growth and flowering performance is left in the branching rhizomes, so that a very old *Iris* plant may be able to yield useful information to an ecologist when he is trying to discover the age of the carr in which it is growing.

Orchids often make a brilliant show of colour in the rushy mowing-marshes of the broads and here, as so frequently elsewhere, the many varied shapes, colours and patterns of the flowers in the spotted orchid (*Dactylorchis fuchsii*), early marsh orchid (*D. incarnata*), common marsh orchid (*D. praetermissa*) and what are sometimes considered to be their hybrids provide material for speculation and experiment. Only recently, some late-flowering plants of distinctive mien have attracted notice in some of the fens where *Cladium* and *Schoenus* are specially common, but their status is not yet decided. The twayblade (*Listera ovata*) is plentiful in many of the local fens and it persists for some time in the partial shade of invading bushes. The fragrant orchid, (*Gymnadenia conoposea*) grows in some of the quaking fens, most usually where the marsh helleborine (*Epipactis palustris*) and black bog-rush are also present. The fen orchid (*Liparis loeselii*) is now a rare and disappearing British plant which has so far managed to survive in broadland. There it is now restricted to special fens where it is associated with the moss *Campylium stellatum*, short reeds, milk parsley, purple loosestrife, fen rush, creeping willow, marsh bedstraw, black bog-rush, marsh pennywort and, less regularly, a dozen or so other kinds of fen plants. The fen orchid is small and inconspicuous, with pale, yellow-green flowers and a pair of broad, sub-erect leaves.

Sweet flag (*Acorus calamus*), with its rippled, yellow-green sword-leaves, grows in more or less floating clumps round the margins of bays in many of the broads and along the riversides. When bruised, it gives off a strong, sweet scent and the leaves were formerly cut to make fragrant litter for the floors of buildings. Sir James Edward Smith, in his *English Botany* (1832) stated that 'the floor of Norwich Cathedral is always strewed with the leaves of this plant upon festival days, which, being trodden upon, perfume the whole building.' During the Second World War, *Acorus* in broadland was sought for use in the tobacco industry.

All British duckweeds of the genus *Lemna* are present on the broads in fluctuating quantities year by year. In very sunny years, they may form great sheets of green completely covering some of the smaller broads and filling the bays of others by the end of July; but in some duller seasons their presence is scarcely noticeable. In either case, they vanish from open water in autumn. Scattered plants of *Lemna minor* are to be found floating in flooded reed-beds even in midwinter. *L. polyrhiza* survives the winter by means of small purple offshoots (turions) which lie at the bottom until spring comes.

The common and unbranched bur-reeds (*Sparganium erectum* and *S. simplex*) both grow in many places round the edges of broads and in neglected dykes. The small bur-reed (*S. minimum*) occurs in a few of the fen dykes, mainly in the northern part of the district. The lesser reedmace (*Typha angustifolia*) is a very common reedswamp plant of the broads and is one of the chief invaders of open water in many of them. The great reedmace (*T. latifolia*, Pl. VI) with its larger, blacker 'poker' heads, is seldom seen in great concentrations here, although it is typically associated with the half-floating beds of rond-grass (*Glyceria maxima*) in the Yare valley. Both plants are much sought after by coypus, which devour their succulent shoots.

Common cotton-grass (*Eriophorum angustifolium*) has a rather patchy distribution here and grows on the least well-drained peat areas, where mowing, burning or intermittent grazing have prevented the advance of taller vegetation.[1] The sea club-rush (*Scirpus maritimus*) is common in brackish waters, chiefly in dykes, but also on riverside 'ronds' up to fifteen miles from the sea. The common bulrush (*Schoenoplectus lacustris*) is present chiefly in the Flegg Broads and grows in smaller quantities in broads of the Bure, Ant and Thurne. It has disappeared from the Yare Broads recently, since the effects of tides have been felt more extensively there. The glaucous bulrush (*S. tabernaemontani*) grows chiefly in brackish waters, but is not confined to them. Black

[1] The rare *E. gracilis* was found in one of the local fens in 1955. (Walters, S. M,. 1956.)

bog-rush (*Schoenus nigricans*), known in this district as ' Black Star ', is a characteristic plant of ' poor ' fen soils where sedge and litter are cut behind the broads. The saw sedge (*Cladium mariscus*) is probably more plentiful in this region than anywhere else in Britain at the present time and dominates some hundreds of acres of old fenland in the Hickling-Horsey neighbourhood, where it is cut periodically as a crop for use in thatching. For students of sedges (*Carex*), the broads are specially attractive, not only because some thirty species have been noticed in the area, but also because the various kinds may be seen growing in a great many different types of lowland habitat, ranging from salt-marshes and boggy pools behind the coast dunes to silt-washed meadows up-river. The great tussocks of *Carex paniculata* give to many of the bays and backwaters of the broads a semblance of tropical jungle. The small tussock sedge (*C. appropinquata*) is locally common on old mowing marshes fairly well back from the water's edge. Extensive stands of the great pond sedge (*C. riparia*), lesser pond sedge (*C. acutiformis*), brown sedge (*C. disticha*) and even a slender sedge (*C. lasiocarpa*) are to be seen here. The false fox-sedge (*C. otrubae*) is specially conspicuous along the shores of broadland rivers in places where the old estuary clay has been dredged and thrown on to the banks and where, incidentally, salty water penetrates. The divided sedge (*C. divisa*) grows as a rank turf alongside some of the dykes of the great grazing levels surrounding Breydon and thrives inland as far up the river Bure as Acle; after prolonged flooding of the grazing marshes by sea water in 1953, this sedge was found to be one of the first plants to spring from badly salted pasture soil.

Of broadland grasses, the reed (*Phragmites communis*) is by far the most obvious and plentiful species fringing the waterways. In some places beds or ' bushes ' of reed cover hundreds of acres of wet marsh and rond, where, from Christmas until April 5th, they are cut, tied in bunches and sold for thatching. Reeds will grow up from the bottom in two to three feet of water, but they thrive best in shallow places where there is some water movement bringing fresh supplies of nutrients. Very thick, tall reeds develop at Oulton and along the lower reaches of the river Waveney, where the waters are inclined to be silty and often a little salt. Reeds growing in brackish water produce very hard, rigid stalks which are durable in thatch. The qualities of reeds vary considerably from place to place and from year to year. A warm, bright summer favours their growth. In some places the shoots are killed by stem-boring larvae of wainscot moths in early summer and the tops are seen to turn yellow before the end of July.

In such cases, secondary shoots arise and grow to almost the normal height, provided there is plenty of sunshine in the ensuing August and September; but in any case, these substitutes are softer and inferior from the reed-cutter's point of view. Many thousands of starlings roost in the reed beds in summer and autumn and their combined weight flattens and spoils the reeds for cutting; but the reeds themselves flourish vegetatively where they are manured by the birds year after year in some of these beds and their growth is lush and soft. It has been noticed that in certain reed grounds distinctive patches of reeds exist side by side in a manner which suggests that each patch originated as a single plant differing in habit from its neighbour. Thus, at Surlingham Broad, when cutting is begun in the winter, one can see an expanse of reeds topped with brown plumes which have already got rid of their downy ' seeds ', while an equally large expanse adjoining bears plumes that are lighter in colour because they are still fluffy with the ' seeds ' not yet freed. Clearly, there are ' early ' and ' late ' fruiting reeds, just as there are ' early ' and ' late ' varieties of fruit trees in orchards. Reed seedlings are rarely seen springing from bare mud or peat, but when the seeding plumes happen to be broken off so that they lie in the water for a time, the seeds germinate and produce a mass of tiny green spear leaves in spring, as in the sprouting ears of ' laid ' corn, seen on the fields when rain and wind spoil the harvest.

Reeds are susceptible to frost damage in spring, when the young shoots or ' colts ' appear. Where cutting has removed the protection which would have been afforded by the old stems, a spell of warm, sunny weather in early spring hastens the growth of the ' colts ', so that they are more likely to suffer from a subsequent frost than those which have developed more slowly in the forests of uncut stalks. Reed-cutting in April tends to involve mechanical damage to the young shoots and the burning of the top reed-growth should not be carried out after the end of March, for the same reason. Where it is intended to destroy reeds, the local practice is to mow the plants in July and again before mid-August, so as to prevent the plants from putting away reserves for the winter.

The reed canary grass (*Phalaris arundinacea*) is apt to be mistaken for true reed by the inexpert, especially when the flowers are not present, because it has much the form of reed, with its broad spear leaves and erect habit. A simple way of distinguishing the two plants is to look at the ligules where the leaves clasp the stems; in the true reed these ligules are fringed with hairs, but in the reed canary grass they consist of a thin skin which is either smooth at the edge or only a little frayed: never hairy. This grass does not grow in the water, but is usually to be found on fairly firm marshland, where, unlike the reed, it retains its bleached leaves all winter. It is a variable plant, producing flowering panicles which may be narrow and compact or widely branched and spreading and which may have purple or greenish-white spikelets. Large stands of plants can arise vegetatively, perpetuating a variant, and a series of *Phalaris* beds occupying a tract of fen sometimes presents a remarkable appearance from the fact that 'clones' at the opposite extremes in variation stand next to one another.

The broad-leaved sweet-grass or rond-grass (*Glyceria maxima*) is a major invader of open waters in the Yare Broads, where rich feeding and tidal rhythm have been shown to favour it. It is a coarse grass with vivid green leaves, many of which are green in winter as well as in summer, although on some of the marshes the dead ribbon-leaves tend to become bleached and beaten down by rain and snow to form a smooth, compact, undulating 'roof' for a period in the winter. Beneath the mat of dead leaves there is a space alternately flooded and drained by tides and here, as in a laboratory 'moist chamber', the spores of many kinds of fungi find conditions favourable for germination and development.

Water whorl-grass (*Catabrosa aquatica*) grows in some of the marsh ditches, but it is comparatively rare in broadland. Purple small-reed (*Calamagrostis canescens*) is locally abundant in the undrained parts of the area, especially favouring old, neglected mowing-marshes and bushy places. Harvest mice are very fond of building their nests out of its comparatively fine leaves and slender stalks. The hybrid purple marram (*Ammocalamagrostis baltica*) is not confined to sand dunes here, but spreads some way on to the sub-maritime fen at Horsey, so that it can be included fairly as a broadland plant. Grasses of the mowing-marshes include varying amounts of red fescue (*Festuca rubra*), meadow fescue (*F. pratensis*) and tall fescue (*F. arundinacea*), rough meadow grass (*Poa trivialis*), common quaking grass (*Briza media*), creeping bent (*Agrostis stolonifera*), purple moor grass (*Molinia caerulea*) and the heath grass (*Sieglingia decumbens*). Creeping bent is very plentiful on some of the fen pastures near the coast. Yorkshire fog (*Holcus lanatus*) abounds on meadows. Perennial rye-grass is a typical constituent of the grassland flora on the great Breydon levels, where it has shown itself very tolerant of salt flooding. Sea barley (*Hordeum marinum*) grows on river and marsh banks within a few miles of the sea. The river walls, along the lower reaches, are crested by quantities of a stiff, bluish-green grass, the sea couch (*Agropyron pungens*), which is sometimes associated with the common couch or twitch (*A. repens*) and forms hybrid populations with it. These tough wiry grasses, with their spreading rhizomes and perennial mode of growth, do much to prevent the erosion of the clay banks through exposure to rain.

GLOSSARY OF NAMES APPLIED TO MARSH AND WATER PLANTS IN BROADLAND

American weed: *Elodea canadensis* (water thyme)
Apple-pie: *Eupatorium cannabinum* (hemp agrimony)
Bean-weed: *Potamogeton lucens* (shining pondweed)
Black star: *Schoenus nigricans* (bog-rush)
Black-weed: *Sparganium ramosum* (bur-reed)
Bolder: *Scirpus lacustris* (bulrush)
Broad Arrow: *Sagittaria sagittifolia* (arrowhead)
Bunds: *Centaurea nemoralis* (knapweed) and *Succisa pratensis* (devil's-bit)
Bulrush: *Typha latifolia* (greater reed-mace)
Bunk: *Angelica sylvestris* (marsh angelica)
Bush-weed: *Ranunculus* spp. (various water-crowfoots)
Cat's-tail: *Equisetum* spp. (horsetails), *Hippuris vulgaris* (Mare's-tail), *Typha* spp. (reed-maces) and *Veronica beccabunga* (brooklime)
Cauliflower-weed: *Ranunculus* spp. (various water-crowfoots)
Cheat: *Carex riparia* and *C. acutiformis* (sedges), *Phalaris arundinacea* (reed canary-grass) and at times other grasses and sedges regarded as 'small stuff' present on a marsh cut primarily for reed, sedge (*Cladium*) or a mixture of these and gladden (*Typha angustifolia*)
Clover: *Lemna polyrhiza* (greater duckweed)
Crowsnot: *Enteromorpha intestinalis* (a floating alga)
Deadly nightshade: *Solanum dulcamara* (bittersweet, woody nightshade)
Dodder-grass: *Briza media* (quaking grass)
Fennel-weed: *Potamogeton pectinatus* (fennel-leaved pondweed)
Ferret's-tail: *Ceratophyllum* spp. (hornworts)
Fiddlesticks: *Scrophularia aquatica* (marsh figwort)
Fishleaf: *Alisma plantago-aquatica* (water plantain)
Fog: *Holcus lanatus* (Yorkshire fog)
Foxtail: *Hippuris vulgaris* (mare's-tail)
Gatter-bush, gattridge: *Viburnum opulus* (guelder-rose)

Gladden: *Typha angustifolia* (lesser reed-mace) and *Iris pseudacorus* (yellow flag), both plants with sword-shaped leaves, viz. *gladius*, a sword
Grass-weed: *Potamogeton pectinatus* (fennel-leaved pondweed)
Halfpennies-and-pennies: *Hydrocharis morsus-ranae* (frogbit)
Hair-weed: *Potamogeton pectinatus* (fennel-leaved pondweed)
Hassocks: *Carex paniculata* and *C. appropinquata* (tussock sedges)
Huv-stuff: commonly *Glyceria maxima* (rond-grass)
King-cup: *Caltha palustris* (marsh marigold)
Lace-weed: *Potamogeton pectinatus* (fennel-leaved pondweed)
Lamb's-skin: floating sheets of various filamentous algae
Maidenhair grass: *Briza media* (quaking grass)
Mare's-fat: *Pulicaria dysenterica* (marsh fleabane)
Nat-hills: *Carex paniculata* (tussock sedge)
Needle rush: *Juncus inflexus* (hard rush)
Penny-weed: *Hydrocharis morsus-ranae* (frogbit)
Pickerel-weed: *Stratiotes aloides* (water-soldier)
Pin rush: *Juncus inflexus* (hard rush) and *J. maritimus* (sea rush)
Poker: *Typha* spp. (reed-maces)
Poker-bolder: *Typha latifolia* (greater reed-mace)
Rattle-basket: *Rhinanthus minor* (yellow rattle)
Ratweed: *Lemna minor* (lesser duckweed)
Raw: tangled mats of coarse filamentous algae, usually *Cladophora*.
Red-weed: *Azolla filiculoides* (water fern)
Rond-stuff: *Glyceria maxima* (rond-grass)
Sags: *Carex acutiformis*, *C. riparia* and other sedges, excluding *Cladium mariscus*
Sedge: *Cladium mariscus* only
Serpent's-tongue: *Sagittaria sagittifolia* (arrowhead)
She-gladden: *Typha latifolia* (greater reed-mace)
She-reed: *Phalaris arundinacea* (reed canary-grass); also second-growth *Phragmites communis* (reed) which lacks flowering plumes
Soft-reed: as 'she-reed'
Soft rush, soft water-rush: *Juncus subnodulosus* (blunt-flowered rush)
Star-grass, starch-grass: *Schoenus nigricans* (bog-rush)
Tenchweed: *Potamogeton natans* (broad-leaved pondweed)
Thack: *Cladium mariscus* (sedge)
Twig-rush: *Cladium mariscus* (sedge)
Water-grass: *Juncus gerardi* (mud rush) and in some places *Agrostis stolonifera* (creeping bent)
Whitsuntide flower: *Viburnum opulus* (guelder-rose)

Willow-weed: *Epilobium hirsutum* (great hairy willowherb) and *Polygonum amphibium* (amphibious bistort)

The names in the above list have been collected from original sources, mainly from men occupied in cutting reeds, cleaning out marsh dykes and clearing weeds from the rivers and broads, during the past twenty years. Their authenticity has been checked in every case by the examination of specimens.

CHAPTER 6

CRYPTOGAMIC PLANTS OF THE BROADS

by E. A. Ellis

Ferns, mosses, liverworts, lichens and fungi flourish best in a moist climate, which East Anglia lacks. All the same, the humidity of the micro-climate in fens and carrs round about the broads satisfies the needs of a rich variety of these cryptogamic plants, so that they are much more fully represented here than the low rainfall of the district might lead one to expect. There is very little industrial pollution of the atmosphere and this is another factor of importance where the growth of lichens in particular is concerned.

In this chapter, considerable space is given to the fungi of the marsh country. Experience has shown that the broads are outstandingly rich in the smaller forms of fungi which find lodging in the reed-swamps and fens. They play an important part in controlling the distribution of the higher plants and in breaking down old plant litter year after year. It will be shown also that many small fungi here, as in tropical jungles, attack a variety of insects and spiders. Even if the broads were not famous for their birds and the beauty of their scenery, British mycologists could make out a very strong case for preserving them for posterity.

FERNS AND FERN ALLIES (*Pteridophyta*)

The broads district is rich in lowland ferns, some of which are to be seen in vast and impressive colonies in the alder carrs. The royal fern (*Osmunda regalis*; Pl. x) grows to magnificent proportions here, mainly amongst alders in the swamps surrounding broads of the Bure and Ant. The delicate, light green fronds of marsh fern (*Thelypteris palustris*) are abundant on many of the fens, often in company with bog myrtle and saw sedge. The rare crested buckler fern (*Dryopteris cristata*; Pl. x) just manages to hold its own in a few places where the peat is poorly drained and supports a certain amount of sphagnum. The broad buckler (*Dryopteris dilatata*) is present in large numbers in the shade of trees and the narrow buckler (*D. lanceolatocristata*) occurs both in the carrs and on more open fen, especially in the vicinity of Horsey. The lady fern (*Athyrium filix-femina*) grows in some of the carrs, usually at higher levels than the bucklers, while the male fern (*Dryopteris filix-mas*) occupies an intermediate zone, sometimes in company with Borrer's fern (*D. borreri*). The hard fern (*Blechnum spicant*) is comparatively scarce, but it grows on the sides of some of the land-spring ditches. Occasional clumps of hartstongue (*Phyllitis scolopendrium*) and polypody (*Polypodium vulgare*) develop on the rotting stumps of trees in the carrs. The adder's-tongue (*Ophioglossum vulgatum*) is plentiful on the mowing-marshes. Bracken appears on marsh banks after fires have prepared the ground for it.

The little ' water fern ' (*Azolla filiculoides*), of American origin, was introduced into private waterways at Woodbastwick in the Bure valley in 1908 and was spread far and wide over the broads as a result of a phenomenal flood brought about by heavy rains in the late summer of 1912. For some years its floating fronds covered the surfaces of dykes all over broadland, where their attractive rosy-magenta suffusion of colour at maturity gained for the plant the local name ' red-weed '. At the present time, it is by no means plentiful in the area; it is known to have suffered severely in hard winters, such as that of 1947.

Only three kinds of horsetails are known to grow near the broads. Of these, *Equisetum fluviatile* appears in shallow, peaty pools and the wetter parts of ill-drained fens; the marsh horsetail (*E. palustre*) is abundant in the mowing-marshes and the common horsetail (*E. arvense*) spreads from higher ground to the fringes of some of the fens.

MOSSES AND LIVERWORTS

The bryophytes of fens in this country are few compared with those of acid moorlands. This is due largely to the fact that the swamp vegetation in base-rich marshes is on the whole tall and luxuriant, producing a light-excluding canopy in summer and an ever-increasing mat of tangled dead stalks and leaves in winter. Mowing-marshes, characterised by the presence of rushes rather than reeds and tall sedges, provide a slightly more favourable habitat than do the reed-swamps, where bryophytes are almost confined to the crowns of tussock sedges (*Carex paniculata*). River banks, dyke-sides where mud and peat have been thrown out, and the exposed bases of overturned willows are colonised by several mosses which are not always typically marsh-dwelling species, and the same may be said of old rotten boats ending their days in forgotten corners of the waterways.

Fen carrs, however, are mossy in the extreme, especially at a late stage in their development when there is an abundance of fallen boughs and many of the sallows and alders have reached such a height that plenty of light falls between them.

No thorough survey of the bryophytes has been made in the broads region as yet, but sufficient sampling has been carried out here and there by W. H. Burrell (1914) and more recently by A. E. Ellis and others to provide a basis for further study.

The only true water moss found in this region is *Fontinalis antipyretica*. It abounds in several of the Bure Broads, in the shallow and often brackish waters of Hickling and Horsey, and in the Waveney above Beccles and the Yare above Brundall. It does not tolerate mud-clouded waters. *Acrocladium cuspidatum* and *Campylium stellatum* in fens and both *Brachythecium rivulare* and *Eurhynchium swartzii* in shady places along river and ditch margins, often grow partly submerged for much of the year. The aquatic liverworts include *Ricciocarpus natans*, which floats like duckweed on Barton and Sutton Broads and on some marsh dykes in the Yare valley, and *Riccia fluitans*, which has narrow, light green fronds floating on some of the fen ditches.

In the following list of fen mosses, the species marked with an asterisk are those found more particularly in the poorly drained and less alkaline mowing-marshes of the Bure-Ant-Thurne region and where these occur in the Yare and Waveney valleys, they tend to be restricted to localities out of the normal reach of tidal flooding. The names used are those given by P. W. Richards and E. C. Wallace in 'An Annotated List of British Mosses', *Trans. British Bryological Society* 1, Part 4 (1950).

**Acrocladium cordifolium*
A. cuspidatum (the most characteristic fen moss)
**A. giganteum*
**Aulacomnium palustre* (not always with *Sphagnum* here)
Brachythecium purum (common in mowing-marshes)
B. rivulare (marginal)
B. rutabulum (widespread, common beside narrow ditches and on sedge tussocks)
Bryum pseudotriquetrum, var. *bimum*

Campylium elodes
C. stellatum (almost the only moss on some Ant valley fens)
Climacium dendroides
Ctenidium molluscum
**Dicranum bonjeani*
Drepanocladus aduncus
**D. revolvens*
Eurhynchium praelongum (on tussocks)
E. swartzii (common)
**Fissidens adianthoides*
Hypnum cupressiforme (tussocks and marsh banks)
Mnium affine
M. hornum (on peat in fens as well as in shady woods)
M. punctatum (not so common as *M. affine*)
M. undulatum (found occasionally)
**Philonotis fontana*
Pohlia nutans
Pseudoscleropodium purum
Rhytidiadelphus squarrosus

The fen liverworts are few, *Aneura pinguis* being the most frequent associate of the mosses in this habitat. *Lophocolea bidentata* grows on sedge tussocks. *Chiloscyphus polyanthus* has been found in swamps at Ranworth and Sutton. *Marchantia polymorpha* flourishes locally from time to time where burning and mowing have taken place.

The mosses of fen-carrs include many of the common species growing on rotten wood and on the trunks of living trees, together with a few that in upland districts develop mainly on moist, clayey soils; there are also fen species which formed part of the ground flora before sallows, alders and other trees and bushes colonised their territory. The following list gives most of the broads mosses occurring in carrs.

Acrocladium cuspidatum (relict from fens)
Amblystegium serpens
A. varium
Atrichum undulatum (elevated ground in alder carrs)
Aulacomnium androgynum
Brachythecium purum
B. rutabulum (very common)
B. velutinum
Bryum capillare
B. pseudotriquetrum, var. *bimum*

Cirriphyllum piliferum
Climacium dendroides (often under sallows)
Cratoneuron filicinum
Dicranoweissia cirrata (on tree trunks)
Dicranum scoparium
Drepanocladus fluitans (marginal, by water)
Eurhynchium praelongum
E. striatum
E. swartzii
Fissidens taxifolius
Hypnum cupressiforme (frequently in slender forms)
Leptodictyum riparium (in very wet, shady places)
Leskea polycarpa (rather commonly on fallen branches in old sallow carrs)
Mnium affine
M. hornum
M. punctatum
M. undulatum
Orthotrichum affine (on tree trunks)
O. lyellii (local, on tree trunks)
O. tenellum (occasionally on tree trunks)
Plagiothecium denticulatum (on the ground)
P. silvaticum (not common)
Pseudoscleropodium purum
Thamnium alopecurum
Thuidium tamariscinum (usually on raised paths)
Weissia controversa

The liverworts of fen-carrs are:

Aneura pinguis
Conocephalum conicum (where the substratum is clayey)
Frullania dilatata (common on tree trunks)
Lophocolea bidentata (rather common on fallen boughs)
L. heterophylla (abundant on rotten wood)
Marchantia polymorpha (occasionally)
Metzgeria furcata (frequent on trunks)
Pellia epiphylla (margins of wet hollows)
Radula complanata (common on trunks and fallen boughs)

The greater range of tides, coupled with the presence of more base-rich mineral matter in the waters of the river Yare, prevents

Plate XIII Non-marine mollusca: 1, 2 *Valvata macrostoma*; 3 *Pseudamnicola confusa*; 4 *Assiminea grayana*; 5, 6 *Planorbis vorticulus*; 7, 8 *Succinea elegans*; 9 *Andonta minima*

Plate XIV *Above: left*, swallowtail butterfly (*Papilio machaon*); *right*, caterpillar of swallowtail butterfly on milk parsley. *Below*, dragonflies: *Aeshna isosceles* (*left*) and *Coenagrion armatum* (*right*)

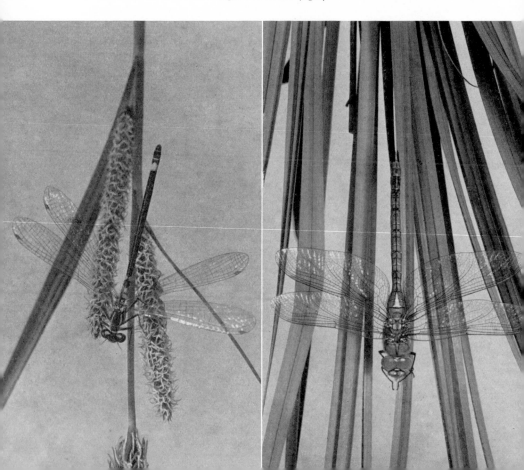

the development of a truly acid peat flora anywhere on its flood plain; but the more stagnant conditions prevailing in the Bure-Ant-Thurne region allow the local formation of sphagnum patches, usually in the form of islands on tussocks, in poorly drained localities. The species of *Sphagnum* in this region have not been investigated ecologically, but the following have been identified by W. H. Burrell and others, chiefly in the Ant valley and near Horning on the Bure: *Sphagnum fimbriatum*, *S. nemoreum*, *S. palustre*, *S. papillosum*, *S. plumulosum*, *S. recurvum*, *S. squarrosum* and *S. subsecundum*. Mosses found in association with these include *Aulacomnium palustre*, *Dicranella cerviculata*, *Drepanocladus exannulatus*, *D. vernicosus*, *Philonotis fontana* and *Polytrichum commune*.

Dyke-dredgings exposed on banks and riverside soil lifted on the roots of overturned willows provide suitable habitats for several kinds of mosses which would not otherwise obtain a footing in the area. These include *Barbula cylindrica*, *B. unguiculata*, *Bryum caespiticium*, *B. capillare*, *B. erythrocarpum*, *Ceratodon purpureus*, *Funaria hygrometrica* and *Physcomitrium pyriforme*. *Funaria hygrometrica* also colonises burnt ground, mainly along marsh banks.

ALGAE

The Fen district of East Anglia is generally regarded as being somewhat deficient in algal species, but in many of the broads and dykes intersecting the east Norfolk grazing marshes a wealth of diatoms and filamentous algae is to be found at certain periods of the year. Special interest is provided by brackish-water species in much of the area.

The range of forms in planktonic algae here is somewhat restricted compared with that found in large deep lakes, although the phenomenon known as ‘ water-bloom ’ occurs in the broads of Ormesby, Filby and Rollesby and in Fritton Lake, and the spherical colonies of diatoms (*Cymbella lacustris*) and the blue-green alga *Anacystis rupestris* var. *prasina*, characteristic of alpine and sub-alpine lakes have been found in this district. (K. B. Clarke, 1958.)

Seasonal fluctuations in the relative quantities of various salts present in the broads doubtless play their part in determining the character of the algal flora, but since most of the waters are shallow and in many cases subject to tidal disturbance fairly regularly, matter in suspension is being mixed repeatedly, so that there can be very little stratification and seasonal turnover such as one finds in deeper waters.

A Comprehensive study of the algae of the broads has yet to be undertaken, although F. Kitton, B. M. Griffiths, K. B. Clarke and others have contributed much to the knowledge of the diatoms. There is a noticeable abundance of diatoms and many of the Volvocales and Chlorococcales in early spring and it is interesting to watch the gradual increase of filamentous and thallus-forming algae from small floating colonies to large spreading masses in some of the waterways between the months of March and June. On warm, sunny days in spring, algae in the shallow dykes and the backwaters of broads seem to effervesce as a result of their great activity and some of the filamentous kinds rise to the surface, buoyed up with the oxygen of their bubbles. Thin, bright green ribbons of *Monostroma*, resembling fragments of oiled silk, drift about in the tidal broads for a time, with small wefts of *Spirogyra*. Later in the spring, these are superseded by other forms. In some summers, large areas of water are covered by the yellow-green, twisted and inflated masses of *Enteromorpha*.

A notable feature of Hickling Broad and neighbouring waterways is the blanket weed, *Cladophora sauteri*, which carpets the bottom perennially and often produces ball-like growths. In bright summers its increase is apt to embarrass navigators in that area and for that reason, the authorities responsible for keeping a passage clear for boats dredge and pump out this weed in vast quantities every year.

Slimy, purple-brown crusts of *Oscillatoria limosa* and other *Myxophyceae* develop on wet mud and produce a conspicuous tide-line on the fringing reed stalks wherever there is any regular rise and fall of water in the rivers and broads.

Velvety green carpets of *Vaucheria* (*V. sessilis* and other spp.) are conspicuous in wet shady places, especially in old sallow carrs. Dark green, gelatinous blobs of *Nostoc* develop occasionally in flooded mowing-marshes, seated upon mats of the prostrate dead leaves of rushes.

STONEWORTS (*Charophyta*)

The broads are famed for their charophytes and Hickling Broad in particular supports what is probably the richest and most spectacular assemblage of different kinds of these plants in Britain. Stoneworts grow best in clear waters and the waters of Hickling in summer are singularly free from mud, even when boat propellers might be expected to churn up the bottom deposits. To look at the starry whorled growths of stoneworts on the bottom is rather like peering through crystal clear water at the fantastic beauty of a coral reef. The following species have been recorded as inhabitants of the broads, but it has to be remembered that charophytes are often only very impermanent colonists of shallow waters and that it is probable that in many instances they owe their introduction to the distributive agency of waterfowl, especially diving ducks such as pochard, which feed on them.

List of species

Nitella opaca: found occasionally in broads and dykes.

N. translucens: recorded once from a deep broad in east Norfolk.

Tolypelle prolifera: rare.

Nitellopsis obtusa: probably confined to Hickling Broad in England.

Chara canescens: rare, Hickling.

C. vulgaris: common and often appearing in newly cleared pools and shallow dykes.

C. hispida: the largest of our stoneworts, plentiful in the Hickling-Horsey area.

C. contraria: not uncommon.

C. baltica, var. *rigida:* recorded only from Hickling Broad, its type locality.

C. aculeata: frequent.

C. aspera: sometimes abundant, chiefly at Hickling.

C. desmacantha: Martham and Hickling.

C. connivens: rare, in Heigham Sounds.

C. globularis: in several broads.

C. delicatula: rare.

LICHENS

Although East Anglia, as might be expected on the drier side of England, is not specially rich in lichens, the humid atmosphere developed in the fen-carrs of broadland favours the growth of a number of the species found attached to trees. Old sallow carrs are quite shaggy with lichens. At the same time, the lack of hard rocks, open, sandy ground and heathland greatly reduces the chances of many species becoming established here. Lichens more or less common on trees in the carrs include *Usnea comosa*, *Evernia prunastri*, *Parmelia perlata*, *P. caperata*, *P. exasperata*, *P. fuliginosa*, *P. sulcata*, *P. dubia*, *Hypogymnia physodes*, *Lecanora allophana*, *L. chlarona*, *L. pallida*, *L. carpinea*, *L. atra*, *L. expallens*, *L. varia*, *L. conizaeoides*, *Lecidea parasema*, *L. dubia*,

Pertusaria amara, *Ramalina farinacea*, *R. fastigiata*, *Caloplaca citrina*, *C. cerina*, *Candelariella vitellina*, *Physcia leptalea*, *Diploicia canescens*, *Buellia myriocarpa*, *Phlyctis agelaea*, *Arthonia radiata* and *Opegrapha atra*. *Cladonia fimbriata* occurs on mossy stumps in open situations.

The names used above are those of W. Watson: *Census Catalogue of British Lichens*, British Mycological Society, 1953.

FUNGI

The fungus flora of the broads area is remarkably rich in the rusts, smuts, mildews, moulds, cup-fungi, pyrenomycetes and small, specialised types of the higher basidiomycetes. Reed-swamps, fens and carrs provide conditions highly favourable to the generation of these organisms; the ever-present moisture, the insular character of the undergrowth zones and the annual decay of much of the vegetation to form porous leaf-mats are influential factors in this respect. Tidal freshwater ronds in particular support immense numbers of fungi at all seasons and it is probable that no comparable marsh habitat elsewhere in Europe is more favourable to the development of so many species as the undrained portion of the Yare valley.

Each major plant community has a recognisable series of fungi belonging to it. This is true not only of the obligate parasites found on the higher plants, but also of the saprophytes. The micro-fungi within each community may also be subdivided into those which develop on their host plants near the tops of stems and leaves where there is plenty of light and free movement of air, those which grow nearer the ground but on the upper parts of the mats of decaying stems and leaves and finally, those which inhabit the really wet and comparatively gloomy hollows beneath the undergrowth. There is a regular succession of fungi attacking the tissues of every marsh plant from the moment it begins to die down until it disintegrates and becomes fen peat. In some cases the conidial organs of a fungus may develop on newly dead material and the perfect fructifications later, at a lower level in the marsh; in other examples the reverse is true, while certain species produce both conidia and ascospores on the same substratum at the same level.

The spores of marsh fungi may be dispersed in several ways. Some are puffed out into the air and borne away like smoke; some are released dry by abstriction and blown away; some are rubbed off by leaves threshing about in the wind or beaten off by rain and hail and many are washed away by water through the action of tides or other flooding. In winter it is common to see a brown scum largely composed of fungus spores floating on the broads and their connecting waterways immediately following a rise in water level, especially if a strong wind has been blowing at the same time. When snow lies on the fens in winter it becomes distinctly soiled after a few days by fragments of lichens blown from the carrs and by the dry spores of various mould fungi (Hyphomycetes), whisked away from the taller sedges and reeds. Numbers of micro-fungi produce slimy spores and there can be no doubt that these are often transported on the feet and beaks of birds. Certain fungi occur mainly along trodden pathways; sometimes this is because their host-plants are rendered more susceptible of infection by being frequently bruised and soiled and in other cases it is likely that infection is due to spores being transported on people's boots. The dematiaceous mould *Deightoniella arundinacea* is a common parasite of the reed where it is regularly trampled, but is seldom encountered where the reed is undamaged. The chytrideaceous fungus *Synchytrium taraxaci* has been found in this area only along pathways, where its host plants, dandelion and marsh thistle, tend to be damaged from time to time.

Many new and interesting micro-fungi have been discovered in the broads district in recent years and some of these will be discussed in a review of the various sections given below.

THE RUST FUNGI (*Uredinales*)

The relatively high humidity of the air in coastal districts and in river valleys appears to favour the growth of rusts, for these parasitic fungi are noticeably more plentiful in such areas than elsewhere. The small airborne basidiospores and aecidiospores produced by rusts lose their powers of germination quickly upon drying, so that it is an advantage to them if the air be moist. Thus the broads are doubly suitable for the reproduction and spread of these fungi and as might be expected the rust-flora is outstandingly rich in rare and interesting species.

Various biological forms of *Puccinia caricina* occur on the sedges and produce orange-coloured clustercups on nettles, and on wild red- and black-currants in the carrs. When sedge litter is used for mulching fruit bushes on market gardens, leaves and fruits of currants and gooseberries are affected by the rust. Leaves of the wild black currants are occasionally attacked by *Cronartium ribicola*, the spores of which have been blown from Weymouth pines planted on the uplands.

The reed, (*Phragmites communis*) bears long chocolate-brown or black sori (spore-cushions) of *Puccinia phragmitis* from midsummer onward as the result of infection from white-spored clustercups appearing on crimson spots on the various marsh docks in spring. The same rust attacks rhubarb grown in the district, but in most years infection is slight. *Puccinia magnusiana*, with orange clustercups on creeping buttercup (*Ranunculus repens*) produces very narrow uredo- and teleuto-sori on the reeds in late summer and autumn; sometimes whole reed-beds appear blasted, like fields of wheat attacked by black rust. The well-known crown rust of cereals and many wild grasses attacks the foliage of both buckthorns in the valley carrs here, but in the temperate climate of Britain it is not dependent upon these carrier-hosts for re-infection of the grasses from year to year. Cluster-cups commonly seen on twayblade, fragrant orchid, spotted orchid and all the marsh orchids of this region belong to the life-cycle of *Puccinia sessilis* with later stages on reed-grass (*Phalaris arundinacea*) whilst cuckoo-pint (*Arum maculatum*), growing in woods close to the marshes, is the vernal host of another race of this rust. Other heteraecious rusts of the marshes include *Puccinia paludosa* on marsh lousewort and the sedge *Carex nigra* (near Barton Broad), *P. persistens* on meadow rue and grasses in the Yare and Waveney valleys, *Uromyces junci* on marsh fleabane and obtuse-flowered rush throughout the district, *U. lineolatus* on parsley water-dropwort (*Oenanthe lachenalii*) growing along the lower reaches of the Bure as well as more generally on sea milkwort (*Glaux maritima*) growing near brackish water, with later stages on sea scirpus; several species of *Melampsora* producing golden uredospores on sallows and osiers in late summer and having their earlier stages on conifers; and *Coleosporium sonchi* on marsh sowthistle as well as the commoner species of *Sonchus*.

Two rusts which have incompletely known life cycles are present in the fens and reedswamps, namely, *Puccinia cladii* on the saw sedge (*Cladium mariscus*) and *Aecidium ranunculacearum*, var. *linguae* on greater spearwort, *Ranunculus lingua*. The former persists year after year on its evergreen host by means of uredospores only and the latter produces clustercups in June and July following infection from an alternating host as yet undetected.

Noteworthy autaecious rusts (developing all their spores on a single host) include several whose distribution in Britain is very restricted. Of these, *Puccinia cicutae* on cowbane (*Cicuta virosa*), appears to be confined to the broads. *Tranzschelia thalictri* is locally common on meadow rue (*Thalictrum flavum*), in the Yare vallev. but elsewhere in Britain it is a very rare species found on other kinds of *Thalictrum*. Milk parsley (*Peucedanum palustre*) is very frequently parasitised by *Puccinia bullata* throughout the fens bordering the rivers Bure, Ant and Thurne, but though the host plant is abundant in parts of the Yare valley, its rust seems to be restricted there to one small strip of fen at Strumpshaw. Possibly the greater alkalinity or richer mineral sources of the Yare flood-plain render the milk parsley a service in enabling it to resist infection by the rust. High humidity appears to favour the development of the goosegrass rust, *Puccinia difforma;* the host plant is infected freely almost wherever it grows alongside our marsh lakes, but very seldom in its other, drier habitats.

Two rusts attack the marsh marigold in Britain; one of these, *Puccinia calthae*, I have found only where the host plant grows on acidic soils and the other, *P. calthicola*, where the soils are of a neutral or basic type; only the second species has been found near the broads.

In the summer of 1950, yellow clustercups of the rust *Puccinia opizii* appeared for the first time in Britain on cultivated lettuces in villages bordering the Yare valley below Norwich. In the following year, uredo- and teleuto-spores of this rust were identified as parasites attacking two kinds of tussock sedges (*Carex paniculata* and *C. appropinquata*) in the local fens. This fungus became established in the area for some years, but appears now to have died out. Happily its effect on lettuces was not of any great economic significance.

The names used for the rusts in this chapter are those given by Wilson and Bisby: List of British Uredinales; *Trans. Brit. Myc. Soc.* 37, 61–86 (1954).

THE SMUT FUNGI (*Ustilaginales*)

The broad, ribbon-like leaves of rond-grass (*Glyceria maxima*) are very commonly striped with light brown, powdery spore-masses of *Ustilago longissima*. This smut is so abundant in some of the Yare marshes in summer that anyone trudging across the swamps is apt to disturb clouds of its spores, which induce sneezing and cover clothes with snuff-coloured dust. Smutted shoots of the grass seldom produce flowers, although they may do so when infection has occurred late in the season. It has been suggested by J. M. Lambert that false 'vivipary' in the florets is caused by this smut.

Clumps of the largest reeds bordering tidal reaches of the rivers Bure, Yare and Waveney and some of their broads are attacked year after year by *Ustilago grandis*, which produces thick cylindrical swellings on the stems, packed with sooty-brown spores. Marsh reed-beds are free from infection by this smut, which appears to be restricted to plants which have a footing in fairly deep water. The fungus prevents flowering, but it does not prevent the reeds from growing vigorously in successive years. A rare stripe-smut (*Ustilago macrospora*) attacks leaves of purple small-reed growing in half-shade at the edge of a fen-carr at Surlingham; it has not been found parasitising this grass elsewhere in Britain.

The purple-brown anther smut (*Ustilago violacea*) prevalent on many of our native campions and chickweeds, attacks flowers of ragged robin in marshes, where it appears almost exclusively on late flowers produced by the plants after the fens have been mown for litter in summer. Water pepper (*Polygonum hydropiper*) is infected by two smuts which fill its ovaries with their spores; one, *Ustilago anomala* is common and widespread here and the other, *Sphacelotheca hydropiperis*, is less common and is most often present in shady places.

The common sedge (*Carex riparia*) has two conspicuous ovary-smuts which often appear side by side on one and the same plant; *Farysia olivacea* bursts out with thready, bright olive-brown spore-masses, while *Cintractia subinclusa* (also found on *Carex lasiocarpa* in broadland) has black powdery spores released only after the splitting of a silvery skin. Another ovary-smut of sedges, *Cintractia caricis*, is seldom found in this district, but it used to parasitise the sedge formerly listed as *Carex trinervis* Degl. in its only British station at Ormesby (this Norfolk plant is now generally considered to be either a variant of *C. nigra* or of hybrid origin).

Great bindweed (*Calystegia sepium*) which commonly climbs reeds and other tall plants in the fens, would be even more abundant here, were it not for the fact that vast numbers of its seeds are destroyed every year by parasitic moulds and the smut *Thecaphora seminis-convolvuli*. Sharp-flowered rush (*Juncus acutiflorus*) at Burntfen Broad, is affected by the smut *Urocystis junci*, which produces dark brown spore-balls in the lower parts of the stems; this fungus has not yet been found elsewhere in the British Isles. The two water forget-me-nots here are commonly parasitised by *Entyloma fergussoni*, which produces white and pale brown spots on the leaves in shady places in the carrs. *Entyloma ficariae* has a similar appearance on leaves of lesser celandine in the marshes.

The names used are those of Ainsworth and Sampson: *The British Smut Fungi* (1950).

Plate XV Slugs. *Above*, milky slug (*Agriolimax agrestis*)
Below, *Arion ater*

Plate XVI Bittern removing egg-shell from nest

BASIDIOMYCETES, *other than rusts and smuts*

Few agarics tolerate very wet habitats and most of those that grow in marshes are comparatively small saprophytes of withered grasses, sedges and the dead stalks of herbaceous plants. Some larger kinds develop on the decaying wood of alder, sallow and other trees and bushes in fen-carrs and on slightly raised, often mossy, ground round the bases of tree stools. At higher levels in mature carrs and where ash and oak come into the composition of woods at the valley margins, many additional kinds of agarics appear in the undergrowth.

The Fen species

Aleurodiscus delicatus forms very thin, peach-pink patches on dead leaves of saw sedge.

Bolbitius vitellinus, a bright yellow, glutinous agaric, common on decaying straw, appears on marsh litter in summer.

Clavaria gigaspora has been found under meadowsweet and fen-rush in autumn.

Clitocybe fragrans, usually a woodland fungus, has been seen developing abundantly on the decaying remains of a swan's nest.

Coprinus martinii, on dead fen-rush.

C. tigrinellus is common on dead culms of marsh grasses in wet places in summer.

C. urticicola abounds on dying stem-bases of many marsh grasses at low levels in reed-swamps and fens, June to November.

Corticium solani spreads over living stalks of water-mint.

Cellypha goldbachii is common on dead grasses, rushes and sedges in summer and autumn.

Cyphella capula grows on the lower parts of herbaceous stems, especially on thistles and marsh bird's-foot trefoil, usually at the junction of dead and living tissues when the plants are dying back in late summer.

Crepidotus phillipsii: in grass and sedge tussocks.

Deconica inquilina: on grass stems.

Epithele typhae forms white and buff crusts on the sheathing leaf-bases of sedges and reedmaces in autumn.

Galerina clavata: on open, mossy sites in fens, summer.

Hebeloma pusillum has been found in sedge fens in July.

Inocybe flocculosa: on mossy tussocks.

Marasmius calopus: on newly dead leaves of sea bulrush, rushes, sedges and grasses in wet places, mainly in summer.

M. graminum: on dead leaves of reed, purple small-reed and other marsh grasses.

M. limosus: in sedge fen.

M. menieri: restricted to fens, where it develops on wet, dead leaf-bases of saw sedge and great pond sedge, from April to July.

Mycena belliae: grows only on standing stems of reed (*Phragmites*) at water level, in autumn.

M. bulbosa: on rushes, summer.

M. clavularis: in sedge fen.

M. cyphelloides: a minute white species on dead leaves of sedges and marsh grasses.

M. olida: in sedge fen.

M. pterigena: a small, fragile, rose-pink agaric growing on newly dead fronds of marsh fern in autumn.

M. pudica: a delicate white agaric plentiful on dead leaves of saw sedge in summer.

M. speirea: a common carr species, but also found on bog myrtle twigs in fens.

M. swartzii: on mossy tussocks.

M. tenerrima: on twigs of bog myrtle.

Pistillaria aculeata: resembling minute white hairs, on soft, rotting leaf-bases of saw sedge; spring to autumn.

Psathyrella typhae: on stems of reed-mace, just above water level, in summer.

Pterula multifida: a pale pinkish buff thready fungus common on dead leaves of fen and reedswamp grasses, sedges and rushes in autumn.

Sphaerobolus stellatus: frequently developing on matted dead stems of fen rush.

Typhula spp.: several species develop from sclerotia on marsh plants in autumn, but they await critical study.

Bovistella paludosa, a chalk-white bog puffball, has been found growing with the moss *Aulacomnium palustre* on a riverside fen in the Yare valley. It is generally regarded as a very rare fungus of *Sphagnum* bogs.

The Fen-Carr species

Amanita inaurata: rare, Surlingham.

A. phalloides: under oaks, especially on marsh walls.

A. rubescens: frequent under birches.

Armillaria mellea: commonly attacks willows.

Boletus scaber: frequent under oaks and birches.

B. testaceoscaber: found occasionally under trees on marsh walls.

Clavaria cristata: very tolerant of flooding, but seems to require some silt mixed with its peat.

C. contorta: sprouts from fallen alder twigs in autumn.

C. inaequalis: appears on mossy or grassy eminences formed by roots of overturned trees.

C. juncea: grows from wet mats of decaying leaves under alders in autumn.

Collybia cirrhata: on the ground.

C. confluens: in clumps and partial rings on leaf-mould.

C. peronata: in the drier carrs.

Conocybe utriformis: on the ground.

Coprinus callinus.

C. ellisii: on leafy rubbish under sallows.

C. urticicola: common at bases of the stems of marsh grasses in wet places in carrs as well as in the rond marshes.

Crepidotus amygdalosporus: on rotten twigs.

C. luteolus: common on sallow sticks.

Exidia recisa: swells like wine-coloured jelly on dead, standing sallow branches after heavy rain has soaked the wood.

Flammulina velutipes: has been found on dead wood of wild red currants, in late autumn and winter.

Galerina hypnorum: on mossy ground.

G. mutabilis: as above.

G. unicolor: on the ground.

Ganoderma applanatum: as brackets old ash and willow trees.

Hebeloma leucosarx: locally abundant under sallows in places often flooded.

H. radicosum: in damp, deep leaf-mould, attached to roots of broad-leaved trees.

Hypholoma fasciculare: on a variety of tree stumps.

Inocybe abjecta: on peaty soil under sallows.

I. flocculosa: on moss tussocks under sallows.

I. geophylla and its var. *lilacina:* common on the ground.

I. griseolilacina: not infrequent, on the ground.

I. maculata: as above.

I. microspora: found occasionally, on the ground.

I. obscura: as above.

I. (*Clypeus*) *calospora:* as above.

I. napipes: as above.

Laccaria amethystea and *L. laccata:* both frequent in fairly damp carrs, especially where birches are present.

Lactarius chrysorheus: common woodland species extending to carrs.

L. cimicarius: as above.

L. glyciosmus: as above.

L. obscuratus: local, under alders.

L. torminosus: under birches.

Lentinellus cochleatus: on rotten alder stumps.

Leptoglossum muscigenum: in moss.

Leptonia euchroa: on the ground.

L. sericella: as above, a typical carr species.

Marasmius epiphyllus: a small, wiry-stemmed agaric common on fallen ash petioles in autumn.

M. ramealis: on sticks.

M. recubans: as above.

M. rotula: as above.

Mycena acicula: common throughout the summer on partly buried twigs of oak, birch, alder, etc.

M. alba, *M. alcalina*, *M. amicta*, *M. capillaris*, *M. fibula*, *M. galericulata*, *M. galopus* and its var. *candida*, *M. hiemalis*, *M. inclinata*, *M. lactea*, *M. leptocephala*, *M. margaritispora*, *M. metata*, *M. oortiana*, *M. polygramma*, *M. speirea*, *M. stylobates*, *M. swartzii*, and *M. tenerrima* have all been found in carrs.

Mycoleptodon fimbriatum forms encrusting wefts on the undersides of fallen boughs of sallow and guelder rose.

Naucoria: several species grow in swarms under trees in carrs, where they are often associated either with alders or sallows; they include *N. celluloderma*, *N. centunculus*, *N. escharoides*, *N. luteolofibrillosa*, *N. rubi*, *N. salicis*, *N. scolecina* and *N. striatula*.

Nolanea tenuipes is a characteristic carr species, appearing in summer and autumn.

Phaeomarasmius erinaceus is common on dead sallow boughs at all seasons.

Pluteolus aleuriatus: summer and autumn.

Pluteus cervinus: not uncommon on dead wood. The more typical species from fen carrs include *P. lutescens*, *P. pallescens*, *P. phlebophorus*, *P. podospileus*, *P. salicinus*, *P. thomsonii* and *P. umbrosus*.

Polyporus betulinus, the birch bracket-fungus, is fairly common; *P. caesius* grows on dead sallows, willows and birches; *P. nummularius* is common on sallow sticks; *P. sulphureus* attacks old pollard willows and *P. radiatus* kills many alders.

Poria purpurea has been found encrusting ash twigs in wet places.

Psathyrella: carr species include *P. canoceps*, *P. fusca*, the common *P. hydrophila* clustering on rotten stumps, *P. microlepidota*, and *P. pennata*.

Russula: one species, *R. delica*, is very tolerant of flooding; other species occurring to a lesser extent in carrs are *R. atropurpurea*, *R. betularum*, *R. cyanoxantha*, *R. firmula*, *R. gracillima*, *R. melzeri*, *R. nigricans* and *R. sororia*.

Solenia anomala, a minute, scurfy, ochre-yellow fungus, grows in patches on dead branches of sallow and buckthorn.

Trametes rubescens (Pl. XI) is the commonest bracket fungus on sallows and alders in this habitat.

Tremella albida, *T. lutescens* and *T. mesenterica* expand in jelly-like, contorted lobes from dead branches soaked by rain.

Tricholoma album, *T. fulvum*, *T. sulphureum* and *T. ustale* have all been found in carrs, on the ground.

Typhula erythropus springs from fallen alder leaves and *T. phacorrhiza* grows chiefly on rotten leaf-mats under ash trees in wet places in autumn.

THE CUP-FUNGI (*Discomycetes*)

The comparatively large and fleshy operculate Discomycetes are not very well represented in the low-lying region of the broads, where waterlogged soil appears to be unsuitable for their development, as is the case with the larger toadstools. The smaller inoperculates, on the other hand, abound on the dying and rotting stems and leaves of marsh plants and many peculiar and interesting species occur here. A selection of the more noteworthy cup-fungi will be mentioned here, in the hope that mycologists may be encouraged to give more attention to the group in marsh and fen habitats.

Operculate Discomycetes

The tall-stemmed morel (*Mitrophora hybrida*) appears in the vicinity of poplars in some of the carrs in late spring. *Helvella crispa*, and *H. lacunosa* appear under various trees and bushes in carrs from time to time. The large crimson-and-white cups of *Sarcoscypha coccinea* develop occasionally on rotting alder twigs on flooded ground. An orange cup fringed with dark brown bristles, usually identified as *Ciliaria scutellata*, is common on wet rotting wood, often amongst mosses. *Taphrina sadebeckii* forms plum-purple leaf blisters on alder and *T. turgidus* is the cause of witches' brooms developing on birch trees. No representative of the *Tuberales* (truffles) has been discovered to date in the broads district.

Inoperculate Discomycetes

Belonioscypha culmicola: on fen-rush, summer.
Calycella citrina: on alder wood, autumn.
C. sulfurina: on ash bark in carrs, summer.
Chlorocibora aeruginella: producing verdigris stains and fruiting in autumn on stems of meadowsweet.
Ciboria acerina: developing on fallen male catkins of bog myrtle in spring.
C. amentacea: springing from the previous year's fallen male catkins of alder and sallow in early spring.
C. aschersoniana: growing on the previous year's fallen fruits of the sedges *Carex appropinquata* and *C. elata* in spring.
C. batschiana: sprouting from buried acorns in autumn.
Cudoniella acicularis: on mossy, rotten wood.
Cyathicula coronata: common on herbaceous stems in the marshes in autumn.
Dasyscypha acutipila: common on reeds, summer.
D. carneola: on purple moor grass, summer.
D. controversa: on reed stems, spring.
D. corticalis: on guelder-rose twigs, spring.
D. crucifera: on dead twigs of bog myrtle.
D. granulosella: on great pond sedge, spring.
D. inquilina: on marsh horsetail, spring.
D. nidulus: on hemp agrimony, spring.
D. nudipes: on meadowsweet, spring.
D. prasina: on great pond sedge, summer.
D. pudibunda: on sallow twigs, summer.
D. pudicella: on grasses, summer.
D. salicariae: on purple loosestrife, summer.
Geoglossum glutinosum: on mossy ground in carrs, summer and autumn.
Helotium calyculus: on rotten wood, autumn.
H. fructigenum: on acorns, autumn.
H. marchantiae: on the liverwort (*Conocephalum conicum*), spring.

H. microspis: on leaf-sheaths of reed, spring.
H. rhodoleucum: on stems of horsetails, spring.
H. robergei: on the previous year's fallen petioles of ash, in carrs, July–August.
H. robustius: on saw sedge (*Cladium*), July.
H. salicellum: on sallow, summer.
H. scutula: in various forms on herbaceous stems, spring.
H. vernalis: on alder bark, spring.
Hyaloscypha deparcula: very common on meadowsweet stalks, summer.
Hyalotricha corticicola: on bog myrtle, spring.
Hysteropezizella exigua: on fen rush.
H. fenestrata: on saw sedge (*Cladium*) leaves.
Leotia lubrica: on mossy ditch banks in carrs, autumn.
Mollisia juncina: common on rushes and sedges. No critical study has been made on this genus of discomycetes, which is certainly represented by a good many species, in the fens of east Norfolk.
Naevia seriata: on newly dead leaves of sedges.
Ombrophila verna: on muddy alder wood, spring.
Pezizella amenti: in swarms on fallen female catkins of sallows in spring.
P. gemmarum: on old fallen bud-scales of poplars, April.
Phialea cyathoidea: a small-spored form has been collected from old stalks of various marsh plants in this area.
Phragmonaevia hysterioides: on leaves of sedges.
Propolis faginea: very common on dead sallow wood.
Pseudopeziza cerastiorum: parasitic on living leaves of viscid mouse-ear chickweed; *P. ranunculi* on buttercup leaves and *P. repanda* on the marsh and bog bedstraws.
Pyrenopeziza millegrana: extremely common on dead stems of meadowsweet; *P. thalictri*, on meadow rue.
Rhytisma salicinum (Pl. XI): produces a tar-spot disease of sallow leaves.
Rutstroemia, cf. *calopus:* appears regularly on decaying leaves and stems of reed sweet-grass in spring.
R. conformata: common on the midribs of dead alder leaves on the ground in spring.
R. henningsiana: on cotton-grass, spring.
Scleroderris fuliginosa: on white willows at Surlingham Broad, where it forms conspicuous black patches on boughs and twigs and appears to cause a die-back disease.
S. ribis: has been found on wild red currant bushes in carrs.

Sclerotinia candolleana: develops from small black sclerotia on old fallen oak leaves in the carrs in May and June.

S. curreyana: produces apothecia from cylindrical *sclerotia* in stems of soft rush in spring.

S. fuckeliana: has been seen occasionally on meadowsweet in spring, and a morphologically similar fungus is not uncommon on dead stems of yellow loosestrife.

S. lindaviana: very common on fallen reed leaves in spring and summer.

S. scirpicola: causes a summer die-back in the bulrushes growing round the broads and its apothecia have been found developing from the sclerotia in spring.

S. sulcata: a common parasite of a number of sedges in the fens, the apothecia appearing in spring.

Stamnaria persooni: on marsh horsetail, May and June.

Stictis stellata: common on dead stalks of hemp agrimony, great hairy willowherb and meadowsweet in spring and early summer.

Symphyosirinia angelicae: on fallen fruits of wild angelica and milk parsley; slimy conidia are produced from sessile synnemata on the newly fallen fruits in autumn and long-stalked synnemata and apothecia develop from the same fruits in the following autumn, disseminating spores just when the new season's fruits become ready for infection.

S. galii: behaves like the previous species, its host being the large-fruited tetraploid subspecies of marsh bedstraw growing with reeds and sedges in the fens of broadland.

Trichoglossum hirsutum: the only earth-tongue which has been found growing in fens.

Verpatinia spiraeicola: produces slender, long-stalked apothecia superficially resembling those of a very small *Mitrula*, growing from black sclerotia on decayed leaves of meadowsweet and bellbine in the broadland fens in spring and early summer.

The names used in the above list are those adopted by R. W. G. Dennis in *A Revision of the British Hyaloscyphaceae* (1949), and *A Revision of the British Helotiaceae* (1956), and for species not dealt with in these two papers, the list of *Discomycetes* recorded from the British Isles, by J. Ramsbottom and F. L. Balfour-Browne, *Trans. Brit. Myc. Soc.*, 34, pp. 38–137 (1951). The two species of *Symphyosirinia* were described by E. A. Ellis in *Trans. Norfolk & Norwich Naturalists*, 1956.

THE PYRENOMYCETES

Acrospermum compressum: develops on dead leaves of reed, rond-grass, sedges, reed-maces, and yellow flag, in addition to the more usual nettle stems; it has been found also on the stout over-wintered stalks of marsh sowthistle.

Anthostomella: two distinct species are common on saw sedge.

Bertia moriformis: has been found on long-dead sallow wood.

Buergenerula biseptata: a distinctive leaf-spotting parasite of the sedge *Carex acutiformis* in broadland.

Calonectria ochraceo-pallida: occurs on sallow.

Chaetosphaeria phaeostroma: commonly associated with *Diatrype* on old branches of sallow and buckthorn.

Clypeosphaeria notarisii: grows on hairy willowherb stems.

Claviceps purpurea: produces ergots in great abundance on flowers of reed and other marsh grasses. The ergots fall and the clubbed heads of *perithecia* develop in the moist litter in late spring.

Cryptodiaporthe aubertii: on bog myrtle; *C. salicella* on creeping willow.

Cryptospora suffusa: on alder.

Cucurbitaria dulcamarae: on bittersweet.

Daldinia concentrica: on ash and occasionally on alder.

Dialonectria applanata: on buckthorn; *D. peziza* on old polypores; *D. sanguinea*, on old *Diatrype* species; *D. wegeliana* on guelder rose.

Diaporthe beckhausii: on guelder-rose; *D. eres*, on sallow; *D. laschii*, on spindle; *D. sarothamni*, var. *dulcamarae*, on bittersweet; *D. striaeformis*, on hairy willowherb; *D. strumella*, on red and black currants.

Diatrype bullata: very common on dead branches of grey sallow.

D. stigma: on dead wood of most kinds of trees.

Diatrypella favacea: on birch; *D. tocciaeana*, on alder.

Didymella nigrella: on angelica; *D. sepincoliformis*, on wild roses.

Didymellina iridis: on yellow flag.

Didymosphaeria palustris: on various sedges.

Endodothella junci: on rushes.

Epichloe typhina: most frequently on cocksfoot, Yorkshire fog and rough meadow-grass.

Erysiphe cichoracearum: a common mildew of composites, attacks hemp agrimony in the marshes. *E. polygoni* attacks many kinds of leaves, including those of marsh marigold, greater spearwort, purple loosestrife and meadow vetchling.

Gibberella zeae: plentiful on dead culms of rond-grass and rather less so on reed and other grasses.

Hyphonectria violacea: has been found parasitising one of the mycetozoa (*Didymium clavus*) on sedge in a marshy habitat.

Hypocrea pulvinata: attacks the birch bracket-fungus; *H. rufa* grows on the bracket-fungus (*Trametes rubescens*) on alder and sallow boughs.

Hypomyces auranteus: has been found on various polypores.

Hypoxylon argillaceum: is present on ash in carrs; *H. fuscum*, on alder; *H. multiforme*, on alder and birch; *H. rubiginosum*, on ash and sallow; *H. serpens*, on ash and sallow.

Lasionectria leptosphaeriae: commonly parasitises another pyrenomycote (*Leptosphaeria doliolum*) on old nettle stalks in damp places.

Lasiosphaeria canescens; on sallow; *L. hirsuta*, on alder; *L. ovina*, on wood and old herb stems; *L. rhacodium*, on ash and guelder rose; *L. spermoides* on alder and birch.

Leptosphaeria: a great many species, many of them awaiting fuller investigation, develop on newly dead stems of marsh plants; those identified here include the common *L. acuta*, on stinging-nettle, *L. agnita*, on hemp agrimony; *L. densa*, on sweet flag; *L. doliolum*, on angelica and stinging-nettle; *L. epicarecta*, on sedges; *L. fuckelii*, on various grasses; *L. microscopica*, on grasses; *L. typharum*, on reed-maces.

Letendriaea helminthicola: on the hyphomycete (*Helminthosporium velutinum*) on spindle.

Lophiostoma salicum: on grey sallow.

Melanconis alni: on alder; *M. stilbostoma*, on birch.

Melanomma pulvis-pyrius: on buckthorn and sallow.

Metasphaeria corticola: on wild roses; *M. cumana*, on saw sedge.

Microsphaera alni: on living leaves of alder and guelder-rose; *M. euonymi*, on spindle.

Nectria cinnabarina: most commonly found on dead stems of wild red currants in the carrs; *N. coccinea* has been found on guelder-rose; *N. punicea* and *N. sinopica*, on ivy.

Niesslia exosporioides: common on newly dead sedges.

Nitschkia cupularis: has been found on sallow wood.

Ophiobolus acuminatus: common on dead stalks of various thistles.

Ophiosphaeria gracilis: common on sedges.

Phyllactinia corylea: attacks living leaves of ash, rather than hazel, its more usual host, in this district.

Pleospora typhicola: on reed-maces.
Rebentischia typhae: on lesser reed-mace.
Rosellinia aquila: common on grey sallow wood.
Scirrhia rimosa: on standing culms of reed.
Sphaerotheca humuli: on wild hops.
Tubeufia helicomyces: on dead culms of rond-grass lying in wet, muddy places.

ENTOMOGENOUS FUNGI

Great numbers of insects and spiders inhabiting reed-swamps, fens and carrs adjacent to broads are killed by various parasitic fungi and their dead bodies in turn are consumed by saprophytic fungi with the utmost regularity in these habitats. Petch (1948) listed ninety-two species of entomogenous fungi as British, and of these no less than fifty have been noticed in the broads region. Nine have not yet been reported from any other part of the world and nine others are as yet undiscovered in other parts of the British Isles.

There can be little doubt that the high degree of humidity in this area is favourable to the development of such fungi, especially when it is coupled with summer warmth so that the atmosphere within the shelter of rank vegetation becomes close in the extreme. It is interesting to find that several of the broads species are known elsewhere only in the tropics.

Of the strictly parasitic *Phycomycetes* which bring about the quick death of their hosts, most are active chiefly between May and September, and innumerable flies of various kinds are to be found transfixed and clinging in death to plant foliage, from the depths of the undergrowth to the uppermost branches of sallows and alders, their bodies glued in place and surrounded by wax-like wefts of fungus hyphae. *Empusa acaridis* attacks the common mite (*Pergamasus crassipes*) in *Glyceria maxima* swamps; *E. muscae* develops on various flies, *E. planchoniana* has been found on aphids, *E. tenthredinis* on larvae of marsh sawflies and *E. thaxteriana* on leaf-hoppers (Homoptera). *Entomophthora americana*, *E. echinospora* and *E. dipterigena* are to be found on various flies in summer, the last being prevalent on the moth-flies (Psychodidae) which breed abundantly in the mats of decaying vegetation in the fens; *E. anglica* kills many beetles, chiefly those of the families Staphylinidae, Cantharidae and Chrysomelidae; *E. aphidis* and *E. occidentalis* occur on aphids; *E. sphaerosperma* parasitises various plant-bugs

(Hemiptera) and *E. aphrophorae* is extremely common on leaf-hoppers (Homoptera) of many species.

Of the Hypocreales (ascomycetes with brightly coloured, soft, fleshy, flask-shaped perithecia), the well-known orange-red clubs of *Cordyceps militaris* are found growing from the mummified remains of moth-caterpillars and pupae in moss and leaf-mould under trees in the carrs, but not in the wettest places. The smaller, yellowish clubs of *Cordyceps tuberculata* have been found on moth pupae occasionally in alder carrs and in closed reed-swamps near the broads; *C. sphecocephala* (parasitic on Hymenoptera), *C. forquignoni* (on flies) and *C. memorabilis* on a Carabid beetle larva have also been collected in this region. *Torrubiella albolanata* kills vast numbers of spiders in fens and reed-swamps of the Yare valley and has been noticed occasionally elsewhere in the broads area, but in no other part of the world; *T. aranicida*, which has a wider distribution, has been found here only once, on a spider at Burntfen Broad; *T. albotomentosa* is known only of small midge-pupae in *Glyceria maxima* beds at Wheatfen Broad.

Of the Moniliales (conidial fungi without the flask-like organs known as pycnidia), most of the entomogenous species appear to be truly parasitic, but some are only mildly so or may follow in the wake of killer fungi, while certain moulds in any case develop on the bodies of insects that have died natural deaths and have come to lie in the damp undergrowth. Slimy-spored species include *Cephalosporium dipterigenum* on plant bugs and leaf-hoppers, *C. muscarium* on many kinds of insects and *C. subclavatum* on larvae and pupae of the round-winged muslin moth (*Comacla senex*); *Hirsutella acridiorum* on leaf-hoppers (Homoptera), *H. aphidis* on aphids, *H. citriformis* on plant bugs and leaf-hoppers attached to sedge leaves, *H. eleutheratorum* on beetles (commonly on the Staphylinid (*Paederus riparius*) in reed-swamps) and *H. saussurei* on small parasitic Hymenoptera; *Oospora ovorum* on cocoons of a Braconid parasite of the drinker moth (*Philudoria potatoria*); and *Verticillium menisporioides* on a dead spider in a sub-maritime fen bordering one of the lower reaches of the river Waveney. Dry-spored species include *Acremonium aranearum* on leaf-hoppers and *A. tenuipes* on spiders and their eggs; *Akanthomyces sphingum* on moth pupae; *Beauveria bassiana* on many kinds of insects, *B. densa* on insects (most often on beetles) and *B. effusa* on insects; *Cylindrodendrum suffultum* very commonly on pupae of moth-flies (Psychodidae) and occasionally on pupae of daddy-long-legs (Tipulidae) and some of the Stratiomyid flies, all in wet marshes; *Cylindrophora aranearum* parasitising spiders; *Gibellula aranearum* very commonly on spiders in fens;

Hymenostilbe arachnophila on spiders, *H. muscaria* on flies under dead leaves on the ground in carrs and *H. sphecophila* found once on a dead ichneumon in flood refuse at the edge of Horsey Mere; *Isaria* (*Spicaria*) *farinosa* on pupae and imagines of many kinds of insects, *I.* (*S.*) *fumoso-rosea* on glow-worms in fens (Pl. XII), *I. tenuipes* on moth pupae under trees in carrs at Wheatfen regularly in late summer (not known elsewhere in Britain), *Spicaria parasina* parasitic on Noctuid caterpillars on grasses in fens, *S. stricta* on a spider at Wheatfen; *Sporotrichum isariae* on other entomogenous fungi, especially *Isaria* (*Spicaria*) *farinosa*.

Species of *Beauveria* and *Isaria* on insects are frequently parasitised by one of the Hypocreales, *Melanospora parasitica;* the long necks of the perithecia of this fungus protrude from the conidial wefts of their hosts like black bristles.

THE HYPHOMYCETES

The reedswamps and fens of the broads have yielded many interesting mould-fungi to those who have troubled to examine the dead stems and leaves of sedges, reeds, rushes and herbs such as meadowsweet and hemp agrimony at various seasons. It is usually most rewarding when the mycologist either squats in the midst of a swamp and takes a close look at all the natural litter within reach, or burrows through the mass of vegetation, peering into the depths of the flooring material (often a spongy mat of tangled stalks and decaying leaves) and scanning all standing plants from all angles, with the aid of a pocket-lens when it comes to detail. There can be little doubt that the humid conditions prevailing in these marsh wildernesses and the tendency for insular micro-climates to exist in the shelter of the rank vegetation of broadland combine to favour the development of plant moulds. While most of these fungi listed below are saprophytes, they are often associated with special plants whose dying tissues provide just what they need at the right season. In many instances there is a succession of different moulds and other micro-fungi on the withered and weathered remains of a plant from the moment the green cells die to the time when the final residue becomes dispersed in peaty tatters.

List of Hyphomycetes found on marsh plants in broadland:

Arthrinium curvatum var. *minus:* on glaucous bulrush.

A. puccinioides: on various sedges.

A. sporophleum: on sedges (commonly on *Carex riparia*).

Arthrobotryum atrum: on over-wintered dead stems of meadowsweet, hairy willowherb, yellow loosestrife and hemp agrimony.

Bactridium flavum: on rotting wood of grey sallow.

Bactrodesmum arnaudii: on poplar.

Botryosporium: an elegant undescribed species with reflexed branches has been collected on a number of occasions from newly-dead leaves of sweet flag and hemp agrimony.

Botrytis: grey moulds of this genus affect many marsh plants, notably meadowsweet, yellow loosestrife and yellow flag.

Cercospora lilacina: produces leaf-spots on marsh violet.

Chalara cladii: on *Cladium.*

Cladosporium herbarum: one of the first moulds to appear on almost all kinds of newly-dead leaves and on the honey-dew deposited by aphids.

Cladosporium: what appears to be an undescribed parasitic species has been found on the leaves and stems of marsh orchids near three of the Norfolk Broads.

Clasterosporium caricinum: a common parasite of the sedge *Carex riparia* where it grows on marshes subject to periodic flooding by both fresh and somewhat brackish waters.

Curvularia crepini: attacks adder's-tongue ferns, producing dark grey circular spots on their leaves in summer.

Deightoniella arundinacea: attacks leaves of reeds where the plants grow on comparatively hard ground fringing marsh causeways; affected leaves have a sooty appearance.

Endophragmia elliptica: on willowherb, meadowsweet and yellow loosestrife.

Heliocosporium phragmitis: abounds on moist, prostrate culms of reed-swamp grasses decaying in the dark interstices of the ground carpet; it appears in cottony, pale grey or pale brown colonies of hyphae bearing helically coiled separate spores.

Hyalodendron album: attacks the living leaves of marsh pea and meadow vetchling.

Myrothecium striatisporum: has been found on dead reed and tussock sedge; *M. carmichaelii* on dead stems of meadow rue and hemp agrimony in spring.

Nigrospora sphaerica: a black-spored mould of bananas, sugar cane, maize and rice in countries where these plants are grown, has been found on sedge leaves at Surlingham Broad.

Ovularia destructiva: grows as a leaf-spot fungus on bog myrtle.

O. sphaeroidea: forms chalk-white patches beneath living leaves of marsh bird's-foot trefoil.

Pachybasium hamatum: a common parasite of the sycamore tar-spot fungus (*Rhytisma acerinum*) grows also on the sallow-leaf tar-spot (*R. salicinum*) here, in spring.

Papularia arundinis and *P. sphaerosperma:* produce masses of sooty spores on culms of reed and occasionally on other marsh grasses.

Passalora depressa: grows parasitically on leaves of angelica, forming angular spots tufted with olive-brown conidiophores.

Periconia: represented by a number of marsh species. *P. byssoides* on herb stems such as those of meadowsweet and nettle; *P. atra* on sedges, rushes and reed; *P. minutissima* on sedges, rond-grass, reed and meadowsweet; *P. paludosa* on sedges (*Carex* and *Cladium*), cotton-grass, rushes and reed; *P. curta* on sedges and rushes; *P. igniaria* on burnt culms of reed canary grass; *P. glyceriicola* on rond grass; *P. hispidula* on reed, reed-maces and sedges; *P. funerea* on sedges and rushes and *P. laminella* on sedges (*Carex* and *Cladium*).

Ramularia alismatis: produces a leaf-spot on great water plantain; *R. calthae* is common on marsh marigold; *R. epilobii* and *R. punctiformis* have been found on willowherbs; *R. cicutae* on living leaves of cowbane; *R. lysimachiarum* on creeping jenny; *R. scrophulariae* on water betony; *R. ulmariae* on meadowsweet and *R. valerianae* on common and marsh valerians.

Septocylindrium aromaticum: is a common parasite of sweet flag.

Speira toruloides: has been found on bittersweet in the marshes.

Sporochisma mirabile: usually found on old wood, has been seen on stems of hairy willowherb.

Sporidesmium cladii: on *cladium; S. eupatoriicola* on meadowsweet and hemp agrimony; *S. paludosum* on *cladium.*

Stachybotrys dichroa: grows on over-wintered dead stems of meadowsweet in early summer.

Tetraploa aristata: abounds on dead standing leaves of saw sedge and has been found also on tussock sedge and reed in this area. The brown spores have four long appendages, like those of many aquatic hyphomycetes, and they are often found floating on water in the marshes.

Triposporium elegans: has been found on meadowsweet.

Tuberculina persicina: a violet-brown mould parasitic on the aecidia of many kinds of rust-fungi in damp habitats.

Volutella arundinis: a common pink fungus on newly-dead reeds and other marsh grasses and on sedges; *V. melaloma* is not uncommon on dead sedges.

AQUATIC HYPHOMYCETES

In recent years an almost entirely new flora of aquatic hyphomycetes has been discovered on submerged leaves of alder and other trees in streams and rivers by C. T. Ingold. A feature of most of these fungi is their production of four-armed spores, which appear to be specially fitted for dispersal in water. A search for them in some of the tidal dykes connected with broads in the Yare valley has yielded rather more than half the recorded British species and spores of a number of species as yet undescribed. For details of these remarkable fungi the reader is referred to papers by C. T. Ingold in *Transactions of the British Mycological Society* from 1942 onwards. The following have been found in the broads district:

Alatospora acuminata
Anguillospora longissima
Articulospora inflata
A. tetracladia
Clavariopsis aquatica
Flagellospora penicillioides
F. curvula
Heliscus longibrachiatus
H. stellatus
Margaritispora aquatica
Piricularia submersa
Tetracladium marchalianum
T. maxilliformis
T. setigerum
Tricladium angulatum
T. gracile
T. splendens

THE COELOMYCETES

These small stem and leaf fungi, bearing spores in pycnidia or in pustules, erupt from most dying stems and leaves in marshes, as elsewhere, and there is a fair sprinkling of parasitic species, producing bleached circular spots on leaves or causing shoots to die back prematurely. The list of broadland Coelomycetes which follows is by no means comprehensive, but it includes a number of the more interesting and characteristic species likely to be met with by a visiting mycologist.

Ascochyta alismatis: on water plantain; *A. equiseti* on marsh horsetail; *A. menyanthis* on bogbean; *A. quadriguttata* on bur-reed; *A. solanicola* on bittersweet; *A. viburni* on guelder rose.

Camarosporium ribis: on wild red currant.

Ciliospora albida: on much trampled rond-grass (*Glyceria maxima*).

Cryptomela typhae: on reed-maces.

Cryptosporium neesii: on alder.

Cytospora myricae-gales: on bog-myrtle; *C. occulta* on alder.

Darluca filum: on many rust fungi, especially those of grasses.

Dilophospora alopecuri: on Yorkshire fog grass and reed canary grass.

Diplodia dulcamarae: on bittersweet; *D. rhamni* on buckthorn; *D. sarmentorum* on saw sedge.

Diplodina salicis: on willows.

Discosia artocreas: on hairy willowherb.

Fusicoccum fibrosum: on buckthorn.

Hendersonia culmicola var. *minor:* on purple moor-grass; *H. culmiseda* on reed; *H. juncina* on lesser reed-mace.

Leptostroma caricinum: on tussock sedge, saw sedge and cotton-grass; *L. juncacearum* on obtuse-flowered rush; *L. phragmitis* on reed; *L. spiraeinum* on meadowsweet.

Melanconium apiocarpum: on alder.

Microdiscula phragmitidis: on reed, reed canary grass and rond-grass.

Neottiospora caricum: on sedges.

Pestalotia caudata: on saw sedge.

Phoma: many species on dead herbaceous stems.

Phomopsis asteriscus: on angelica; *P. calystegiae* on great bindweed; *P. caulographa:* on milk parsley; *P. denigrata* on self-heal and marsh woundwort; *P. dulcamarae* on bittersweet; *P. durandiana* on great water dock; *P. lysimachiae* on yellow loosestrife; *P. ramealis* on spindle.

Phyllosticta opuli: on guelder-rose; *P. pirolae* on larger wintergreen; *P. rhamni* and *P. rhamnicola* on buckthorn; *P. thalictri* on meadow rue.

Scolecosporium typhae: on lesser reed-mace.

Septoria epilobii: on hairy willowherb; *S. brissaceana* on purple loosestrife; *S. dulcamarae* on bittersweet; *S. hydrocotyles* on marsh pennywort; *S. lysimachiae* on yellow loosestrife; *S. menyanthis* on bogbean; *S. scutellariae* on skullcap; *S. sii* on narrow-leaved water-parsnip.

Stagonospora caricis: on sedges; *S. elegans* on reed; *S. equiseti* on marsh horsetail; *S. gigaspora* on tussock sedge; *S. sparganii* on bur-reed; *S. subseriata* on meadow fescue; *S. typhoidearum* on reed-maces.

Thyriostroma spiraeae: on meadowsweet.

THE PHYCOMYCETES

Little attention has been paid to this class of fungi in the broads, whose waterways offer a virgin field for the study of aquatic moulds. The downy mildews on some of the marsh plants have been identified and a number of the Entomophthorales have been discovered parasitising insects (these are dealt with in the section on Entomogenous Fungi). It is hoped that the brevity of the following list of Phycomycetes may encourage further research in this direction.

Chytridiales: *Physoderma menyanthes*, on living leaves of bog-bean; *Synchytrium aureum*, on ribwort plantain and water forget-me-not; *S. succisae*, on devil's-bit scabious; *S. taraxaci*, on dandelion and marsh thistle.

Blastocladiales: *Gonapodya prolifera* (aquatic).

Monoblepharidales: *Monoblepharis* sp. (aquatic).

Saprolegniales: *Achlya* spp., *Dictyuchus* sp., *Leptolegnia* sp. (all aquatic).

Peronosporales: *Peronospora alsinearum*, on mouse-ear chickweed; *P. aparines*, on goosegrass; *P. effusa*, on white goosefoot and hastate orache; *P. ficariae*, on lesser celandine; *P. viciae*, on meadow vetchling; *Phytophthora* spp. (aquatic and in marsh soils); *Plasmopara densa*, on red bartsia and yellow rattle; *P. nivea*, on angelica and milk parsley; *Pseudoperonospora humuli*, on wild hops; *Pythium* spp. (aquatic and in marsh soils).

Mucorales: *Phycomyces nitens*, on greasy papers dropped by picnickers; *Thamnidium elegans*, on dung of water-voles.

MYCETOZOA

The elegant fruiting bodies (sporangia) of these organisms, looking variously like miniature puffballs, stalked or sessile, and often brightly coloured yellow or red, are most commonly sought on rotting trunks and leaf-carpets in woodlands. Few students of the group have thought to search for them in marshy habitats. Nevertheless, not only the fen carrs, but also the mowing-marshes and reedswamps of the broads yield a fair number of mycetozoa. many of which occur regularly within the same zones of vegetation year after year. The brief account of them given here is based on H. J. Howard's *The Mycetozoa of Sand Dunes and Marshland* (S. E. Nat. & Antiq., liii, 26–30, 1948) and amplified by records of additional species verified by the author of that paper.

Beds of rond-grass (*Glyceria maxima*), sedges such as *Carex riparia* and *Cladium mariscus*, fen rush (*Juncus subnodulosus*), meadowsweet (*Filipendula ulmaria*) and plants commonly associated with them, provide masses of decaying stalks and leaves on which thrive colonies of *Arcyria cinerea*, *A. pomiformis*, *Comatricha pulchella*, *Craterium leucocephalum*, *C. minutum*, *Diderma globosum*, *Didymium clavus*, *Mucilago spongiosa*, *Physarum compressum*, *P. sinuosum* and the ubiquitous *P. nutans*. Other fen species, found less commonly, include *Diachaea leucopoda*, *D. subsessilis*, *Diderma spumarioides*, *Didymium melanospermum*, *Perichaena pedata* and *Physarum contextum*. The universally common *Didymium difforme* is often present in heaps of marsh litter, where it is sometimes accompanied by *Perichaena vermicularis*. A very rare moorland species, *Badhamia lilacina*, has been found associated with *Sphagnum* on a mowing-marsh in the broads area.

Fallen boughs in the wettest carrs produce very few mycetozoa, but as the detritus accumulates and less of the newly fallen material becomes waterlogged, the number of species increases. The following have been found mainly in mature carrs of sallow, alder and their usual associates, but some grow on ash where this tree enters into the composition of fen carrs in the Yare valley:

Arcyria cinerea: on sallow.

A. denudata: on white willow and ash.

A. incarnata, *A. pomiformis*, *Badhamia capsulifera*, *B. utricularis:* on woody fungi.

Ceratiomyxa fruticulosa: on ash and elder.

Comatricha nigra, *Cribraria violacea:* on ash and white willow.

Diachaea leucopoda, *D. subsessilis:* on fallen alder twigs and leaves.

Didymium difforme var. *repandum:* on fallen twigs.

Didymium clavus, *D. squamulosum*, *Dianema depressum:* on willow bark.

Diderma effusum: on fallen alder leaves.

D. montanum var. *album:* on rotten logs.

Enteridium olivaceum, *Hemitrichia clavata*, *Lachnobolus congestus:* usually well up the limbs of dead but still standing sallows and white willows.

Lycogala epidendrum: on all sorts of soft rotten wood, even in the wettest places.

Perichaena corticalis: on ash.

P. depressa: on ash.

Physarum bitectum, *P. nutans*, *P. psittacinum*, *Reticularia lycoperdon:* on alder, willow and birch trunks and often on marsh gate-posts.

Trichia affinis, *T. decipiens*, *T. persimilis*, *T. scabra* and *T. varia:* all very common.

Invertebrate Animals

CHAPTER 7

LIFE IN FRESH WATER, WITH SPECIAL REFERENCE TO THE AQUATIC FAUNA OF THE BROADS, AND AN ACCOUNT OF THE CRUSTACEA

by R. Gurney

It may be taken as certain that life originated and the main groups of the animal kingdom were evolved in the sea and it is interesting to speculate how the freshwater fauna arose. In the most distant past, the sea was less salt than it is now, and it is conceivable that salinity itself was no barrier; but now, that alone is an almost complete bar between the fauna of the sea and the fresh waters. It has been maintained that the salt which is found in the blood of all vertebrates, and is so essential to their life, owes its presence there to inheritance from remote marine ancestors. In the sharks and rays, which are some of the most ancient fishes and are now seldom found away from the sea, the blood contains less salt than the sea of the present day. It may well be that their ancestors developed their present circulatory system in a sea which was not so salt as it is now. That the sea has become more salt through the ages is certain, and that there is some relation between the salinity of blood and the salinity of the sea is most probable; but this is one of those rather fascinating subjects for speculation about which there cannot be any certainty.

The world has been going on for a very long time, and the fauna of fresh water of these days is made up of components of different ages: those which entered it in very remote times, such as the Branchiopods; those which have evolved in fresh water from distant ancestors; those which have colonised fresh water in comparatively recent times and may be in the process of doing so even now; and those which have returned to fresh water from the land (the aquatic insects). We need only concern ourselves with the more recent immigrants, to speculate on the ways by which they have overcome the barriers between salt and fresh waters. These barriers are: (1) Salinity, (2) Density, (3) Currents and (4) Temperature.

1. *Salinity or chemical composition.* Any animal in water has to maintain a certain balance between the salinity or salt contents of its own body fluids and that of the water around it; but most invertebrates are unable to control the diffusion of salts through their skins, so that a change of external salinity means also a change in the internal fluids, which may be lethal. Water will diffuse through animal membranes from water of low salinity to water of high salinity until the density on either side of the membrane is balanced. An animal unable to control transfusion, if transferred from sea to fresh water, will swell up and become heavier, with fatal consequences. The lethal effect may be due to the absorption of certain salts, for some are more deadly than others. For instance, minute traces of potassium nitrate will kill water fleas (*Daphnia*), although these may survive the addition of an appreciable amount of common salt to their fresh water. Eels, salmon and sticklebacks can control the diffusion through their skins and can live in either salt or fresh water. The three-spined stickleback (*Gasterosteus aculeatus*) has an astonishing power of adaptation to changes of salinity; but when it lives in salt water it changes its appearance, developing bony plates down the sides of its body. The power to control diffusion depends upon the activity of the spleen in the stickleback; but the common eel can adapt itself to changes in salinity even when the spleen has been removed.

Many examples could be given of animals whose distribution appears to be influenced directly by salinity. In the Crustacean genus *Gammarus*, a series of distinct species occupies aquatic habitats from the sea, through brackish estuarine waters to the perfectly fresh waters farthest upstream; each zone has its typical kind of *Gammarus*. The commonest species in the broads is *G. zaddachi*, which flourishes in brackish waters. Rather more delicate subdivisions in the range of tolerance are exhibited by three of the opossum shrimps in this region: *Macropsis slabberi*, a transparent creature with long-stalked eyes, lives in Breydon and the lowest reaches of the broadland rivers; *Macromysis flexuosa* has much the same range, but reaches farther up the rivers; *Neomysis vulgaris*, most abundant of all, is a shrimp of remarkable tolerance, being found in myriads in the lower waters of the river Bure and ranging almost into fresh water in some of the broads and marsh dykes. Some plankton copepods have a distribution corresponding closely to the salinity. The sea water brings in with it *Centropages hamatus* and *Acartia clausi*, but neither of these can stand any dilution. Above their range, but overlapping into sea water, comes *Acartia bifilosa*, a typical estuarine species and above that again is found *Eurytemora affinis*, which is ultimately replaced by *E. velox*.

It has sometimes been suggested that such and such a form may owe the differences it shows from near relatives to the direct action of local conditions. A classic example is the ditch prawn (*Palaemonetes varians*), which in this country lives in brackish water and has a free-swimming larva, whereas in south Europe there is another form which lives in fresh water and has large eggs from which the young hatch in the form of the parent. It used to be suggested that the two forms owed their differences in the mode of reproduction to the influences of their different surroundings; but it is now known that the southern freshwater form is inherently distinct, so that it is improbable that either form would show any marked response to an experimental change in conditions within any practicable period of years.

Animals, as well as plants, are in many cases acutely sensitive to the acid or alkaline reaction of the water by or in which they live and it is therefore of great importance to ascertain the reaction of soil or water in all studies of ecology. Nowadays it is possible, by using a simple system of colour tests, to estimate the 'hydrogen-ion concentration', the results being stated in degree of 'pH'. Thus, pH 7·0 is neutrality and any figure below this indicates an acid water and above it an alkaline one. The limit of acidity tolerated by living things is about pH 4·7, while pH 8·5 is about the limit of alkalinity. The acidity generally depends upon the amount of carbon dioxide (CO_2) dissolved in the water and this changes quite a lot according to the activities of plants and animals present. Aquatic plants absorb CO_2 from the water in sunlight and so decrease acidity and raise the pH, whereas the respiration of animals releases CO_2 and so increases the acidity.

2. *Density of the water.* Everyone knows that it is easier to swim in the sea, with its water of comparatively high density, than in fresh water, and animals transferred from the one to the other find their floating and swimming arrangements upset. The difference of density, apart from its chemical effects, is no doubt a very serious barrier for floating animals and plants (plankton); but it is probably of much less importance to bottom-living animals, except in the case of their free-swimming larvae in some instances.

3. *Currents.* It has been supposed that the currents of fresh water, sweeping steadily towards the sea, must be a serious barrier against

immigration and that they have largely determined the fact that so few freshwater animals have floating larvae. No doubt there is some truth in this, but it is to be doubted whether such currents have had any great effect in this direction. It must be remembered that rivers are generally tidal in their lower reaches, and that the duration of the ebb is not much greater than that of the flood there. Consequently, there is no difficulty in larvae being carried several miles up such rivers and metamorphosing at the extreme end of their run. An interesting example of the transportation of marine animals inland by tidal currents is to be seen in the Bitter Lakes of the Suez Canal. The canal from Suez to the lakes is about fifteen miles long and through it a current flows, carrying with it the larvae of Red Sea animals. In this case, the salinity of the lakes is higher than that of the sea, but that has proved no obstacle. The lakes now contain a rich marine fauna almost entirely derived from the Red Sea, including many creatures which could not have found their way there as adults. It is certain that in the past there must have been many rivers with still lagoons within the reach of tidal currents and in which marine immigrants could settle down and prepare for taking another step forward into the fresher waters of the rivers. It would seem more likely that the suppression of free larvae in freshwater animals is a consequence of low density and rapidly fluctuating temperature rather than of inability to swim against currents. The mussel *Dreissena polymorpha* has a free-swimming larva much like that of marine mussels, but it has spread all over Europe and is now to be found commonly in many of our rivers; it is a recent colonist of broadland.

4. *Temperature*. Marine animals are generally very sensitive to changes of temperature and the distribution of many of them is determined by it. One of the greatest difficulties to be overcome in studying marine animals in the laboratory is that of keeping the temperature sufficiently steady and low. In fresh water, owing to the relatively small volumes and depths involved, fluctuations of temperature may be very rapid and violent, and in shallow water temperatures may become very high right down to the bottom in summer. In a deep lake there is usually well-marked stratification of water according to temperature; but in rivers the waters tend to become mixed more thoroughly. While the contrast in respect of temperature between sea water and fresh water will not be very marked in estuaries and rivers, it is very great between the open sea and shallow lakes, such as the broads. Freshwater pools in northern climates are subject to frost and the smaller bodies of water may become exposed also to

summer droughts and, generally speaking, marine animals are not exposed to these conditions.

SOME GENERAL OBSERVATIONS ON THE AQUATIC FAUNA OF THE BROADS

The main physical features affecting aquatic life in the broads, combining to produce a fauna of unique character in Britain and hardly to be matched anywhere in the world, may be outlined as follows:

1. The area is one of low rainfall and of limited range of temperature.
2. The broads are all shallow, without thermal stratification, and respond rapidly to changes of temperature.
3. The water is derived mainly from soils rich in carbonates and to a large extent from cultivated land. The broads are obviously eutrophic.
4. The rivers have a very slight fall and do not erode their beds.
5. The influence of the sea is felt both by way of the tides and by subterranean infiltration.

The fact that almost the whole of the broads is affected to some extent by their connection with the sea makes the factor of salinity highly important. It is convenient to express salinity in terms of sodium chloride alone and no serious error is likely to arise from doing so. Between sea water with a normal salinity of about 35 parts per thousand and fresh water of about 0·1 parts per thousand is a wide range which, for the convenience of ecologists has been divided into zones: oligohaline, in which some adaptable freshwater species can live; mesohaline, which is the real brackish-water region; and polyhaline, in which some marine animals can live.

The mesohaline, or brackish-water, region has its own specialised fauna, and the same species are recorded from this zone in nearly all localities investigated. But there may be some difference of opinion as to whether or not certain species are characteristic of any one zone. For instance, Redeke, who invented the zoning system, included as mesohaline species the crustaceans *Sphaeroma rugicauda*, *Jacra albifrons* and *Corophium lacustre*, the hydroid *Cordylophora caspia* and the polyzoon *Membranipora crustulenta*. In the broads district none of these belongs properly to the mesohaline region. The first two are polyhaline; *Corophium lacustre* appears to be confined here to the Thurne river, which might just come within the definition of oligohaline; the position of *Cordylophora* is disputable and *Membranipora* is certainly polyhaline in Norfolk.

The dividing line between these regions in the river Bure changes from day to day with the state of the wind and the tides. Very rarely, the river is full of fresh water right down to Great Yarmouth, where on occasion, duckweed has been seen floating out of the harbour mouth. On the other hand, high tides may drive salt water, and a salt-water fauna, up the river as far as Ludham Bridge. In that region of the river which is most subject to these fluctuations, between Acle and Stokesby, the plankton necessarily changes with the state of the tide, but the bottom fauna does not. Thus some species, such as the isopod crustacea *Cyathura carinata* and *Heterotanais örstedi* live in the river about Stokesby permanently and barnacles (*Balanus improvisus*) may sometimes be found established on piles. Although the river water thereabouts may be fresh one day and salt the next, it is not certain that some of the animals are really exposed to the full force of the change. It is quite possible that there are holes and pockets in the river bed which may retain for a long time water of high salinity and that certain of the animals live chiefly in such holes.

Apart from the semi-marine animals which invade the lower reaches of the broadland rivers and give them their zoological peculiarity, there are a few other creatures more capable of withstanding dilution and these have managed to establish themselves in fresh water in some of the broads. Examples of these are the copepo *Tachidius littoralis*, *Mesochra rapiens* and *Nannopus palustris*. The white prawn, *Leander longirostris* is the largest of the river crustacea here and goes up into quite fresh water, although it has to go to the sea to breed.

In the river Bure above Horning and in some of the Bure Broads and those of the Ormesby group, the water in summer is sometimes very thick and green with the growth of microscopic algae. So far as the animals are concerned, the plankton is characterised by the abundance of the Crustacea *Bosmina longirostris*, *Daphnia cucullata*, *Ceriodaphnia pulchella* and *Cyclops vicinus*, and the frequency of the copepod *Eurytemora velox*. The absence of certain typical lake planton species such as *Bosmina coregoni* and the genera *Leptodora* and *Bythotrephes* is significant. So far as Britain is concerned, the plankton of the broads differs radically from that of the Cumberland, Scottish and Irish lakes. If we look outside Britain for a plankton like that of the broads, we will look in vain. It has been said that the Danish lakes are like those of Norfolk; but there are differences in the plankton which point to radical differences in the physical conditions. The plankton of the Friesland Meres is different again; there, many of the physical features resemble those of the broads, but it is noticeable that the Friesland waters are in general more peaty and acid in reaction, as may be judged by the eroded condition of the freshwater mussel shells.

OBSERVATIONS ON THE CRUSTACEA

The crustacea of the broads and their rivers, although very numerous and often of the greatest scientific interest, are unlikely to attract the attention of the casual visitor to the area. On some rare occasion a holiday-maker may happen to be looking on when an eel-catcher's net is hauled in; then he may see, amongst the eels and perhaps a few small flounders, some whitish prawns running up to three inches long. These prawns are of rather special interest, belonging to a species common in the rivers of Holland near the sea and, until recently, known in England only from broadland rivers. They are *Leander longirostris*, a true river prawn, ranging into quite fresh water and going to the sea, or at least to tide-water, only in summer, for the purpose of breeding, just when their larvae are ready to hatch. The larvae are carried out to sea by the tides and do not return to the rivers until nearly ready to moult into the adult form. Most of them complete their larval life in the sea and return as little prawns about six millimetres long. These prawns are very common in Breydon Water at times and there they are known as jack shrimps; but they are not used for food, probably because of their white colour. They can be kept easily in freshwater aquaria, feeding greedily on pieces of worm or raw meat and they are so indifferent to changes in salinity that they can be transferred from fresh to salt water without injury. Their estuarine companions, the common shore crab (*Carcinus maenas*) and the brown shrimp (*Crangon vulgaris*), which abound in Breydon, are strictly limited to salt water and do not go upriver except when there are very high salt tides.

The ditch prawn (*Palaemonetes varians*) is abundant in salt and brackish ditches, but not in the rivers. It is quite a small prawn, whitish in colour and easily recognised by the narrow rostrum which is usually equipped with five teeth above and two below.

Most of the other crustacea of the broads are small and inconspicuous, even microscopic in size. One more of the larger kinds may be mentioned, an 'opossum shrimp' (*Neomysis integer*). The name 'opossum' has been applied to it because it carries its eggs in a sort of pouch until they hatch. It is a grey shrimp, up to about an inch long, and may often be seen in great numbers swimming at the edge of a rising tide along muddy river banks. It frequents brackish water and is periodically common in Hickling Broad and Horsey Mere, especially after sea flooding has occurred.

Anglers are familiar with the fish louse (*Argulus foliaceus*) in east Norfolk. It is a very active crustacean, clinging to the fish with its suckers, but readily leaving its host to swim rapidly about. It is often taken in plankton. When *Argulus* is introduced into a fish pond, it may multiply to such an extent that the fish are destroyed; but under ordinary conditions the numbers are not great enough to do any harm. Its eggs are laid on water weeds and those laid in autumn hatch out into free-swimming larvae of peculiar form in the following spring. Only one other kind of crustacean fish-parasite has been found in the broads; this is *Thersitina gasterostei*, which is attached to the gills of sticklebacks.

A kind of barnacle (*Balanus improvisus*) which inhabits the lowest reaches of the broadland rivers where the water is often salty, sometimes spreads much farther upstream and even grows attached to reeds in the broads for a season following exceptional salt flooding. It is sometimes abundant in Oulton Broad. The old trading wherries plying between Yarmouth and inland staithes used to become encrusted with these barnacles underneath.

The broads are naturally very rich in crustacea of the smaller kinds. Amongst these, two of the water fleas (*Cladocera*) are specially common: *Daphnia cucullata*, which teems in the summer plankton of the Bure Broads, and *D. longispina*, a larger and more robust species which abounds in ditches and weedy broads. These water-fleas produce 'resting eggs' in autumn, so that, if the adults all die off in winter, the population is renewed in the spring from these eggs, which can stand drying and freezing without damage. In the broads, the shape of the head of *Daphnia cucullata* varies very little, but in Denmark, for instance, where the same species occurs, enormous head-crests are developed in individuals of the summer generations so that it is difficult to believe that they belong to the same species as specimens with rounded heads found in the spring generation. This seasonal variation in form, known as cyclomorphosis, is a striking phenomenon observed in the planktonic Daphnias of continental lakes and it leads to extraordinary difficulties in defining the limits of species, especially since each lake may have in summer its own peculiar 'race' of *Daphnia*, whereas in spring all look exactly alike.

Beds of stoneworts (*Charophyta*) in Hickling Broad harbour only a few species of small crustacea, but there is a great abundance of individuals of water-fleas, such as *Simocephalus vetulus* and *Eurycercus lamellatus*. The high salinity of Hickling accounts for the presence of the copepods *Nitocra lacustris* and *Mesochra rapiens*, while *Horsiella brevicornis* is another broadland copepod which prefers a rather high salinity and is commoner in Hickling Broad and Horsey Mere than elsewhere in the region; this last is found in decaying stems of reed-mace and bulrush. The thick masses of pondweeds and water-lilies in Sutton Broad harbour a rich variety of small crustacea. By contrast, the comparatively weedless broads of the Ormesby group have far fewer water-fleas and copepods, in quantity and variety. On the other hand, they have a relatively rich bottom fauna, including all the three known British species of *Ilyocryptus* (mud-dwelling water-fleas).

LIST OF FRESHWATER CLADOCERA OF THE BROADS AND THEIR RIVERS

Sida crystallina, *Diaphanosoma brachyurum*, *Daphnia longispina*, *D. cucullata*, *Scapholeberis mucronata*, *Simocephalus vetulus*, *Ceriodaphnia reticulata*, *C. quadrangula*, *C. pulchella*, *Bosmina longirostris*, *Ilyocryptus sordidus*, *I. agilis*, *I. acutifrons*, *Eurycercus lamellatus*, *Acroperus harpae*, *Alona quadrangularis*, *A. affinis*, *A. rectangula*, *A. protzi*, *Pleuroxus trigonellus*, *P. aduncus*, *Chydorus ovalis*, *C. sphaericus*, *Anchistropus emarginatus*

Mention has been made, earlier in this chapter, of the special isopods found in the fluctuatingly brackish portions of the broadland rivers. One of these, *Corophium lacustre*, builds mud-tubes upon the hydroid *Cordylophora caspia* which grows on reed-stalks and river piles. It has not yet been found living in completely fresh water, but it is able to penetrate farther upstream than any other species of its genus, except for a variety of *C. curvispinum* found in some European rivers. *C. volutator* is a larger mud-borrowing species found in shallow pools on the salt-marsh 'ronds' bordering the lowest reaches of the east Norfolk rivers and at the edge of Breydon. The 'swimming woodlice', (*Sphaeroma rugicauda* and *S. hookeri*) occur commonly in the more brackish waters of this region. The sea slater (*Ligia oceanica*), which is terrestrial rather than aquatic, lives not only amongst the piles of the harbour at Gt. Yarmouth, but also along the banks of Breydon and the lower reaches of the rivers, coming up the Yare as far as Reedham. It crawls forth by night and hides under stones and driftwood by day.

The shore-hopper (*Orchestia mediterranea*) is common under clods of turf and flood litter alongside brackish ditches in the estuarine parts of broadland. *Orchestia bottae*, an inland riverside species which was not seen in Britain until a colony was discovered on a bank of the Thames at Richmond in 1942, appeared amongst driftwood and other rubbish along the north shore of the broadland river Yare at Brundall in 1944 and was later found to be abundant in reed litter at Rockland Broad. This shore-hopper is without much doubt a very recent introduction and may have arrived in Norfolk as a passenger on a barge from the Thames.

[*Note added by E. A. Ellis:* Another recent colonist of the broads is the small gammarid (*Eucrangonyx gracilis*), thought to have been introduced into this country from the U.S.A. a few years ago. It was found fairly plentifully in Barton Broad in 1952.]

CHAPTER 8

MISCELLANEOUS INVERTEBRATES

FRESHWATER POLYZOA

by E. A. Ellis

The Polyzoa of the broads are better known than those of any comparable freshwater lake areas in Britain, on account of the research carried out by H. E. Hurrell, Norfolk's most able microscopist, over a period of nearly fifty years. Most of the information about to be given has been derived from his notes, or from experience enjoyed when collecting these beautiful aquatic animals in his company on a number of occasions prior to his death in 1942.

'Moss animals', as polyzoa are sometimes called, form branching colonies attached to submerged stones, wood and water plants. They dwell in horny tubes and are furnished with crowns of elegant, translucent tentacles used for capturing diatoms and other forms of plankton. Most of them thrive best in quiet, clear waters which are at the same time well supplied with oxygenating plants and microscopic life. The broads have hitherto provided very favourable conditions for most of the British species; but there have been signs of deterioration in the past twenty years, which may be attributed to increasing pollution of some of the waters and in some places, to the fact that certain broads have become increasingly tidal during that period. All the species represented require plenty of free oxygen in the water and a pH of between 7·5 and 8·5. Excessively turbid waters are avoided and they do not appear to be very tolerant of salt tides, although in the Hickling-Horsey region some of them are used to mildly saline conditions. It is of some interest that they are seldom, if ever, found attached to stoneworts (charophytes). All are normally deciduous in habit, the colonies dying down at the end of the summer and leaving behind the reproductive bodies known as statoblasts. One species (*Paludicella articulata*) is devoid of statoblasts, but produces winter buds called hibernacula. Some statoblasts sink to the bottom of the water and rest there until the time comes for the liberation of the young polyps in spring; others float and are frequently washed ashore, where most of them perish. It has been found that statoblasts swallowed by amphibians and ducks commonly remain viable after passing through the alimentary systems of these creatures.

Two orders of ectoproct polyzoa are represented in the broads. One freshwater species only is included in the Gymnolaemata, characterised by the possession of a circular lophophore (the base of the tentacular crown) and the lack of a protective epistome. This is *Paludicella articulata*, an inconspicuous polyzoon usually found associated with the horny mats of *Fredericella sultana* on submerged roots, but sometimes found in pure colonies on the water-moss (*Fontinalis antipyretica*). The tiny zooecia are club-shaped and the crown of some sixteen tentacles issues from a distinctively square-cut opening. *P. articulata* occurs in broads of the Bure, Ant, Thurne, Yare and Waveney. All the rest of the species are included in the order Phylactolaemata, in which the lophophore is commonly horseshoe-shaped, but may be oval or circular, while the mouth is always furnished with a protective epistome.

Cristatella mucedo is a light-loving species, specially favouring clear waters. Its colonies form long translucent chains wreathed about the stems of water-lilies or clinging to the free roots of waterside reeds and willows. The statoblasts are circular, with a ring of hooked spines and when the colonies die down in autumn they often become tangled together in clusters which may be as large as walnuts. *C. mucedo* has been found in all the main divisions of broadland waterways and it was formerly very plentiful, especially in the Yare Broads; but it is now scarce or absent where the waters are rendered turbid during the summer months.

Lophopus crystallinus is the largest polyzoon present. It grows in pearly tufts on the submerged parts of various water plants, on tree roots and sunken branches, piles and sluices and on the shells of water-snails. The yellowish colour of massed frustules of diatoms in process of digestion in its stomach is visible even without the aid of a pocket-lens. The statoblasts are elliptical, pointed at both ends and without spines. In mild winters, the living colonies can be found at any time in some of the freshwater tidal dykes sheltered by trees. This species is common in the Yare Broads and in Fritton Lake; it has not been recorded as occurring in any of the broads of the Bure and its tributaries.

Fredericella sultana forms thin mats of slender, often antler-like, branched, brownish, horny tubes on submerged roots of willows and alders and on reeds. Glassy skeletons of diatoms are often to be seen embedded as strengthening material in the tubes. This species tends to avoid light and its propensity for blocking water-pipes is well known. It is unique amongst freshwater polyzoa in being able to live at considerable depths (e.g. at 713 feet in Lake Lucerne) and it is better able to withstand low temperatures than other species. The kidney-shaped statoblasts do not float, but remain firmly embedded where they are produced in autumn. *F. sultana* is widely distributed throughout broadland.

Various forms of *Plumatella repens* abound in these waters. The creeping forms cover the lower surfaces of water-lily leaves and are attached to many other water plants and to objects lying at the bottom. A luxuriant tufting form, var. *coralloides*, is plentiful on submerged parts of rond-grass floating at the edges of freshwater tidal channels of the Yare Broads. The spindle-cluster form, var. *fungosa*, builds huge masses a foot or more in length and as thick as a man's fist on submerged tree-roots in very many broads. The statoblasts are oval and without spines and they are liberated throughout the summer. The var. *fungosa* also produces many larvae round about midsummer and these float on the surface for a time, like miniature balloons.

Much more remains to be discovered regarding the biology of these animals and their reactions to physical changes in their environment and it is to be hoped that they will attract further attention in the broads.

One brackish-water polyzoon, *Membranipora crustulenta* var. *fossaria*, is very common in salt ditches in the marshes near Great Yarmouth, where it forms crisp, friable encrustations on submerged parts of reed stems and on water-weeds such as *Potamogeton pectinatus*. This species flourished in the broads of the Horsey-Hickling area for a season following the sea-flood of 1938, but when the salinity of the water fell below 12 parts per thousand in the following autumn, conditions ceased to be favourable for it.

LEECHES (*Hirudinea*)

by E. A. Ellis

Only seven of the thirteen British leeches have been noticed so far in the broads district, where they have never been a subject of intensive study. The following species are known to occur.

Piscicola geometra: a common parasite of freshwater fishes in broads.

It is long, thin and of a translucent pale yellow-green colour; specimens are to be seen swimming with an undulating motion in clear shallow waters. When fishes are caught by anglers, these leeches often curl up and drop from them.

Theromyzon tessulatum: a small, pinkish-brown leech which attacks the soft parts of water birds. Numbers are seen from time to time attached to the eyelids of wild-ducks and domestic geese which have fed in the broads and nearby dykes. Specimens not so attached have been found chiefly amongst decaying leaves in ditches overhung by trees.

Glossiphonia heteroclita and *G. complanata:* known as snail-leeches from their habit of extracting nourishment from water-snails, are common in all the local fresh waters.

Helobdella stagnalis: preys on various aquatic invertebrates, is extremely common and generally distributed.

Haemopis sanguisuga: the large olive-brown horse-leech, abounds everywhere. It attacks earth-worms, often leaving the water for this purpose, and devours the flesh of dead fish and frogs in the water and at the waterside.

Erpobdella octoculata: this rather long, narrow, reddish brown leech, speckled with black on the back, is probably the most universally distributed in local waterways of all kinds, occurring even in both polluted and somewhat brackish waters. It preys upon a variety of small aquatic invertebrates. The closely related *Erpobdella testacea* has so far escaped notice here, but it is almost certain to be present somewhere in the area, since it is a common and widely distributed British species.

MOLLUSCA

by A. E. Ellis

The broads district is naturally rich in freshwater and marsh mollusca. All but a dozen of the freshwater species inhabiting the British Isles are to be found in the broads, rivers and marsh drains of East Anglia, and nearly every marsh-dwelling land-snail is represented. Some of these are rare or unknown in other parts of the country. The slender amber snail (*Succinea elegans*, Pl. XIII, 7 and 8) is known for certain only from east Norfolk, where it is abundant on sedges, flags and other plants growing along the margins of the waterways, and on the floating leaves of frogbit in the dykes. A slug, *Agriolimax agrestis*

Plate XVII Marsh harrier

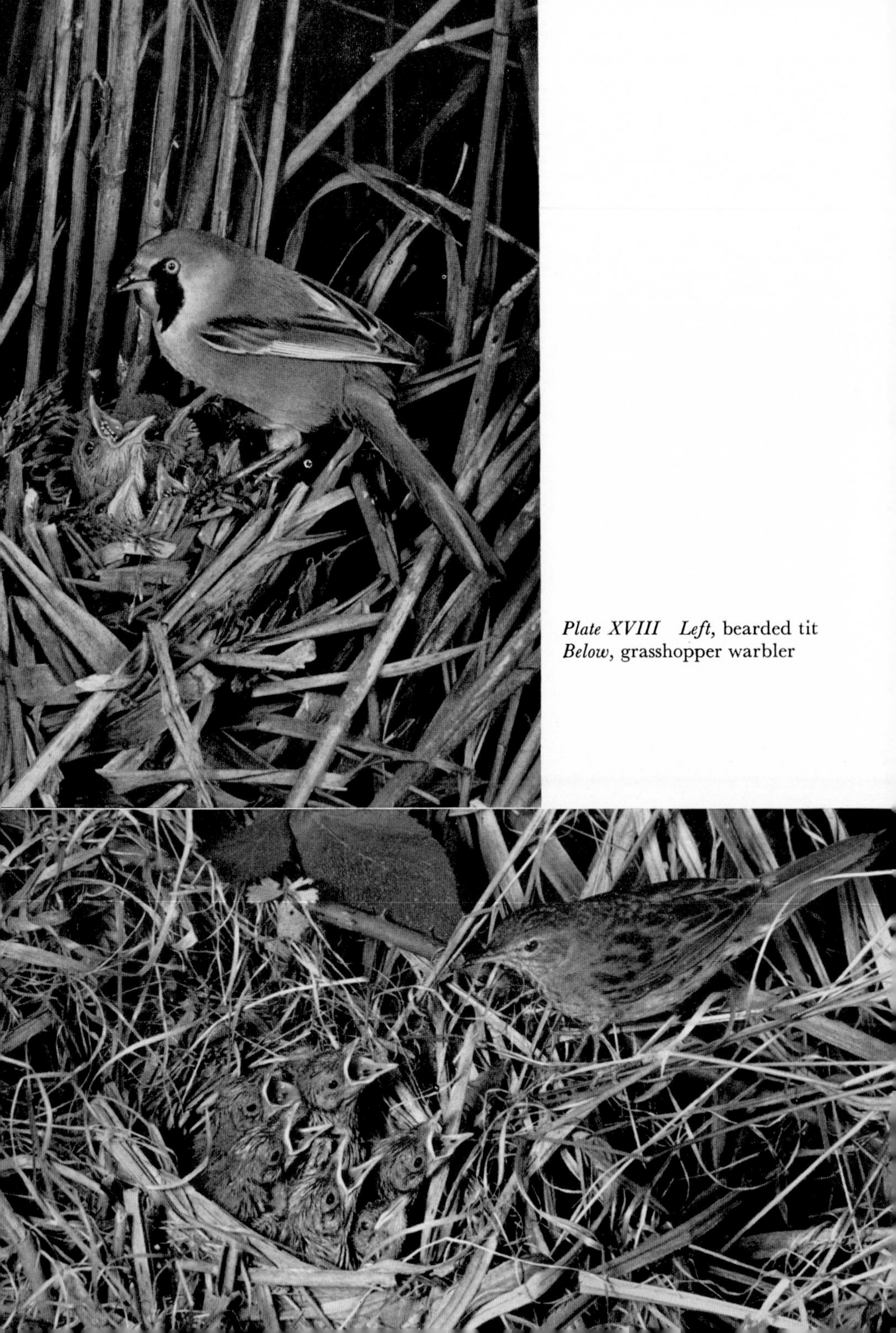

Plate XVIII *Left*, bearded tit
Below, grasshopper warbler

(Pl. xv), has been identified recently from marshes at Surlingham, where it is locally plentiful amongst fen and reed-swamp vegetation, being particularly partial to wild angelica; so far this is its only known locality in England. One of the tiny whorl snails, *Vertigo moulinsiana*, of which there are only a few scattered colonies in the south of England, is frequent in the reed-swamps of the broads, where it may be found in large numbers on sedges, particularly *Cladium mariscus* and *Carex paniculata*, and the grass *Glyceria maxima*, in company with its common relative, *V. antivertigo*. One of the ram's-horn snails, *Planorbis vorticulus* (Pl. xiii, 5 and 6), which inhabits marsh drains in the valleys of the Yare and Bure, is known outside this region only from Sussex, while a species of valve snail, *Valvata macrostoma* (Pl. xiii, 1 and 2), found in dykes at Brundall and Surlingham, is recorded from only a few widely separated localities in the south-east. The river Yare provides an outlying station for the lesser swan mussel (*Anodonta minima*, Pl. xiii, 9), the nearest localities for which outside Norfolk are the Thames and the Ouse at Bedford.

Some thirty species of Mollusca occur in the broads themselves, of which the most conspicuous, owing to their size, are the river snails (*Viviparus viviparus* and *V. fasciatus*), the great ram's-horn snail (*Planorbarius corneus*) and three of the pond snails (*Lymnaea stagnalis*, *L. peregra* var. *ovata* and *L. auricularia*). The swan mussel (*Anodonta cygnea*) is abundant in the broads and lower reaches of the rivers, but the duck mussel (*A. anatina*) and painter's mussel (*Unio pictorum*) are in this area practically confined to flowing waters, and in the upper reaches of the rivers occur to the exclusion of the swan mussel. The zebra mussel (*Dreissena polymorpha*) is locally abundant, attached to rhizomes of reeds along the banks. This mussel differs from all other non-marine species in passing through a free-swimming larval stage, which prevents it from travelling upstream beyond the influence of tidal flow. In other parts of the country it is almost restricted to canals. Some species, such as the shiny ramshorn (*Segmentina nitida*), inhabit marsh drains rich in aquatic vegetation, but not the broads themselves. These drainage dykes swarm with Mollusca, and in spring and summer incredible numbers of pond-snails may be seen crawling on the muddy bottom and on the water plants. Thick deposits of their empty shells accumulate in some of the channels of the broads, into which they are swept by tidal currents. Shallow drains and pools, with a flourishing aquatic vegetation, are far more populous than the deeper waters of the broads. The plants provide food and oxygen, while air-breathing pond-snails only live in shallow waters where they can easily reach the surface. Where there is a deep sediment of liquid mud and decomposed plant material Mollusca are scarce or absent, and few species will tolerate water overshadowed by trees or a dense growth of reeds.

The reed-swamp which perpetually encroaches on the open water of the broads soon becomes tenanted by paludal land-snails, which gradually replace the aquatic species (*Valvata cristata*, *Planorbis planorbis*, *P. leucostoma*, *P. contortus*, *Segmentina complanata*, *Sphaerium corneum*, *Pisidium personatum*, *P. obtusale*) which still persist in the initial phases of open reed-swamp. The amphibious marsh snail (*Lymnaea palustris*) is abundant and the dwarf marsh snail (*L. truncatula*), the intermediate host of the liver fluke, is often present in myriads on wet mud, particularly in the *Glyceria maxima* swamp. The amber snails (*Succinea putris*, *S. elegans*, *S. pfeifferi*), shiny snail (*Zonitoides nitidus*), tawny snail (*Euconulus fulvus*), rayed snail (*Retinella radiatula*), beautiful snail (*Vallonia pulchella*), dwarf snail (*Punctum pygmaeum*), slippery snail (*Cochlicopa lubrica*) and marsh slug (*Agriolimax laevis*) are prevalent in these very wet swamps, with the copse snail (*Arianta arbustorum*) and, in the Yare valley, the silky snail (*Ashfordia granulata*). As reed-swamp is succeeded by fen additional land snails and slugs come in, while a few of the aquatic species (*Valvata cristata*, *Lymnaea palustris*, *Planorbis leucostoma*, *P. contortus*, *Pisidium personatum*) may still retain a footing, where the fen is subject to frequent flooding. Nearly three dozen species of Mollusca have been observed on a small area of fen at Surlingham, including some terrestrial species which do not normally penetrate into reed-swamp: two kinds of whorl snail (*Vertigo pygmaea* and *V. substriata*), the chrysalis snail (*Lauria cylindracea*), hairy snail (*Trichia hispida*), grove or brown-lipped snail (*Cepaea nemoralis*), smooth snail (*Retinella nitidula*), cellar snail (*Oxychilus cellarium*), garlic snail (*O. alliarium*), crystal snail (*Vitrea crystallina*) and two slugs (*Arion ater* Pl. XV; and *A. intermedius*). Some of these are much in evidence when the fen is flooded at exceptionally high tides, when they may be seen in hundreds, in company with beetles, spiders and other temporarily ‘displaced persons’, climbing up the stems of rushes and other tall plants, like shipwrecked mariners clinging to the masts. Most snails, however, can remain submerged for some hours or even days without drowning, particularly in winter when they are in a state of torpor with the mouth of the shell sealed with a mucous film or epiphragm. After floods, the dead shells often deposited in heaps by the receding water are mostly those of land snails less tolerant of prolonged immersion than the habitual swamp-dwellers. Incidentally, careful sifting of flood refuse often brings to light minute species, such as *Vertigo* and *Punctum*, which are otherwise difficult to find.

The carrs, wet woods of grey sallow, alder, ash, etc., which succeed reed-swamp and fen, shelter, in addition to many of the same species, some characteristically woodland Mollusca, such as the pellucid snail (*Vitrina pellucida*), the toothless chrysalis snail (*Columella edentula*) and three kinds of slug (*Arion hortensis*, *A. circumscriptus*, *Limax marginatus*). About the same number of species inhabit carr as occur in fen.

As the broadland rivers approach the sea, some interesting species of semi-marine and salt-marsh snails make their appearance, namely: the dun sentinel or rond snail (*Assiminea grayana*, Pl. XIII, 4), the spire shells (*Pseudamnicola confusa*, Pl. XIII, 3; *Hydrobia ventrosa*, *Peringia ulvae*) and the primitive pulmonate, *Phytia myosotis*. *Assiminea* inhabits the Thames estuary and extends up the coast to King's Lynn. It occurs by Breydon Water and up the rivers Yare and Waveney to Cantley and Somerleyton; it is also found at the mouth of the river Bure and by Lake Lothing. This little snail is abundant on the reed-ronds bordering the rivers and also lives on salt-marsh, showing a wide range of tolerance of varying degrees of salinity (from 1 to 30 parts per thousand chloride). Near the sea it is associated with the laver spire shell (*Peringia ulvae*), while *Hydrobia ventrosa* and the isopod *Sphaeroma rugicauda* accompany it at the fringes of the estuaries, extending up the Yare as far as Reedham. Jenkins' spire shell (*Potamopyrgus jenkinsi*) is present in most of its stations, but penetrates into fresh water (at least as far as Norwich). At the inland limit of its range *Assiminea* lives together with marsh snails such as *Succinea* spp., *Vallonia pulchella*, *Cepaea nemoralis*, *Ashfordia granulata*, *Cochlicopa lubrica* and *Lymnaea truncatula*. The swollen spire shell (*Pseudamnicola confusa*), which is known elsewhere in Britain only from Lincolnshire and by the river Arun in Sussex, occurs with *Assiminea* at Lake Lothing, St. Olave's and Somerleyton; it extends up the Waveney to Beccles and up the Yare to Cantley.

WOODLICE

by A. E. Ellis

Three species of woodlice, *Ligidium hypnorum*, *Trichoniscus pusillus* and *Philoscia muscorum*, are abundant in the broadland marshes, where they play an important part in the reduction of dead vegetable matter and soil formation. The various species of woodlice differ in the degree of their adaptation to life on land, and while all require a fairly moist environment, some are more dependent on damp conditions than others. *Ligidium hypnorum*, which until recently was known from very few localities in England, is the least tolerant of low humidity and the most imperfectly adapted to terrestrial life. It is more closely related to the sea slater (*Ligia oceanica*) than to the rest of our species, and represents an early stage in the evolution of land isopods. In *Ligidium* the abdominal appendages or pleopods, which serve as breathing organs, are not modified for air-breathing, so that respiration is entirely branchial and the animals quickly die in a dry atmosphere. The favourite habitats of *Ligidium hypnorum* are in tussocks of sedge in reed-swamp, fen and carr, at the roots of grass and other marsh plants, and amongst damp moss and humus. It is very agile and runs swiftly when disturbed. This woodlouse is frequent in suitable habitats in the broads district, often being associated with the very common *Philoscia muscorum*, from which, in spite of a superficial resemblance, it can be distinguished by its long, many-jointed antennae. At St. Olave's both species are abundant in the same marsh as *Sphaeroma rugicauda* and the snails *Assiminea grayana* and *Pseudamnicola confusa*.

Trichoniscus pusillus, a tiny reddish-coloured woodlouse, is the most abundant species in damp places, occurring in countless myriads in marshes and carrs. Though able to withstand lower humidities than *L. hypnorum*, this active little woodlouse is more intolerant of a dry atmosphere than any of our other species. In *Trichoniscus* the inner branch or endopodite of the pleopods is branchial in function, the outer branch or exopodite serving as a protective covering to conserve water. There is no special modification for breathing air.

The third species, *Philoscia muscorum*, is an abundant and ubiquitous woodlouse, living amongst moss and humus, under logs and stones and at the roots of grasses, sedges and other plants. In late summer it may be seen in numbers fully exposed on brambles, nettles, bracken and other herbage, showing a curious reversal of its usual love of seclusion. Though often living in company with *L. hypnorum*, this species avoids excessive moisture; in very wet fen it finds harbourage amongst tussocks of sedge, especially *Carex paniculata*, which forms islets raised above the water level. In adaptation to life on dry land, *Ph. muscorum* occupies a position intermediate between *T. pusillus* and *Oniscus asellus*. As in the latter species, air-chambers at the margins of the exopodites of the pleopods indicate an incipient adaptation to aerial respiration, though the principal breathing organs are still the branchial endopodites.

Five other species of woodlice occur in the carrs: *Oniscus asellus*, *Porcellio scaber*, *Haplophthalmus danicus*, *H. mengii* and *Trichoniscoides albidus*, the last two being rare. The common slater (*O. asellus*) is frequent in woodland and fen-carr, lurking beneath loose bark and logs, but shunning very wet places although it often lives in situations too moist to suit *P. scaber*. The latter is likewise common beneath the loose bark of dead trees and logs, its favourite habitat, but avoids excessively damp spots. In this species the exopodites of the two anterior pairs of pleopods have extensively branched air-tubes or pseudo-tracheae, opening by a single large spiracle near the articulation of the exopodite. Uropodial glands, on the terminal appendages of the abdomen, the function of which is said to be to moisten the pleopods, are well developed in *Porcellio* and in the pill louse (*Armadillidium*). As a consequence of these adaptations, these woodlice are able to live in comparatively dry situations. Respiration is still partly carried out by the branchial endopodites of the last three pairs of pleopods, and both methods are essential: if deprived of either the first two or the last three pairs of pleopods, the animal dies within about four hours. *P. scaber*, like *O. asellus* and *Armadillidium vulgare*, is of a sociable disposition, individuals often being found crowded together in groups. This gregarious tendency in woodlice has been shown to be exhibited under conditions of sub-optimal humidity, and the bunching habit probably has some survival value in conserving water. Two other species of *Porcellio*, *P. spinicornis* and *P. dilatatus*, sometimes live about buildings close to the broads; the former has been seen in spring in considerable numbers on the walls of Burgh Castle, where *Porcellionides pruinosus* also occurs.

The pill louse (*Armadillidium vulgare* or *A. cinereum*) lives only in the drier parts of the woods, hedges and lokes, and is more fully adapted to life on land than any of the foregoing species. The exopodites of the first and second pairs of pleopods are provided with air-tubes, opening by several pores situated along a furrow. The chitinous plates covering the back of this animal are relatively thick, thus checking evaporation, while the very convex shape and reduced area of ventral surface probably assist in water conservation.

HARVESTMEN

by A. E. Ellis

Thirteen of the twenty British species of harvestmen (Opiliones) occur in the broads district, although only one, *Oligolophus tridens*, is particularly, and then not exclusively, associated with marshes. Like other terrestrial Arachnids, harvestmen are completely adapted to life on dry land and are air-breathing. They are carnivorous, feeding on dead animal matter or any small insects and other creatures they can capture by means of their crab-like pincers. Harvestmen lack the poison-glands and spinnerets of spiders, from which they are distinguishable at a glance by the absence of a narrow waist between the cephalothorax and abdomen, and on closer examination, by the single pair of relatively large eyes, which are raised on a characteristic eye-eminence or ocularium. The legs of some species are remarkably long and slender and enable the animals to scamper amongst herbage with baffling agility. The legs become detached readily, but amputation of a few limbs does not seriously hamper the locomotory powers of harvestmen.

The following species occur in closed reed-swamp and carr: *Nemastoma lugubre*, *N. chrysomelas*, *Leiobunum rotundum*, *L. blackwallii*, *Oligolophus agrestis*, *O. tridens*, *Mitopus morio* and *Lacinium ephippiatus*. *N. lugubre* is a very distinct little black Phalangid with a pair of conspicuous white spots on the back, slow and deliberate in its movements; adults are to be found at all seasons. *N. chrysomelas*, remarkable for the great length of its pedipalps and the golden metallic spots on its abdomen, is mature, like most harvestmen, in late summer and autumn. *Leiobunum* is at once recognisable by the small round or oval body and exceedingly long tenuous legs. Though most harvestmen are nocturnal, the two species of this genus are frequently to be seen on the move in daylight, quartering the ground and foliage as though in quest of prey. *L. blackwallii* is more frequent on the marshes than its congener, which is more common amongst trees. The two species of *Oligolophus* are very abundant, *O. tridens* predominating in damp habitats; in the wettest parts it is usually the only harvestman present. *Mitopus morio* is very common, especially amongst shrubs, brambles, nettles and tall-growing plants, frequently resting fully exposed on the leaves. *Lacinius ephippiatus* is found chiefly on fen, but occurs also in closed reed-swamp and carr. This species is mature in June and July and by August few individuals remain, though specimens have been collected early in September. *Platybunus triangularis*, another early harvestman, occurs in fen and woodland, and *Odiellus palpinalis*, a slow-moving, lethargic animal, lurks amongst dead leaves and plant debris in the carrs and on marsh walls. *Phalangium opilio* has also been observed on the raised banks of the marshes and *Opilio parietinus* in the neighbourhood of dwellings by the broads. *Megabunus diadema*, a very striking harvestman when examined under a lens, inhabits woodland in the broads district, but is not common.

SPIDERS OF THE BROADS

by E. Duffey

Of the major groups of invertebrate animals found in this country, spiders have probably been the most neglected by biologists. This is surprising when one realises how widespread and numerous the order is; it is probably true to say that almost every building, tree, garden and open ground from mountain tops to salt-marshes in this country has its own spider fauna or is frequently visited by spiders. The available information about the spiders of Britain has been gathered almost entirely through the remarkable labours of a small band of enthusiasts, mainly chemists, doctors and clergymen, working in their spare time. It has therefore been impossible for these few investigators to cover the whole country or even the major geographical areas in Britain and it so happens that the broads district, together with many other parts of East Anglia, has been little studied. For this reason, any account of the spider fauna of the broads must be given in fairly general terms; but enough information is available to suggest that this area has certain distinctive features where spiders are concerned, when comparisons are made with other damp habitats in East Anglia, such as the fens and heathland bogs.

The floras of the fens, bogs and broads in south-east England are so different in many respects that the botanist considers them to be quite distinct communities. Zoologically, however, there is a very considerable overlap, and habitat preferences in carnivorous invertebrates such as spiders depend more on vegetation form than on the actual species of plants present. This may be important not only from the point of view of web construction but also on account of the anatomy and colour of the spider. For many species, of course, the availability of water or the degree of relative humidity are limiting factors restricting them to particular habitats; interesting experiments confirming this have been carried out by Nørgaard in Denmark.

A good example of the influence of vegetation structure is to be seen in the distribution of a common hunting spider (*Lycosa nigriceps*). This species is found only in localities where the ground vegetation is tall and thick, but it appears to be little affected by the species of plants present or by the nature of the substratum. For instance, *L. nigriceps* may be found on the gorse- and heather-covered slope of a Norfolk heath, on the marram grass of an east coast sand dune, or on the lush, mixed fen vegetation of the broads. It appears to avoid the shade of a wood or reed-swamp and it is not found on short turf or where there is a thin growth of creeping or prostrate vegetation. Trapping has shown that *L. nigriceps* hunts predominantly on the leaves and upper parts of the herb layer, in contrast to most other lycosids, some of which live deep in the vegetation close to the ground, while others are confined to dry sandy areas, woodlands, mountains, or marshes.

It is likely that there are many new discoveries yet to be made with respect to the lycosids of marshes in the broads, although a good cross-section of the British species can be found there easily. The most interesting species is undoubtedly *Pirata piscatorius*, the largest and most handsome in its genus. This spider is not uncommon at Hickling Broad and has been seen in other Norfolk localities. When mature, it is deep red-brown in colour and the cephalothorax is edged on either side with pure white hairs, forming lateral bands. *P. piscatorius* has the narrowest tolerance range of environmental conditions of all the British species of the genus and is found almost exclusively by the water's edge, whether it happens to be living in a bog, at a lake-side or along a stream. It roams about in wet vegetation and on plants growing above the surface of the water. It may frequently be found in a silken tube which is probably built for moulting purposes and as a retreat for the female when she is carrying her egg-sac. When alarmed, this species will run down the stem of a marsh plant into the water.

Although the five British *Pirata* species are typically associated with marshy localities and are undoubtedly most numerous in such places, the comparatively mild, moist Atlantic climate of these islands makes possible a wider habitat range than is usually found in the same species on the Continent. For instance, *P. uliginosus*, *P. piraticus* and less frequently, *P. hygrophilus*, may occur here in thick vegetation well away from water or marshland. The probable explanation is that in our climate the dead plant material which accumulates on the ground where the vegetation is tall and lush, is nearly always very moist because it is shielded from solar radiation and exposure to drying winds, and we seldom have long periods without rain. In this ' litter ', many spiders and other animals live in an atmosphere which probably has a relative humidity of not much less than 90 per cent during any month of the year. A further example is provided by *Lycosa pullata*. In Britain, this species is probably the commonest lycosid and may be found almost anywhere, providing there is a vegetation-covering on the ground. On the European mainland, however, it tends to be less numerous and reaches its optimum population density in marshy places.

At this point, reference should be made to the water spider (*Argyroneta aquatica*). It is unique in the British fauna in that it is entirely aquatic: hunting, moulting, courting and mating beneath the water surface. It is widespread in this country and in spite of the few Norfolk records, it is probably quite common in the broads area. It makes an interesting aquarium animal and the construction of its underwater retreat filled with air can be observed. The spider, which lives on small aquatic animals, has a silvery appearance in the water, caused by the layer of air trapped by numerous hairs covering its body.

In considering further the characteristic spiders of the broadland vegetation-types, attention should first be directed to the very large areas of *Phragmites* reedswamp. A reed-ground may vary considerably in density of stems, height of growth and uniformity and it soon becomes apparent to the araneologist that what is best for the reed-cutter is usually the poorest in species and numbers of spiders. The collector finds his richest reward in those reed-beds which have been neglected for some time and allowed to dry out a little, so that the reed-stems are comparatively thinly distributed and the spaces between them have been colonised by invading grasses, sedges and other flowering plants. In such an environment, the open nature of the vegetation and the diversity of plant form greatly increases the range of micro-habitats available to marsh-loving spiders.

In this type of hydrosere the naturalist very often first notices those animals which are more or less on a level with his eye and the spiders which come into this category are those which live on or visit the flower heads of the reeds and other tall marsh plants. Several species are found at this level in the field layer, depending on the time of year. The most numerous is *Araneus cornutus*, distinguished by the foliaceous pattern on its dorsal abdominal surface. It may be found in this position during any month of the year, although its tough orb-web spun between the stems will only be seen during the summer. Why this spider should be the most numerous on vegetation in wet places is rather difficult to understand, because it is always on the higher parts of the tall plants and never appears to come in contact with the ground water or within the influence of the highest humidities, except perhaps in localities where there are large areas of open water. Other *Araneus* species may be most numerous in other types of habitat; thus *A. redii* favours the gorse and heather of a dry heath and *A. sclopetarius* is usually found near water, but with an apparent preference for bridges and other buildings. Food preferences, competition and the physical structure of the environment may all form parts of the answer.

One of the most interesting species found on the flower-heads of reeds is the jumping-spider (*Marpissa pomatia*), one of the largest of the British representatives of its family. Until recently, it was thought that this spider could only be found commonly in Wicken Fen, near Cambridge; but in recent years it has been found to be widespread over the greater part of the broads area and along the rivers Lark and Waveney in Suffolk. *M. pomatia* is of a tawny colour with darker areas on the fore part of the cephalothorax and two dark longitudinal stripes along the dorsal surface of the abdomen. The cocoon is usually placed within a silk chamber situated amongst the florets of *Phragmites* and the female has been seen to remain with the young until they disperse.

A third species commonly found on reed-heads is the crab-spider, (*Xysticus ulmi*). As with *M. pomatia*, *X. ulmi* is restricted almost entirely to marshy places and is specially numerous in mixed reedswamp vegetation. Both species are conspicuous on reed-heads because the female very often constructs her egg cocoon in such places. Before reaching maturity, these spiders seek their prey at a lower level in the vegetation, on the stems, leaves and flowers of marsh herbs and grasses. It appears strange that they should climb to the highest point available to them before laying their eggs, but it may well be an adaptation to make dispersal of the young more easy. When the young spiderlings hatch out, they do not crawl down the vegetation, but let out a strand of silk which is caught by air movements and at the right moment each baby spider becomes airborne and floats away. In this manner the young are dispersed over a wider area.

The egg cocoons of many other kinds of spiders may be found on the leaves of *Phragmites* or hidden among the florets. Sometimes the cocoon may be a flat disc attached to the underside of a leaf, as with *Tetragnatha extensa*, in which the white silk containing the eggs is camouflaged by a cover or cap of a different type of silk, dark grey in colour. A method used commonly by various spiders of the genus *Clubiona* is to twist a leaf or curl down the tip so that it forms part of the retreat in which the eggs are laid. Probably the most numerous species is the aptly named *Clubiona phragmitis*, which in late summer may be found in the same flower-heads as *M. pomatia*, *X. ulmi* and *A. cornutus*. Most of the species of *Clubiona* are rather sluggish animals, hunting by stealth, and they normally move about deep in the ground vegetation; but several climb tall plants when they are ready to lay their eggs.

Some typical spiders of the reed-swamp and mixed fen vegetation have been described and mention should be made of the fauna associated with a very distinct type of plant form, the tussocks of the sedge (*Carex paniculata*). This plant, which has a wide distribution in the broads and is a typical inhabitant of many places in the Yare and Bure valleys, may be found growing in open situations, along the sides of fen channels, or in the shade of alders in swamp carrs. In the valley of the Lark, it grows in rather drier situations, sometimes in peaty depressions on a gravelly substratum. A well-developed tussock may be three feet high and four feet in diameter across the leafy top. The tussock ' stem ' is a broad column lined by dry dead plant material, while the growing leaves spring from the apex and droop down over the sides. A relatively large, complex structure such as this has much in common with a tree in that both have a vertical zonation of different types of micro-habitats. Just as the trunk, boughs and foliage of a tree are exploited by different vertebrate animals (e.g. birds), the spider fauna of a *C. paniculata* tussock also shows a distinct zonation. In the dead plant material around the base of the tussock and shaded by the overhanging leaves, many small species of the Linyphiidae can be found and the majority will probably be black, dark brown or reddish in colour, without any sort of patterning. Many other families are also represented in this stratum, particularly Clubionidae and Lycosidae.

The dead plant litter around the tussock forms a damp, dark world for the inhabitants; but above this zone, on the sides of the tussock ' stem ', it is much drier and some light manages to get through the shading leaves. Most of the spiders found here are again Linyphiidae, but rather larger than the litter species and in most cases their horizontal sheet-webs are easily detected. Common species include *Linyphia clathrata*, *Bathyphantes pullatus*, *B. gracilis*, *B. approximatus*, *Taranuchus setosus* and one may find *Linyphia impigra* and *Theridion instabile* (Theridiidae). An examination of these species reveals some interesting features associated with their coloration. Although the shades and intensity of the colours vary, most of these spiders differ from the ' litter ' species in that they possess some sort of patterning.

Although they live in a dimly lit environment, camouflage is now of some importance and suitable patterning enables the spider to blend into the background of light and shade. The condition known as counter-shading, the upper parts dark and the under parts light, is very widespread in the animal kingdom and its effectiveness in reducing conspicuousness has been demonstrated convincingly. Spiders also include many examples of this type of coloration but it is not generally realised that the opposite condition, *reversed* counter-shading, is quite common as well. Many lyniphiid spiders which build their horizontal sheet-webs in the ground-vegetation and wait for their prey by hanging upside down, are uniformly dark on the belly, which of course faces upwards, while the dorsal surface is light-coloured or patterned. *Linyphia clathrata* and *L. triangularis* are good examples of this.

In the upper parts of the tussock, among the leaves and crown, a large variety of species can be observed, including some of those found round the ' stem '. At Wheatfen, several species usually found in the ' litter ' have been taken from the sedge foliage and in this case it is possible that the tidal rise and fall in the fen channels causes a movement upwards which would not occur elsewhere. Spiders of particular interest which inhabit the upper parts of the foliage and are frequently seen on the surface include *Zora spinimana*, *Marpissa pomatia*, *Tibellus oblongus*, *Euophrys frontalis*, *Xysticus ulmi* and *X. cristatus*, *Lycosa nigriceps* and other lycosids. Two rare and interesting species which come into this ecological category and which have been taken from *Carex paniculata* tussocks beside the river Lark, are *Thanatus striatus* and *Lycosa rubro-fasciata*.

In this case also we find that there is an interesting colour difference, when the ' top ' species are compared with those from the lower strata. On examination the eight species mentioned above will be found to be predominantly yellowish or light brown in colour, on which background darker longitudinal stripes (chevrons in *E. frontalis*) are displayed. There can be little doubt that such coloration is protective. These spiders live in a well-lighted vegetation zone where leaves and stems create, by their shading, a background consisting of alternate light and dark lines. It follows that an effective cryptic coloration will be one which most closely resembles this. The necessary conditions are fulfilled by these species, which include representatives of several different families.

Egg cocoons also vary in colour according to where they are deposited. The marsh-haunting *Pirata* species, which live within the lower vegetation layers and carry the egg-sac attached to the spinnerets, have pure white cocoons, as do most ' litter ' spiders. Lycosids which are commonly seen on the vegetation surface (e.g. *L. nigriceps*) construct cocoons which are at first white but soon become greenish in colour. Some species of *Theridion* found on tall plants also produce greenish cocoons, while *Agroeca brunnea* covers the exposed cocoon with a layer of mud which, when hard, also serves as a protection against parasites. *Xysticus ulmi*, which deposits its white egg-sac on the upper leaves of fen plants, covers the cocoon with its cryptically coloured body until the young are hatched.

A curious feature of fens and marshes, noticed by araneologists and specialists interested in other groups of invertebrates, is that heaps of cut reed, grass and sedge often harbour a much greater concentration of animals than exists in comparable areas of the surrounding natural vegetation. Such man-made structures have the effect of greatly increasing the extent of a particular micro-habitat, in this case, the ' litter ' layer, which is normally richer in species and individuals than any other zone within the ground vegetation. A heap of grass and herbs rots down quickly in the warmth and moisture of a fen, but reed and especially sedge (*Cladium mariscus*) are tougher and retain their rigidity for a longer period. If a heap of sedge is examined, the surface layer will be found to be dry and hard and on this, many fen spiders, chiefly lycosids, will be found running about. Inside the heap the sedge material will be wet and slimy with fungal growths, but the rigid structure of the stems maintains numerous air-spaces where beetles and other insects and spiders can move about and where small Linyphiidae can build their tiny webs. If the sedge has been lying for some time, the lowest layers will be much disintegrated and a different fauna will be found. Many of the special fen ' rarities ' have been collected from such heaps.

This short account has dealt with only a few of the interesting features associated with the spider fauna of marshes and fens; emphasis has been placed on the ecological approach rather than on the presentation of a species list which would mean little to the average reader and in any case would be very incomplete.

There remains one further point to be considered; this concerns the past history of the faunas of the East Anglian fens and broads. The collecting of spiders in such places as Wicken Fen, Woodwalton Fen, the broads and various wet heaths of Norfolk and Suffolk, has revealed certain faunistic affinities and differences which can perhaps be explained by reference to the history of the different sites. The spider fauna of Wicken Fen is the best known of the places mentioned, with an imposing list of locally abundant species which have been found in few other localities. As our knowledge of the spider fauna of the broads increases, many similarities to the Wicken Fen type of community become evident. The best example so far is *Marpissa pomatia*, a Wicken ' speciality ' now known to be widespread in the broads. Different types of marsh communities in the valleys of the rivers Lark and Waveney also reveal close affinity with that of Wicken in the presence of rare species such as *Lycosa rubro-fasciata*, *Thanatus striatus* and *Crustulina stricta*. On the other hand, at the two ' fens ' at Holme and Woodwalton in Huntingdonshire, the spider fauna seems to be of a different type. *Marpissa pomatia* is absent from the reed-beds and there is only a very restricted number of ' litter ' linyphiids, while at Woodwalton occurs the rare *Lycosa paludicola* which is not known from any other locality in East Anglia. It is also puzzling to find that *Lycosa pullata* is relatively uncommon in these two ' fens ', while *L. prativaga* and *L. amentata* are very numerous. At Holme Fen, the last two species are often very dark in colour and without the usual patterning. These faunistic differences may well be associated with the fact that both Holme and Woodwalton ' fens ' were originally raised bogs which, as a result of the activities of Man in various directions, have become gradually altered in character, more especially in becoming less acid and so permitting colonisation by fen plants in place of bog plants. The fauna as well as the flora appears to be still in the process of change and several typical fen spiders have not yet taken up residence.

CHAPTER 9

INSECTS

by E. A. Ellis

The shallow waters of the broads, with their rich variety of vegetation and microscopic life, teem with insects, several of which are found nowhere else in Britain. The luxuriant beds of reed-swamp plants, the flowery fens and the carrs of sallow and alder also abound in peculiar insects, many of them beautifully adapted to withstand seasonal flooding at one or more stages in their lives.

An ordinary visitor notices the many fine dragonflies, the lordly swallowtail butterfly, the swarms of pale moths which come to lighted cabin windows at night, and the metallic reed-beetles crawling over water-lilies and other plants. In August, innumerable insects of a great many types are attracted to the flowering umbels of angelica and milk parsley on the fens. There are also plagues of mosquitoes and horse-flies at times.

In this chapter attention is drawn to a few insects of particular local interest. A more detailed account of the various Orders so far studied by entomologists in this region is given in Appendix B. Unfortunately, information about some ecologically important groups is not yet available and it is to be hoped that in due course special studies will be made of the springtails (Collembola), psocids (Psocoptera), thrips (Thysanoptera) and aphids (Aphidoidea).

The most noteworthy grasshopper occurring here is the large *Mecostethus grossus* which lives among bog myrtle in some of the fens of the Bure and Ant valleys. One of the grouse-locusts, *Tetrix subulata*, is common on marsh soil and adults may be found at all seasons.

Only a few kinds of stoneflies breed in still or slow-moving waters and the only species seen here in quantity is the vernal *Nemoura variegata*. The rare and peculiarly East Anglian *N. dubitans* is on the wing in a few places in March and early April.

Mayflies are comparatively scarce, owing to the stagnant character of most of the local waters. The recent discovery of *Caenis robusta* on the broads is of interest; previously it was known only in the marshes of Holland.

The dragonflies *Aeshna isosceles* (Pl. xv) and *Coenagrion armatum* (Pl. xv) are rare insects confined to the Norfolk Broads in this country. *Libellula fulva*, which has a wider distribution, is locally plentiful in this district and rare elsewhere. Of the remaining species, most are common in the southern half of England; but *Ceriagrion tenellum* is a rare insect which maintains a precarious hold only in a few widely scattered localities.

The broads and marsh ditches provide attractive habitats for swarms of water-boatmen, pond-skaters, water scorpions and other amphibious and aquatic bugs. Some of these are widespread while a few are restricted to specialised habitats and may show tolerance of saline waters. Many will be seen running on wet mud and peat. Some are associated with special food plants, and most of the bugs peculiar to fens in this country are found near the broads. *Eurygaster testudinarius*, a rare tortoise-bug, lives in some of the very wet fens. *Picromerus bidens*, a thorny shield-bug, climbs about tall plants and preys on caterpillars. *Cymus glandicolor* abounds on the flowers of sedges. *Ischnodemus sabuleti* is a recent colonist of the marshes which swarms over reeds and other grasses and sedges. *Chilacis typhae* lives in the heads of reed-maces, where it may be found all through the year. *Adelphocoris ticinensis*, a graceful red insect of fens, is locally common on purple loosestrife, water mint and bog myrtle. Rare and local aquatic species include the pale brown *Hydrometra gracilenta* found under sedge tussocks among alders, and *Microvelia umbricola*, another floating insect of shaded ditch margins.

The froghoppers and their allies all suck plant juices through beaks and all are terrestrial. Most of them range freely over a wide range of vegetation, but several are specially associated with certain fen plants. Large hoppers of the genus *Aphrophora* are common here on sallows and alders in summer. The vivid green *Tettigoniella viridis* is a characteristic reed insect everywhere. Galls are produced by *Livia juncorum* on rushes and by *Trioza galii* on bedstraws in the fens.

The sluggish alder fly (*Sialis lutaria*) is common round the waterside in spring and early summer, and the small dusky-winged lacewing (*Sisyra fuscata*) abounds as a predator of freshwater sponges.

Most of the caddis-flies whose larvae inhabit quiet waters occur here and they include some which are able to breed in brackish waters. A few species normally associated with fast-running streams manage to breed locally in some of the little becks of the broadland valleys and in sluices. The inconspicuously coloured and rather moth-like caddises fly mainly at night; during the day they rest on tree trunks

Plate XIX Above, reed warbler
Below, sedge warbler

Plate XX *Above*, water shrew (*Neomys fodiens*) with earthworm
Below, water vole (*Arvicola amphibius*)

or hide in thick marsh vegetation. The cases formed by their larvae are mostly cylindrical and decorated with snail shells, fragments of dead or living leaves and an assortment of rubbish. A few live in sticky webs under the leaves of water-lilies and use their webs for the capture of other insects.

The moths of broadland include many species whose range in this country is restricted to the fenland and east Norfolk. Notable among these are some of the ' wainscots ' associated with reedswamp and fen food-plants. Moths with aquatic larvae are well represented, as are those whose caterpillars feed on sallow and alder. Owing to its nearness to the North Sea coast, the area receives many migrants from time to time and some of these tend to become established as breeding species for a few years. Probably the holiday-maker will notice few moths, because most of these insects are night-fliers. In spring the emperor moth may be seen flying strongly over the marshes by day and its caterpillars are sometimes abundant on meadowsweet in summer. The drinker, a large, sandy-coloured moth, quarters the marshes at dusk on summer evenings. The pearly white china-marks moth often swarms over duckweeds in the ditches.

One does not have to be an entomologist to take pleasure in the sight of broadland's lordliest insect, the swallowtail (Pl. XV). Happily, although the indigenous race of this butterfly (*Papilio machaon britannicus*) survives only in this part of East Anglia, it abounds in all suitable localities within the district and is at least as plentiful as it was fifty years ago. The first sunny days of May bring about the emergence of the first swallowtails, which may be seen with spread wings basking on reed and sedge bleached white by winter. Emergence continues until about mid-June and the butterflies not only patrol the marshes in search of wild flowers such as ragged robin and marsh valerian, but visit also a variety of blossoms in riverside gardens; some travel far from the water, especially when strong breezes are blowing, and have been observed imbibing nectar from bluebells and rhododendron flowers in woodlands.

The butterflies of the first brood almost invariably lay their eggs on the milk parsley (*Peucedanum palustre*), which is peculiar to fens. The young caterpillars (Pl. XV) are black, with a broad white band across the middle; after the third moult they become bright green, with black, orange spotted rings. When alarmed, they erect a bright orange-coloured horn from just behind the head and this horn emits a scent resembling that of pineapple. Late in July, or in August, the caterpillars fix themselves, head downwards, by silken attachments to reeds, sedges and the lower twigs of bushes, such as bog myrtle, and assume the chrysalis state. It is usual to find two distinct varieties of the chrysalids in about equal numbers; one kind is greenish yellow and free from black dots; the other is of a pinkish buff colour and copiously marked with black and brown.

As a rule, only a very few swallowtails emerge from these chrysalids to produce a second brood of caterpillars in the same year. The autumn caterpillars have been found feeding on a greater variety of plants than those produced in early summer; in addition to milk parsley, they have been seen many times on angelica and occasionally on garden carrots and ragged robin.

From 1921 onwards, black swallowtails have been met with in the vicinity of Ranworth Broad from time to time and on one occasion in the Yare valley at Surlingham; 'smoky-winged' specimens have been seen also. The melanic insect in pristine condition, velvet black with only the smoky blue crescents of the hind wings showing in faint relief, basking in the spring sunshine, all considerations of its rarity apart, is a magnificent creature. Too many of Norfolk's black or dusky swallowtails have been snatched away as prizes for collections for any honest estimate of the survival value of their melanistic tendencies to be made; but it is certain that under the natural conditions prevailing where the mutation arose, the melanistic trend persisted and spread with some success among the local swallowtail population.

It has been stated that the swallowtail is plentiful in broadland and it might be assumed from this that the insect is in no danger of extinction within the next few decades. It owes its present abundance very largely to the fact that considerable areas of watery fens which used to be mown regularly in summer (and burnt off occasionally in early spring) have been left to run wild during the past thirty years or so. In these places, the insect's chief food plant has flourished and the larvae and pupae have been undisturbed. Many of these fens have now become overgrown with bushes and so become less suitable for the breeding of swallowtails. Many tracts of marginal land have been drained and cultivated very recently and others have been burnt or treated with herbicides and transformed into rough pasture. The reed industry has been showing signs of expansion and the practice of burning marshes to improve conditions for reed-cutting has been extended in consequence. There are extensive nature reserves in the vicinity of the broads; but breeding grounds of the swallowtail form a comparatively small proportion of the areas covered by them. Like other insects, the swallowtail suffers from natural disasters, due in the main to unfavourable weather. So far, the local population has had the reserves necessary for full recovery to be achieved in a good season. The time may come when, because of local changes in land utilisation, the minimum reserve population of this butterfly necessary for survival will not exist to meet emergencies. The insect died out at Wicken Fen recently after part of the conserved area had been given up temporarily to cultivation. If the swallowtail is to remain a part of England's glorious inheritance for ever and ever, its safeguarding in the broads must become the conscious responsibility of all would-be collectors who visit its native paradise.

Mention will be made now of wind as an agent in the dispersal of Norfolk swallowtails. A few years ago, just when the emergence of these butterflies had reached its peak, an easterly gale sprang up suddenly and swept many of the insects far inland, where they surprised a number of people in towns and villages up to fifty miles distant from the nearest broad. In centuries past, when fens were to be found in a great many parts of the country, such an occurrence might well have proved beneficial in helping to increase the insect's breeding range. In the present state of the land, such enforced wandering only serves to deplete the native stock.

That other lovely butterfly of the East Anglian fens, the British large copper, became extinct about the year 1851. Its disappearance followed the draining, mowing and burning of its home grounds and, in the last stage, when it had become very localised, over-collecting. A smaller and less brilliant race of the same insect, *Lycaena dispar rutilus*, inhabiting a large part of Europe and extending into western Asia, was introduced unsuccessfully at Wicken Fen, Cambridgeshire, by G. H. Verrall, in 1909; but in 1914, E. B. Purefoy succeeded in establishing a colony of it in Ireland and in 1926 more than five hundred butterflies of Capt. Purefoy's Irish stock were released at Woodbastwick, Norfolk, in the hope that they would settle down and multiply round the broads. This experiment failed, mainly, it was thought, because the insect's food plant, the great water dock, grew alongside the waterways more than in the mixed vegetation of the marshes where conditions would have been more suited to the needs of the insect in the early stages of development.

In 1915 another race of the large copper was discovered in Friesland. It so closely resembled the lost British *L. dispar dispar* that it was at first thought to represent a relict colony of the same race, but it was later separated on account of very small but constant differences in marking and named *L. dispar batavus*. The Dutch large copper was introduced successfully at Wood Walton Fen, Huntingdonshire, in 1927, where a flourishing colony has been maintained ever since.

In 1949 an attempt was made to establish *batavus* in fens of the Yare valley at Surlingham by introducing larvae from Wood Walton. Eighty of the butterflies were released between 26th June and 29th July; the weather proved very favourable and large numbers of eggs were laid on the local water docks. From 30th July to 2nd August strong winds and rain swept the area and all the butterflies vanished from the fen; one was seen nine miles away to the south-east on 5th August. Young larvae were seen in plenty during August and they went into hibernation in brown, curled up leaves of the docks. The winter proved mild and dry and a fair number of the caterpillars wintered successfully and produced butterflies in the following summer, which again proved encouraging for the insects. More eggs and caterpillars were seen in 1950 than in the previous year. A wet autumn and winter followed and in April 1951 at the critical period when the larvae had come out of hibernation and moulted, so that they were vulnerable to flooding, exceptionally high tides rose over the marshland and drowned them all except for perhaps half a dozen. In view of the risk of tidal flooding, the experiment was discontinued. At the same time, an increase in the feral population of coypus resulted in the destruction of a great many of the water docks by these rodents and this development would have been very discouraging for the large coppers. Until the coppers were introduced in broadland it had not been suspected that birds played a significant part as predators so far as the butterflies were concerned, although it was known that the pupae were often attacked by sedge warblers. At Surlingham, white-throats nesting on the marsh banks acquired the habit of pursuing the coppers in flight, usually of an evening. The birds ate the bodies of their victims and discarded the wings. They attacked migratory Large White butterflies passing over the marshes in the same way.

The water-beetles of this area were studied in some detail by F. Balfour Browne at the beginning of this century and it was shown that there was some differentiation between species inhabiting water-ways on peat and silt respectively. Families of Coleoptera well represented in the broads district include the Carabidae found running on damp soils, the Staphylinidae (often abundant in flood refuse), the Cantharidae and Malachidae (on fen flowers), Coccinellidae (lady-birds), Chrysomelidae (including the brightly metallic reed-beetles) and Curculionidae (weevils).

The marshes abound in sawflies, whose larvae feed on living plants, but there are no aquatic species. Of the other Hymenoptera, mention should be made of the great number of bumble-bees to be seen visiting sallow catkins in spring; most of these have their nests on marsh banks and high ground away from the valleys. A solitary-bee, *Prosopis pectoralis*, often occupies old cigar-galls in reeds; another, *Macropis labiata*, also makes its nests in hollow stems and specialises in collecting pollen from yellow loosestrife flowers. The only common ants in the fens are *Myrmica laevinodis*, which nest in sedge tussocks.

A great many flies have aquatic larvae and these very naturally proponderate in much of broadland. They include some of the craneflies, moth-flies, mosquitoes, non-biting gnats, drone-flies, marsh-flies and shore-flies. The mosquito *Anopheles algeriensis* has been found breeding freely in some broads, but it has not been found to transmit malaria in this country, although it is one of the species capable of doing so. Clouds of Chironomyd gnats often gather, dancing, over bushes by the waterside, when they are sometimes mistaken for black smoke. Small black flies of the genus *Hilara* may be seen over the water and darting down to pick up still smaller insects which are then consumed by the females during their mating flights. Various Chloropid flies, including some which form cigar-shaped galls in reeds, are much eaten by bearded tits and other insectivorous birds of the reed-beds.

Vertebrate Animals

CHAPTER 10

FISHES

by E. A. Ellis

About two hundred and fifty kinds of freshwater fishes inhabit Europe; in the British Isles there are forty-five, of which Norfolk has twenty-nine and the broads district almost the same number, if one includes species that stray from upper reaches of the rivers and those that normally live in the small local streams or becks. The non-migratory fishes which appear to be truly indigenous to the broads and the slow-moving waters of their rivers comprise the pike, tench, roach, rudd, silver bream, bream, perch, ruffe, three-spined stickleback and ten-spined stickleback. All these seem likely to have arrived by way of freshwater connections with the European mainland after the termination of the Pleistocene and most probably while Mesolithic Man was roaming the land of forest, marsh, rivers and lakes inundated later by the North Sea. In the broads, all of these fishes come in contact with salt water of varying strengths from time to time and although many succumb to the effects of sudden tidal inrushes, all prove themselves capable of living in slightly saline waters for lengthy periods; such a measure of adaptability may have helped their forebears spreading through the lowlands of the Rhine Delta in early post-glacial times.

The PERCH was formerly much more plentiful in local waters than it is now. A. H. Patterson suggested that a factor contributing to its decrease was the introduction of motor-propelled craft, which disturbed the spawn violently and tended to pollute the surface waters with oil when the eggs were floating. Many perch used to be taken in Breydon, in the mixed fresh and salt water, but since the estuary has become silted up and the main river channel running through it has become more strongly tidal, they are only occasional visitors, swept downstream on a strong ebb. They still frequent the slightly brackish waters of the rivers for some miles above the estuary and occur, in varying numbers, in most of the broads.

RUFFE. According to Cuvier, this fish was first made known to science by Dr. Caius, who discovered it near Norwich in the sixteenth century. It abounds chiefly in the upper reaches of the rivers here, but is also widespread in the broads and is able to adapt itself to life in somewhat brackish water, notably in Horsey Mere.

MILLER'S THUMB. This is found in most of the little streams or ' becks ' of the district, but not in the broads or the tidal reaches of the main rivers.

Migratory shoals of GREY MULLET enter Great Yarmouth harbour periodically and visit Breydon; odd examples have been known to travel upstream as far as Barton Broad.

The THREE-SPINED STICKLEBACK, known locally as the 'Stannickle ', is abundant in most of the marsh ditches, in the rivers and in some of the more tidal broads. It goes right down to the sea where large numbers are taken at times in the longshore fishermen's drawnets and even in the nets of herring drifters much farther out. It is exceptional among fishes in being able to survive sudden extreme changes in water salinity. In arctic regions, this species is largely marine; in Spain and Italy it is said to be confined to fresh water. Specimens living in salt water tend to possess bony plates along the sides; these are not usually seen in those that inhabit fresh water exclusively. It has been observed that when the river Yare has been polluted temporarily after heavy rainstorms, roach and bream have been killed in large numbers, while the three-spined sticklebacks gave no appearance of suffering any ill effects. After spawning in spring, the females tend to become segregated and swim off in shoals, while the ' redbreast ' males stay to guard nests and young. Females preponderate in the shoals found in the sea. Many of these fishes living in brackish ditches are parasitised by small copepods (*Theristes gasterostei*) which live under the gills. Local sticklebacks are devoured regularly by eels in the rivers and by pike in the marsh dykes. They are caught by herons and kingfishers and common terns sometimes come in from the sea to fish for them in ditches.

The TEN-SPINED STICKLEBACK or ' Sweep ', as it is called here, is common and widely distributed in the marsh dykes and broads, but appears to be much less tolerant of salt in the water than the three-spined.

BURBOT. This freshwater representative of the cod family was present in small numbers in east Norfolk rivers up to about a century ago, since when it appears to have died out. A. H. Patterson (1857–1935) never saw a specimen caught locally in his lifetime.

FLOUNDER. Although generally regarded as a salt-water fish, the flounder, alone among our flat-fishes, is well able to live in fresh water, although it has to go to the sea to breed. Spawning takes place in late winter and early spring and the eggs float at the surface of the sea, some of them and the young fry being carried by tidal streams into harbours and estuaries. Many young and some adult flounders ascend the local rivers for many miles and commonly reach the broads, where they feed on small molluscs and crustaceans. Small specimens may be found in fresh water inland at all seasons; but the adults move downstream to salt water in late autumn in a regular migration. The flounder appears to be able to tolerate river pollution to a considerable degree and the bodies of many specimens are often found to be stained in the vicinity of sewage effluents at Great Yarmouth and elsewhere.

The SALMON only very rarely enters the rivers of this district. The migratory SEA TROUT arrives off the Norfolk coast in summer and autumn and a few specimens ascend local rivers from time to time; but they are unable to penetrate upstream to suitable areas for spawning because of obstructions in the form of locks. Non-migratory RIVER TROUT inhabit the upper reaches of east Norfolk rivers and occasionally get carried downstream; some were placed in Filby Broad a good many years ago but gradually disappeared. The SMELT is another fish that runs up rivers from the sea, in this case for the purpose of spawning in fresh water. Considerable numbers used to ascend the river Yare to lay their eggs on the river bed in the neighbourhood of Norwich in March and April annually and there was a regular cast-net fishery for them there. The river at Norwich is too highly polluted for their liking now; but they still enter all the broadland rivers in comparatively small numbers, and there has been recent evidence of their breeding in Oulton Broad. Observations made on the growth of smelts in this district by Thomas Southwell, of Norwich, showed that the young fish attained a length of one inch within three months of hatching out; by early August their average length was a little under three inches and by the following March, four inches.

PIKE abound in most of the broads and monsters weighing up to thirty-six pounds have been taken in local waters. Pike-fishing is a popular sport here in autumn and winter. Spawning takes place in shallow water early in spring and both eggs and young tend to be dispersed freely over marshland in spring floods, while others reach dykes on the grazing levels through imperfect or temporarily weed-fouled sluices. Some of the dykes contain very many young pike, which often fall a prey to the patient heron. The young fish feed largely on crustaceans, aquatic insects and molluscs; later, they devour other fishes, including fellow pike, and take toll of swimming water-voles and water birds; but it does not follow that a large fish confines its attention to the capture of correspondingly large prey: A. J. Rudd records that on one occasion he found the stomach of a twenty-five-pound pike full of freshwater shrimps (*Gammarus* spp.). Salt-water flooding at times kills a great many pike in the broadland rivers, yet once, at least, a sizeable pike was taken on rod and line by an angler in Yarmouth harbour, on a very low tide when the river brought a great body of undiluted fresh water right down to the sea. Until towards the end of the nineteenth century, pike were commonly netted in the broads, while many were caught on ' trimmers '—baited hooks on long lines attached to more or less floating bunches of rushes. Local boys used to snare jack pike in the marsh dykes.

The SPRAT, although not a freshwater fish, has invaded the broads in large numbers on two occasions in recent years as an immediate result of sea flooding. Sprats abound off the East Anglian coast in early winter and were present close inshore when the sea broke through at Horsey in February 1938 and again on the night of January 31st, 1953, when there was an even greater inundation of the low-lying marshland. Quantities of sprats were taken with smelts in grids where the flood waters were pumped off the marshes during the weeks that followed these catastrophes.

Although the TWAITE SHAD migrates far up some English rivers, notably the Severn, it is only an occasional visitor to east coast estuaries, including Breydon Water.

The EEL is very much at home in the broads and other fresh waters of the district and for more than five hundred years it has been taken here in eel-sets—nets with a series of cone-like pods stretched across the rivers to catch the migratory fish in autumn. This fishery has declined in recent years, as has the practice of spearing the fish with eel-picks as they lie in the mud in winter. The sport of eel babbing is still carried on to some extent by those who live near the broads, usually on warm summer nights. The babber moors his boat in about five feet of water and dangles a bunch of earthworms threaded on worsted and weighted at the end of a line from a hazel rod. The eels hang on to the worsted thread inside the worms just long enough for the angler to lift them gently into the boat, where they drop off. The natural history of the eel is full of complexities, but its outlines may be sketched here. Eels spawn at a depth of two hundred to three hundred fathoms in the Sargasso Sea in spring and summer. The small larvae rise gradually towards the surface and drift with the help of ocean currents. Those that eventually reach Britain take about two and a half years to cross the Atlantic while they are ribbon-like *Leptocephalus* larvae. They have become translucent elvers just before entering our rivers, first those of the west coast in February, then those bordering the North Sea in March and April. In many years only a very few reach the Norfolk river mouths. On arriving in estuarine waters they lose their translucence and become dark above and yellowish below. They travel upstream mainly at night, working along the sides of the rivers and finding their way into broads and marsh ditches everywhere; they are seen climbing weed-encrusted sluice-gates and wriggling over wet ground at such times. Thereafter, they feed and fatten in fresh water as sexually immature yellow eels. It has been shown that the males take at least eight years to reach maturity and the females not less than ten years. Every August, those about to mature gradually cease feeding, change colour to become silver eels and in early autumn migrate down the rivers to the sea, where the eyes become much enlarged and sexual maturity is reached. Travelling at speeds estimated as between thirty and sixty miles a day, they reach the Sargasso Sea by the following spring and die there after spawning.

It is still commonly believed that broad-nosed and sharp-nosed eels constitute distinct species, but research has shown that these merely represent extremes of variation in a graduated series. Male eels rarely exceed twenty inches in length, whereas females may attain a length of nearly six feet. It has been discovered that in about ten per cent of eels the sex is predetermined genetically as female; in the rest of the population the young go through a remarkable series of sexual vicissitudes, being at first neutral, then temporarily feminised and still later potentially hermaphrodite; ultimately, their sex is determined by environmental conditions.

There is evidence that not all of the silver eels passing to the sea in autumn undertake an ocean journey at once; many return to the broadland estuary of Breydon and the tidal reaches of local rivers in spring; moreover, they have not ceased feeding. In very hot summers, many eels perish in local waterways, especially in the shallower ditches, where they appear to be poisoned by the gases given off by decaying vegetable matter in the ooze. Silver eels on migration sometimes die in large numbers on reaching estuarine waters; such fish become red underneath and the local name for this condition is ‘ red rot ’. It is possible that in certain circumstances the eels are not adjusted speedily enough to life in salt water and that their fatal inflammation results from the physiological upset involved. What are known as 'slink' eels are taken from local waters occasionally; in these, the head is of normal size and the body may be a yard or more long and yet little thicker than a pencil; such fish are lively enough when caught and appear to be healthy apart from their extreme thinness.

Broadland eels eat quantities of sticklebacks, freshwater shrimps (*Gammarus* spp.) and aquatic insects. Large specimens have been known to swallow frogs and water voles. In the estuary they consume many sand shrimps and shore crabs. In their turn, they are eaten commonly by herons, bitterns, cormorants, otters and pike.

CARP are known to have been present in most of the broads up to the end of the nineteenth century; but they are now very scarce. In some instances the reasons for their disappearance are not known, but increased tidal effects have been held responsible so far as broads in the Yare valley are concerned. Specimens have been found killed by salt water on Breydon occasionally and since carp are bottom-rooting fish they are in greater danger of being overwhelmed by inland-thrusting fronts of salt water than are the species keeping more to the upper layer of fresh water. It appears likely that carp were introduced to the broads to provide a source of food for the local inhabitants some few centuries ago. The smaller, silver-eyed CRUCIAN CARP used to abound in the ponds of east Norfolk and east Suffolk, but was exterminated in many of them by the great drought of 1921. There can be no doubt that it was introduced here as a food fish in the first place, although Sir Thomas Browne made no mention of it when he described the local fauna in the seventeenth century. At the present time it is most commonly met with in Fritton Lake.

The GUDGEON is not a characteristic inhabitant of broads; but it is present in the upper reaches of local rivers and in becks, including those of the Flegg Island. Specimens swim well down the rivers from time to time and wander into broads; some take up residence near the outfalls of sluices occasionally, in waterways otherwise unsuited to their needs.

The TENCH is a fish of still, fairly deep waters where there is soft mud below. Up to the end of the nineteenth century it was the common local practice to take tench from the broads with bow nets and sometimes a sunken bunch of flowers was used as a lure. The fish were marketed and priced according to their length rather than weight, those of 14 to 17 inches being considered the most suitable table fish. Young tench move about the waterways more actively than their elders and are present even in the tidal reaches of the Yare, where some of them succumb to salt in the water from time to time. Spawning takes place in instalments between late April and early August and the eggs are laid on submerged weeds.

The MINNOW is present in becks and the upper reaches of local rivers, but not in any of the broads.

The CHUB is not indigenous to any of the eastward-flowing rivers of Norfolk although it occurs in the west of the county. It has been introduced into the rivers Bure and Waveney very recently, but there is little likelihood of it ever becoming established in the broads.

The DACE abounds in the upper parts of local rivers and wanders downstream occasionally to reach some of the broads. Since small dace are often used as live-bait, it is possible that some of those found in unexpected situations were introduced by anglers as discarded bait.

The ROACH is the most widely distributed and abundant of broadland fishes and provides sport for an immense number of anglers nowadays. Towards the end of May, vast shoals assemble in certain reaches of the rivers, in main dykes and channels of the broads, for the ' roding '. The spawn adheres to waterweeds in translucent masses and the young fish sink to the bottom and stay there for a week or so after their liberation. The roach feeds largely on freshwater algae. Growth is comparatively slow in some of the broads, more especially where there is most salt in the water. Roach weighing 1 lb. are considered good fish in this area; on rare occasions, specimens of 2 lb. and a little over have been taken. It has been observed many times that roach carried far down the rivers to Breydon estuary on ebb tides manage to retreat upstream safely when the tides change; during periods of drought, salt water tends to extend farther inland than at other times and when this happens suddenly, many roach are killed.

Some roach-like fishes in the broads are difficult to identify; this is because hybridisation occurs between roach and rudd, roach and bream, roach and silver bream, rudd and both kinds of bream and between the two breams themselves.

The RUDD flourishes in several of the broads, notably those of the Ant and Thurne, and in the river Waveney. It may be distinguished from the roach by its rather deeper body, golden sides and the straight-edged dorsal fin arising from a point some way behind a vertical line taken from the base of the ventral fins. In addition, the fins, especially that of the tail, tend to be of a more brilliant red than those of the roach. Shoals of rudd often frolic at the surface and snatch at floating insects. Their spawning follows much the same course as that of the roach. Specimens weighing as much as two and a half pounds are not uncommon.

The SILVER BREAM in Britain is confined to rivers of the eastern counties from Suffolk northwards to Yorkshire. It is present in most of the broads and is specially abundant in Fritton Lake. From the common bream it is distinguished by its much smaller size at maturity, the presence of reddish colouring on some of the fins, the silvery whiteness of the scales and the almost symmetrically forked tail; in the common bream the lower tail-lobe is much the longer of the two. Any doubts may be dispelled by examining the throat teeth in a dead fish; these are in double rows in the silver bream and in single rows in the other species.

The COMMON BREAM swims in large shoals in the slow-moving rivers and broads. Spawning takes place in May, when the fish assemble in comparatively shallow waters, rolling and leaping like porpoises in their excitement. The yellowish eggs are deposited among water weeds. The young swim near the surface for a time, feeding on plankton; then they resort to bottom-feeding and root about in the mud for molluscs, worms and insect-larvae, mainly at night. It is not unusual for them to swim into reed beds, agitating the reeds as they press between the submerged stems. Before fresh-water fishery acts came into force, enormous quantities of bream were netted in the broads; some were sent to the London and Birmingham markets and others were used for baiting lobster pots off the Norfolk coast. These fish can live in slightly brackish water but are often killed in large numbers when overtaken swiftly by salt tides; their habit of keeping very much to the depths renders them more liable than surface feeders to be caught by salt water.

The LOACH lives in some of the local becks and abounds in the upper reaches of the rivers, but very seldom wanders into sluggish waters lower down. Specimens have been found living below the outfalls of sluices in the broads.

The STURGEON is an exceedingly rare visitor to this region; a few specimens have entered the estuary of Breydon and travelled up the Yare and Waveney in the past three centuries, but in no case has one been reported as having been captured in a broad.

The LAMPREY used to be taken in numbers annually from the rivers Yare and Waveney, as many as five hundredweights having been secured in a single night's haul. In the past fifty years there has been a great decline in the numbers visiting this area and specimens are taken only very occasionally in local eel-sets.

The LAMPERN comes up all the broadland rivers annually in moderate numbers and breeds in their upper reaches; specimens wander into the broads from time to time but most of them keep to the rivers on their migrations to and from the sea.

The parasites of freshwater fishes in this district have received very little study. In 1907–8, Minshin found nine species of trypanosomes occurring as blood parasites in the perch, tench, bream, rudd, pike and eel inhabiting Sutton Broad. The parasites are known to be transferred from one fish to another by leeches. There is no evidence that the trypanosomes produce any markedly ill effects in their hosts. Trematodes (flukes) are common in the livers of pike and perch and in the gills of sticklebacks and most members of the carp family (Cyprinidae). Bream, roach, pike and perch act as intermediate hosts of certain tapeworms which parasitise, in order, copepods, fish and fish-eating birds. Only one kind of fish louse (*Argulus foliaceus*) has been identified in the broads and it appears to be ubiquitous in seeking its temporary victims. The parasitic copepod *Theristes gasterostei* has been found under the gills of three-spined sticklebacks living in brackish water in some of the local dykes. The fish-leech (*Piscicola geometra*) abounds in the broads and attaches itself to a variety of fishes; it is often found on the pike.

CHAPTER 11

AMPHIBIANS AND REPTILES

by E. A. Ellis

Although it would be natural to assume that in a comparatively static region of the English countryside like that of broadland, changes in the local status of reptiles and amphibians would take place only slowly, such has not been the case here in recent years. In the past thirty years all kinds have become scarcer with the exception of the grass snake, which has become more plentiful and widespread. Some decreases may have been due in part to the protection enjoyed by harriers, bitterns and herons, all of which prey on amphibians and reptiles to a sufficiently significant extent. In fens of the Yare valley, grass snakes have been blamed for the disappearance of frogs, toads and lizards from many of their former haunts. The extensive sea flooding which affected the Horsey-Hickling area in 1938 and the lower portions of the Yare and Waveney valleys in 1953 must have overwhelmed a good many of these animals while they were hibernating in marsh embankments. The heavy mechanical equipment used for dyke and river dredging and bank-mending claims victims among the amphibians and reptiles. More toads are killed crossing roads than formerly. The ploughing and re-seeding of grazing marshes and the use of herbicidal sprays are bound to have had a deleterious effect on frogs and toads. The viper and viviparous lizard have lost many patches of rough common and heathland to cultivation in many broadland parishes. It is possible also that the climatic oscillations experienced in the course of the last few decades have had an adverse effect on some of the species concerned.

The reptiles present are listed below.

SLOW-WORM: hardly ever met with in marshes subject to flooding, but inhabiting some of the adjacent ground, usually where this is sandy and supports a vegetation composed largely of grasses, gorse and bracken. At the present time, few slow-worms in this district are found except in village churchyards. Blue-spotted specimens have been found here occasionally and an all-blue male was taken from the churchyard at Haddiscoe a few years ago.

VIVIPAROUS LIZARD: fairly common and widespread on heaths, sandhills and hedge-banks and present on many of the river and marsh walls; it frequents some of the marginal fens, but rarely penetrates the wetter reedswamps. It used to abound in many of the local mowing-marshes and numbers would be seen sunning themselves on the litter-heaps in summer. It has vanished from many of these marshes since mowing has ceased.

VIPER: formerly very common round about broads of the Thurne and Ant, where it frequented not only the marsh walls but, in summer, large tracts of fen and sedge-fen. It is still found there, but in much smaller numbers and its main stronghold today lies in the coast dunes and their adjacent heaths and sub-maritime fens. It occurs sparingly in the valleys of the Bure and Waveney, but appears to be absent from all land bordering the river Yare.

GRASS SNAKE: distinctly rare in the greater part of the broads district comprising the land about the valleys of the Bure, Ant and Thurne. In the vicinity of the rivers Yare and Waveney, however, it is common at the present time and there is good evidence that it has become more abundant and widespread in this part of the district during the last quarter of a century. A regular migration of grass snakes to and from the marshes has been observed annually at Wheatfen Broad. In spring, the snakes are seen first on hedge-banks and paths in woods bordering the uplands; they appear soon afterwards on marsh walls and nearby parts of the fen (where numbers have been found lying clustered in sunny hollows, and mating has been seen to occur); in June and July the snakes are met with in the wetter reedswamps and are seen swimming in the river Yare and the broads. A return movement is noticed during August and September. The eggs have been found in heaps of marsh litter on staithes and in manure heaps on farms close to the marshes. As in other parts of Britain, the young emerge from the eggs at various times, according to the temperatures prevailing; it is most usual for hatching to take place here in September.

The amphibians of the district are as follows:

PALMATE NEWT: local distribution imperfectly known; it has not been noticed in any of the broads or their marshes, but has been taken from ponds at Brumstead, in the north-eastern part of the area and at Herringfleet, in the south-east 'island' of Lothingland.

WARTY or GREAT CRESTED NEWT: widely distributed in ponds and in marsh dykes bordering the valleys. It is not known to breed in any of the broads, although it has been found in waterways closely and directly connected with them.

SMOOTH NEWT: common in ponds and ditches throughout the district and found occasionally in some of the quieter broads during the breeding season.

NATTERJACK: formerly plentiful and breeding in marsh ditches in the most easterly portion of the area, including Hickling, Horsey, Winterton, Ormesby, Great Yarmouth, much of the 'island' of Lothingland, and Reedham, on the river Yare. It was well known as the 'running-toad' and many people were familiar with its loud rattling choruses on the marshes at night during May and the early part of June, when spawning took place. It was attached to sandy ground within easy reach of water and was to be found living in large colonies in the most suitable spots. As many as eighty specimens of all sizes have been discovered occupying one hole in a sandy hedge-bank alongside a fen. Since 1930 the natterjack has disappeared from many of its former haunts and has become very much scarcer in nearly all the localities where it has survived. Its decline is not thought to have been brought about by any one change of circumstance, but rather by the combined operation of several adverse factors, some of which were mentioned earlier in this chapter. In Lothingland, grass snakes have become more numerous while natterjacks have become scarcer, but the same is not true for haunts of the natterjack north of Great Yarmouth.

COMMON TOAD: common and widely distributed, but noticeably scarcer than it was in many localities, say, twenty-five years ago. Where the toads have to cross busy roads in travelling to spawning places in early spring, their habit of embarking upon mass migrations proves fatal for many and the cumulative effect of the losses inflicted over a number of years can result in the almost complete extinction of a local breeding colony. On the other hand, toads are known to have deserted old breeding grounds in parts of broadland where their disappearance cannot be assigned to this cause. Although it is usual for toads to leave the water and return to drier ground immediately after spawning, it has been noticed that in the tidal broads of the Yare a few toads remain attached to the water until late in summer, where they persist in croaking out of season. Many are established along marsh embankments, which are a substitute for the dry upland sites sought by their kindred breeding closer to the sides of the valleys.

COMMON FROG: generally distributed but has become scarce in some parts of the district, notably in the Yare valley, since the 1930's.

Spawning occurs in ponds and dykes and occasionally in pulks and shallow bays of broads. Herons sometimes kill more frogs than they can eat at the spawning sites, leaving numbers of mutilated victims by the waterside. Lumps of rather firm white jelly found on the marshes in autumn and winter are derived from the oviduct glands of frogs which have been dismembered by their predators.

CHAPTER 12

BIRDS

by B. B. Riviere and E. A. Ellis

While many ornithologists are attracted to the broads because bearded tits, bitterns and marsh harriers live there nowadays, the interest attached to these few rarities need not obscure a more general view of the bird life of this area, nor detract from a study of the local ecology of common birds. To the true naturalist, the gathering of sand-martins in their legions over the waters of a summer evening when gnats are rising provides as spell-binding an experience as the muffled booming of a bittern in an April mist. To those who know the wren in gardens and woodlands, it comes as a surprise to find its nest lodged in sedges on a quaking swamp. The tawny owls of broadland hold nightly chorus with the wild-duck and the water-rail. It is interesting to find that the pheasant, as in much of its home territory in the east, roosts and nests in the reed-beds and amongst the tussock sedges and behaves as a true marsh bird, summer and winter.

The element of surprise figures largely in broadland bird-watching. At Hickling, for instance, on a shimmering July day, a party of spoonbills may circle down out of the hazed blue sky to alight on the Rush Hills, a favourite haunt of waders. At Horsey, in May, the secret flute of a golden oriole may tease you for hours on end. You may happen on a passage visitation of black terns and find them taking their fill of gnats or resting, Andalusian blue in the sunshine, on golden reed-stuff, and if you know anything about the history of birds in Norfolk, you will give a thought to the hey-day of black terns in broadland, when vast numbers nested at Upton and elsewhere, early in the nineteenth century. Landing at a river's edge during the holiday month of August, you may see goldfinches lively on the seeding thistles. Winter brings other surprises. Flocks of fieldfares and red-wings seek night sanctuary in the sallow bushes and reed-grounds after they have been feeding in the uplands during the day. Magpies gather together in chattering parties amongst the alders as night falls. Waxwings come to swallow the berries that glow in fiery clusters upon the guelder-rose bushes in the carrs. You may catch a glimpse of a lordly peregrine upon a sentinel tree, or a little merlin flying off with a blackbird almost as big as itself.

So far as the open water is concerned, not all the broads attract the same swimming and diving birds. Coot, for instance, seem to require plenty of room, so that they are only prevalent on the larger broads, both in the breeding season and in winter. Great crested grebes show some preference for the large, deep broads; rather more than a third of their broadland population in the nesting season is concentrated in the Ormesby-Rollesby-Filby chain of broads (ninety-two were counted there in 1954), while shallow Hickling Broad, despite its large acreage, does not support a comparable number of these birds. Nevertheless, most broads have at least one pair in the spring. Diving ducks, such as pochard, tend to frequent those broads which abound in submerged water-weeds, notably the stoneworts characteristic of the Horsey-Hickling area.

The yachting traffic on those broads which are accessible to the public is not very considerable in the birds' nesting season and appears to make little difference to the birds as they are now distributed. All is well, so long as there is no deliberate human interference with nests. Certain birds, requiring the seclusion of land-locked waters devoid of such traffic, abound only on such broads as answer this description. The nesting colony of black-headed gulls at Alderfen Broad is the most obvious example of this. If the black terns ever become re-established in the area, they must almost certainly colonise secluded waters if they are to succeed. It has been encouraging to find that even where boating access has been permitted on some of the broads nature reserves, careful guardianship on the part of wardens has made it possible for pioneering pairs of common terns to form the nuclei of colonies which have grown in the past few years; thus, thirteen pairs of these birds nested at Ranworth Broad in 1954, where a first attempt had been made some five years earlier. The Norfolk Naturalists' Trust owns the Whiteslea Estate at Hickling, the greater part of Barton Broad, Ranworth Broad, Alderfen and Surlingham Broads, while Horsey Mere is administered under an agreement with the National Trust. The future of bird life in this part of the country may therefore be regarded with optimism. The Nature Conservancy also participates in the management of some parts of the area.

It seems worth while recalling that by the end of the nineteenth century, exploitation by Man had robbed the broads of its nesting colonies of ruff, black-tailed godwit, avocet and black tern, while

Savi's warbler and the bittern had also vanished and the great crested grebe had become scarce. Local protection saved this last species from extermination in the early years of the present century. The bittern (Pl. XVI) returned to the broads as a breeding species in 1911 and great care was taken to prevent the molestation of its nest. Since then there has been an overall increase until, in 1954, it was estimated that there were sixty booming males in Norfolk, concentrated mainly about Barton, Hickling and Horsey. Bitterns generally start booming in February and cease to do so about mid-June. The boom is usually repeated from three to six times and is preceded by short grunts. The best time to see bitterns on the wing is after the young are hatched, when the females are flying between their feeding grounds and their nests.

With the encouragement given by four decades of protection, marsh (Pl. XVII) and Montagu's harriers became re-established as regular nesting species in small numbers in broadland. In the vicinity of Hickling and Horsey and occasionally elsewhere, they could be seen beating over the marshes with alternating flaps and glides every summer, until very recently. Alas, the slim and graceful Montagu's has vanished from the Norfolk scene within the last few years and the marsh harrier now breeds only irregularly. Both species have shared in the regression suffered by all birds of prey in England since certain poisons came into agricultural use.

Broadland has long been the home of the bearded tit (Pl. XVIII), resident in the reed-beds in considerable numbers at the present time. Its status is always considered precarious partly because of its rather specialised requirements and partly because it suffers severely in hard winters, particularly when there are heavy snowfalls. The arctic conditions which prevailed during the first three months of 1947 reduced the local population almost to vanishing point; only one bearded tit was seen in the whole of the broads district in the ensuing summer, although two or three pairs nested near the Suffolk coast. The following winter was unusually mild and in the summer of 1948 at least two pairs nested in Norfolk and ten pairs in Suffolk. Since then, re-establishment has progressed steadily. These attractive little birds, often called ' reed-pheasants ' on account of their very long tails, are more often heard than seen, their ringing, metallic notes revealing their presence unmistakably to anyone who has once heard them. Their nests, generally built in saw sedge (*Cladium mariscus*) would be very hard to find if the birds were not so confiding as to go to them quite openly. It is a delightful experience to lie still in a boat among the reeds in late summer, surrounded by a family party of bearded tits searching for insects in the reed-tops.

Both reed-warblers and sedge-warblers (Pl. XIX) are abundant here from the end of April until late August and their songs are to be heard on all sides. The reeling of grasshopper-warblers (Pl. XVIII) has a ventriloquial quality and the small songsters tend to secrete themselves in sallow bushes dotted over the marshes, so that they are rarely visible while performing. The shifting emphasis of the song is produced when the warblers turn their heads from side to side as they utter their curiously vibrant notes.

Reed-buntings are common, the cocks being conspicuous with their black heads when they perch on the tops of reeds and bushes. Yellow wagtails avoid the dense vegetation of the reedswamps and fens, but abound on the grazing levels. Both species are apt to be preyed upon by the harriers rather extensively.

The best wader-grounds in broadland are at Hickling and the tidal estuary of Breydon, with its extensive mudflats. Here during spring and autumn the rarer passage migrants may be looked for: ruffs and reeves, black-tailed godwits, spotted redshanks and wood sandpipers, with an occasional avocet and Temminck's stint.

The osprey now visits the broads with some regularity during the spring and autumn migrations, individual birds often remaining within the area for several weeks at a time. Its method of fishing—the preliminary hover, the vertical headlong plunge and emergence with talons grasping a fish—affords one of the most spectacular sights which can reward the bird-watcher. An osprey on the wing bears some resemblance to a great black-backed gull and may at first sight easily be mistaken for one.

Hickling and Horsey are near enough to the sea to come within range of the great migratory movements of late autumn and over them may pass the fringe of the hosts of rooks, lapwings, starlings, skylarks and other birds which follow the coast-line from east to west throughout October. Late on October afternoons, when the herring fleet is out, may also be seen—and it is a sight not easily forgotten—many hundreds of great black-backed gulls arriving on Horsey Mere to drink and bathe in comparatively fresh water. These are birds which have followed the drifters from the herring grounds into Great Yarmouth harbour, from whence they fly up the coast to Horsey; from Horsey they follow the coast westward, the great flocks often lined up in V-formations, to roost on the stretch of sands between Blakeney and Wells.

At dusk, during late summer and autumn, vast hordes of starlings, hurrying like dark clouds across the evening sky, pass on their way to the reed beds of Rockland, Barton, Hickling and other broads, where they spend the night.

As the days shorten, so the broadland landscape changes, till stark alders and butter-coloured reeds form a background to grey waters under wintry skies. With winter come the migratory ducks—mallard, teal, wigeon, pochard and tufted, with a few scaup, goldeneye and smew. Every year, herds of wild swans, both whoopers and Bewick's, visit the larger broads. While the great crested grebes are away in winter, some of the rarer grebes visit the broads: red-necked, black-necked and Slavonian. Dabchicks, which nest on ponds and in the higher reaches of local rivers, descend to the broads for a few months each winter. The Montagu's harriers depart and as a rule a few hen-harriers take over their broadland territory for the winter.

In late autumn and winter, flocks of wild geese spend their days feeding on the grazing levels of the Yarmouth estuary; in recent years, white-fronted geese have predominated over the pink-footed here. Bean-geese have visited the Yare valley with some regularity for a number of years.

In winter, many hundreds of black-headed and herring-gulls, with a few great black-backed, roost on tree-sheltered broads such as those of Wroxham, Hoveton, Rockland and Ranworth, at night. Small numbers of cormorants come inland to fish and to roost in riverside willows at this time. Conversely, many of the kingfishers move down to the coastward marshes where they can obtain stickle-backs in the brackish ditches during hard weather.

From what has been described so far, it will be realised that broadland bird life has a complex territorial pattern which is affected in the first place by the distribution of open water (deep or shallow, exposed or sheltered, as the case may be), reedswamps, scrub-carrs, fens, grazing marshes and mudflats and in the second place, by the impact of the changing seasons which produces internal adjustments as well as major exchanges of bird populations with the outside world.

The rest of this chapter will be devoted to brief descriptions of the local status of most of the birds known to frequent the broads.

A LIST OF BROADLAND BIRDS, WITH NOTES ON THEIR LOCAL STATUS

Black-throated diver. An occasional winter visitor.

Red-throated diver. Odd birds come to the broads in late autumn and winter, usually when gales have wearied them at sea.

Great crested grebe. A summer resident; population estimated at 262 in 1954. Most birds arrive on the broads during February and depart for the estuaries and coastal waters in autumn.

Red-necked grebe. A passage migrant and winter visitor, usually in small numbers and most often during hard weather.

Slavonian grebe. A fairly regular passage migrant and winter visitor, most often seen in hard weather. A few have been recorded in the spring.

Black-necked grebe. A spring and autumn passage migrant and winter visitor in small numbers; most often seen in spring.

Little grebe. Resident in the district, but seldom seen on broads until autumn and winter, when considerable numbers put in an appearance, chiefly in the rivers.

Cormorant. Formerly nested in trees at Fritton and elsewhere. Now a fairly regular visitor to the broads in small numbers, chiefly in winter.

Shag. A rather rare winter visitor in small numbers.

Heron. Resident; about 140 nests counted in 13 heronries in 1954 (37 nests at Wickhampton, 40 at Buckenham, 18 at Mautby, other colonies much smaller). Passage migrants and winter visitors arrive in autumn and weather movements take place in hard winters. On the Yare, which is strongly tidal, herons which have been feeding in the shallows of Surlingham and Rockland Broads sometimes leave in a body at high tide and fly eastward to Breydon, which they reach as the tide is approaching the bottom of the ebb; conditions on the estuary are then suitable for a further spell of feeding. In severe winters, herons have been found to die of privation very quickly.

Little bittern. A rare and irregular visitor, formerly a summer resident in small numbers.

Bittern. Resident; about 60 booming males recorded in 1954. Nesting occurs throughout the whole extent of suitable reed-grounds and the population has probably reached saturation point, although a hard winter always brings a severe setback.

Spoonbill. A fairly regular, but non-breeding, summer visitor. Single birds or small parties are most frequent, but flocks of up to 17 have been seen. Breydon is their favourite resting place, but the Hickling marshes have been visited increasingly in recent years, the length of stay varying from a few hours to several weeks, mainly between April and July. This species formerly nested in the broads area, but ceased to do so in the seventeenth century.

Mallard. An abundant resident and winter visitor. Immigrants come in during the autumn, the timing of their arrival and the extent of their numbers depending largely upon the severity of the winter in northern Europe.

Teal. Although nesting only sparingly in broadland, the teal comes here in very large numbers as an autumn passage migrant and winter visitor.

Garganey. A summer resident in variable, but never large, numbers. The rattling call of the drake is one of the oddest sounds to be heard on the waterways in spring.

Gadwall. The presence of this species in Norfolk is accounted for by the introduction of a pinioned pair on Narford Lake, in the west of the county, in 1850. From these progenitors, in the course of a little over a century, the colonisation of local meres, lakes and more recently, the broads, has proceeded. As yet, only a very few gadwall nest in broadland, but many more are visitors in winter.

Wigeon. A passage migrant and winter visitor, generally preferring coastwise waters and the mudflats of Breydon, but not infrequently visiting broads in large numbers in late winter.

Pintail. An uncommon winter visitor to broadland, but more frequent on the coast. It has nested in local marshes in recent years.

Shoveler. A summer resident, passage migrant and winter visitor in considerable numbers, the breeding population being probably replaced by fresh arrivals in the autumn. It has increased in numbers steadily during the past half-century. Fifty pairs bred at Ranworth Broad in 1954 and 500 shovelers were counted on the same broad at the end of January in that year.

Scaup. Essentially a sea duck, this species is only an occasional visitor to the broads except during spells of hard weather in winter.

Tufted duck. Although breeding in some numbers in west Norfolk, this bird has seldom done so on the broads. It is a common winter visitor and of all ducks is the most inclined to use the rivers.

Pochard. A resident and winter visitor. Since 1928, a few pairs have nested round the broads. Fairly large numbers frequent Horsey Mere, Hickling Broad and Ranworth Broad in winter and at times visit other broads, such as Rockland, especially in hard weather.

White-eyed pochard. An occasional winter visitor in small numbers, usually in hard weather. A few examples of Paget's pochard, a hybrid between this species and the common pochard, have appeared on the broads from time to time.

Goldeneye. A ' hard weather ' winter visitor, occurring more frequently than the scaup in this area.

Goosander. A fairly regular winter visitor in small numbers; immature birds usually predominate.

Smew. A winter visitor, usually during severe weather; adults rarely appear before January. Thirty-two were counted at one time on Rockland Broad in February, 1954.

Shelduck. Although this species nests in sandy areas not far removed from the broads and is a common summer bird on the Breydon estuary, it rarely visits the broads themselves.

Gray lag goose. A very scarce winter visitor. In recent years, birds from semi-domesticated and full-winged flocks kept in the district have acquired the habit of visiting the broads, where a few pairs nest each year.

White-fronted goose. A regular winter visitor in numbers which have greatly increased during the past few decades. The flocks visit the grazing marshes by day and fly out to sea at night.

Bean-goose. A winter visitor in small numbers. A flock which came to the Yare valley marshes with considerable regularity between 1924 and 1952 and reached a maximum of 250 birds in 1944, failed to arrive in the winters of 1953–4 and 1954–5, after marked signs of diminution had been noticed, but returned subsequently.

Pink-footed goose. A regular winter visitor to the grazing levels in somewhat variable numbers. In recent years, this species has decreased as the white-fronted goose has become more plentiful.

Canada goose. This north American goose was introduced into England certainly as long ago as 1678 and for many years flocks in a semi-wild state have been kept on the lakes of some Norfolk estates, notably at Holkham. A few pairs now breed round the broads and have shown signs of increase recently.

Mute swan. Resident and abundant. Flocking takes place after the nesting season and numbers up to 300 are often present on Hickling Broad. There is abundant evidence to show that many riparian landowners in the broadland parishes of Norfolk kept swans under royal licence in the fifteenth and sixteenth centuries, marking the bills of their birds with distinctive notches. N. F. Ticehurst (*Transactions of the Norfolk and Norwich Naturalists' Society*, 1928) illustrated no less than 195 east Norfolk swan marks out of some 600 known to him from this area. The distribution of ownership suggests very strongly that the sheets of water known as the broads were in existence in that period; indeed, it seems not unlikely that they were exploited as an extremely valuable amenity by their owners, for swans in large numbers must have required a great deal of living space. At the present time, very few swan rights are exercised, although many local families and manors still possess them. Norwich Corporation, which in the course of the centuries has amassed a number of the swan rights formally owned by its burgesses and religious houses, still perpetuates the custom of swan-upping, whereby cygnets are caught, marked and pinioned on the river Yare every summer.

Whooper swan. A fairly regular passage migrant and winter visitor, herds often spending the winter on Hickling Broad and Horsey Mere.

Bewick's swan. A passage migrant and winter visitor, usually in rather smaller numbers than the whooper.

Sparrow-hawk. Resident and occasionally nesting in the broadland carrs. Immigrants arriving from the Continent in autumn swell the local population in winter.

White-tailed eagle. A rare and irregular winter visitor.

Marsh harrier. In the 1950's between two and five pairs bred annually in broadland. For a long time, this species was regarded as a summer visitor only, but in recent years winter occurrences, mainly of immature birds, have been not infrequent. This species has now become scarce and nests irregularly.

Hen harrier. A winter visitor in small numbers.

Montagu's harrier. A summer resident in small numbers: seldom more than three pairs nested in the whole of the broads district in any one year, up to the 1950's. It has now ceased to nest in Norfolk.

Osprey. A spring and autumn passage migrant, few years passing without one or more visiting the broads, usually in May or September.

Hobby. Appearing occasionally as a spring or autumn passage migrant.

Peregrine. A fairly regular passage migrant and winter visitor, in small numbers.

Merlin. Not uncommon as a winter visitor and autumn passage migrant.

Kestrel. Resident and fairly common, a hovering kestrel being a typical feature of the skyscape over the open marshes. Favourite nesting sites are the derelict windmills, but nests are built on the ground occasionally. Arrivals from overseas take place in autumn.

Quail. A few pairs nest in some summers on fields in the broads district and during the spring migration quails are heard calling occasionally in the marshes.

Pheasant. A common resident, specially favouring fens and reedy marshes and often roosting on tussock sedges. Its very mixed diet includes leaves, berries and seeds of a great many marsh plants, including buttercups, frogbit, marsh horsetail, seeds of water-pepper and great bindweed and fruits of guelder-rose. Amphibious snails (*Succinea* spp.) are often picked from the waterside vegetation.

Water rail. Resident and usually common. It is more usual to hear the grunting and screaming of water rails in the reeds than it is to catch sight of them in the open. Once in a while a rail may be surprised in the act of breakfasting on water-snails and sedge fruits along the waterside; then it steps with the elegance of a sandpiper over the vegetation, leaving only the slightest of footprints on the mud between. In some winters, large numbers of these birds arrive from north-west Europe and in very hard weather they tend to desert the broads for sheltered ditches and streams round the fringes of uplands. At such times as many as a score may be seen together, probing the mud in company with snipe, jack snipe and redshanks.

Spotted crake. Formerly a broadland breeding species and now met with fairly regularly as a passage migrant in autumn. A few birds have been seen during the winter in recent years.

Moorhen (almost invariably called 'waterhen' here). Resident and usually abundant. Weather movements occur in winter. Outside the nesting season, many of these birds roost in sallow bushes bordering the waterways.

Coot. Resident and abundant on the larger broads, with the addition of wintering birds from the Continent. Local wildfowlers say that they can distinguish the 'flighting coot' (immigrants) from home bred birds, by the whiter under-parts of the former in winter.

Lapwing. Present in fair numbers at all seasons. Those that breed in the marshes usually arrive at their traditional nesting sites in February or March and depart in September. Passage migration occurs on a large scale in some years and many winter visitors arrive to take the place of the local birds in autumn.

Ringed plover. A summer resident and passage migrant and an occasional visitor to the broads from its usual habitat on the coast.

Little ringed plover. A visiting bird of this species was identified at Hickling Broad in 1954. Has nested in west Norfolk.

Grey plover. A passage migrant and winter visitor. Essentially a bird of mudflats and tidal estuaries, it is only very occasionally seen on the freshwater marshes of broadland.

Golden plover. A regular spring and autumn passage migrant and winter visitor, visiting not only the coast, but also the freshwater marshes and uplands.

Turnstone. Although almost wholly a bird of the coast-line, this species visits the wader grounds of Hickling Broad occasionally.

Common snipe. Resident and fairly common, but not nearly so plentiful as formerly. An immigration of passage birds and winter visitors takes place in autumn.

Great snipe. An occasional autumn passage migrant.

Jack snipe. A passage migrant and winter visitor in small numbers.

Woodcock. A resident and winter visitor. A few breed within the broads area and may be seen on their 'roding' flights up and down the rivers at dusk. In hard winters, very large numbers arrive from northern Europe.

Curlew. A double passage migrant and winter visitor. A bird of tidal estuaries and common on Breydon, it seldom alights on the marshes of broadland, but is often to be seen and heard calling overhead. Large flights of curlew passing from east to west have been observed here in June and July.

Whimbrel. A spring and autumn passage migrant in large numbers. It is often abundant on Breydon and occasionally visits the freshwater marshes.

Black-tailed godwit. Before 1830, this species used to breed at Horsey, Thurne, Buckenham and elsewhere in broadland. At present, it is a spring and autumn passage migrant in small numbers.

Bar-tailed godwit. A spring and autumn passage migrant, often abundant on Breydon but only occasionally seen on the broads. Some birds winter in the district.

Green sandpiper. A passage migrant in small numbers. It has been met with on the broads in every month of the year, but most frequently in spring and autumn.

Wood sandpiper. A spring and autumn passage migrant in small numbers.

Common sandpiper. Occurs on passage in spring, summer and autumn.

Redshank. Resident and common throughout the year. An arrival of passage migrants and winter visitors takes place in autumn.

Spotted redshank. A spring and autumn passage migrant in

small numbers, visiting Breydon and occasionally observed at Hickling Broad.

Greenshank. A regular spring and autumn passage migrant.

Knot. A passage migrant and winter visitor, common on Breydon, but seldom visiting the freshwater marshes.

Dunlin. A passage migrant and winter visitor in large numbers. Although very much more abundant on the mudflats of the Yarmouth estuary, it often visits the broadland marshes, especially when the tides are high on Breydon.

Ruff. A fairly regular spring and autumn visitor to Hickling, usually in small numbers. This species formerly bred in large colonies in broadland; a few nesting pairs lingered at Hickling until late in the nineteenth century and a few spasmodic attempts have been made since that time. The re-establishment of ruffs and reeves as residents at Hickling would be hailed with delight by British ornithologists and special efforts are being made to provide suitable conditions which may attract the birds.

Avocet. An occasional visitor to the broads in spring, summer and autumn.

Greater black-backed gull. Small numbers frequent many of the broads by day, chiefly in winter. Larger numbers roost on the broads with other gulls during severe weather in winter. Broads near the coast are visited by passing flocks of these birds for the purpose of drinking fresh water.

Lesser black-backed gull. An occasional visitor to the coastwise broads in spring and autumn.

Herring-gull. Birds which have been feeding on the land by day during the winter often repair to the broads to roost in fairly large numbers.

Common gull. Frequents the broads chiefly for roosting purposes in winter. It is sometimes very abundant here in hard weather.

Little gull. A fairly regular passage migrant in small numbers, visiting broads in the manner of the black tern.

Black-headed gull. A very common species throughout the year. A colony of 500–600 pairs nests annually at Alderfen Broad and a few smaller colonies exist elsewhere in the area. In winter, the local birds are largely replaced by continental birds, which occupy large roosts on some of the broads at night.

Black tern. A spring and autumn passage migrant, often in considerable numbers, especially during the first half of May. Formerly nested here.

Common tern. Many visit the broads on passage migration, while birds resident in coastal districts in summer pay occasional visits to these inland waters in search of fish. Small numbers have nested on Ranworth, Hickling and Ormesby Broads during the past few years (13 pairs at Ranworth in 1954).

Little tern. Birds nesting along the coast commonly feed at Horsey Mere, Hickling Broad and on the rivers adjoining, possibly more regularly than in the sea.

Sandwich tern. An occasional visitor from the coast.

Stock dove. A fairly common resident round the fringes of broadland and often feeding on marshes and in the waterside carrs.

Wood pigeon. A very common resident and winter visitor, breeding throughout the year, the peak period being in late summer. Immigration takes place in late autumn and winter, when at times enormous flocks come into this area. They have been seen to descend through mist and settle amongst guelder-rose berries glowing like fog lamps on the marshes.

Eastern collared dove. This newcomer to the British fauna is well established at and near Great Yarmouth.

Turtle dove. A common summer resident, frequently nesting in the fen carrs.

Cuckoo. A common summer resident, in this area most often parasitising the yellow wagtail, pied wagtail, meadow pipit and hedge sparrow. The reed warbler is also victimised, but since its nest is so often attached to reeds over water, any cuckoo nestling runs a grave risk of breaking down the rather frail nest and tumbling into a watery grave before it is ready to fly. Adult cuckoos are sometimes seen perching on old reed stalks, which bend, yet bear their weight.

Barn owl. Resident and not uncommon, but sparsely distributed, nesting in derelict mills, local church towers and farm buildings. It quarters the marshes not only towards dusk, but often also in broad daylight. In winter, it has been seen patrolling over snow in search of shrews.

Little owl. A fairly common resident, nesting in hollow trees and old buildings. It appears to be more numerous towards the coast, especially in the vicinity of Horsey, than farther inland.

Tawny owl. Resident and common in the broadland carrs.

Long-eared owl. Resident in small numbers, not infrequently nesting on the ground, usually within the shelter of a wood or carr, but sometimes on a dry marsh in the open. A few passage migrants are seen occasionally in autumn.

Short-eared owl. A regular autumn passage migrant and somewhat irregular summer resident in broadland. It has been suggested that the presence or absence of breeding birds and their numbers may depend upon the comparative abundance or scarcity of field voles in the area.

Nightjar. A summer visitor to some of the heaths and woods fringing parts of broadland but much scarcer than formerly.

Swift. An abundant summer visitor and passage migrant. At times, vast numbers may be seen over the broads, especially of an evening, when they are taking toll of insects which have risen from the waters.

Kingfisher. Resident and fairly common. Its numbers were greatly reduced by the severe winter of 1947 but recovery followed.

Green woodpecker. Resident and fairly common in broadland carrs and fens.

Greater spotted woodpecker. Resident and common in the carrs. It is known to destroy many wood-boring caterpillars of the goat-moth in dying willow-trees.

Lesser spotted woodpecker. A thinly-distributed resident, nesting in rotten alders in some of the broadland carrs.

Skylark. An abundant resident of the grazing levels and fields, but does not use the fens and reedswamps for nesting purposes. Considerable numbers of passage migrants and winter visitors arrive from overseas in autumn.

Swallow. A very common summer visitor and passage migrant, nesting in boat-houses, marsh-mills and farm buildings everywhere. The wealth of insect life associated with the broads attracts vast flocks of swallows, which exploit successive hatches of gnats and ephemerids to the full. In autumn, many swallows roost in the reed-beds just before their departure.

House martin. A common summer visitor and passage migrant. The ready availability of mud for nest-building in the broadland villages makes the area attractive for this species. The house-martin does not appear to roost in reed-beds at any time.

Sand martin. A common summer visitor and passage migrant, nesting in the coast cliffs and in sandpits. From July onwards, until they emigrate, thousands of sand-martins come at sundown to roost in the reed-beds.

Golden oriole. A fairly regular spring passage migrant in small numbers, more often heard than seen.

Carrion crow. Resident and not uncommon. Nesting in riverside trees and in the secluded carrs, it has become more numerous in broadland than in any other part of East Anglia in recent years. The flocking of young carrion-crows has been observed regularly during late spring in the Yare valley, a maximum of fifty-five birds being counted in a single roost on one occasion at the end of May. This species takes tremendous toll of early eggs and young of marsh and water birds, yet in places where it is most numerous, such birds hold their own successfully, which suggests that in the long run, losses suffered early in the spring are repaired through successful nesting later in the season.

Hooded crow. Present in winter in varying, but never very large, numbers, mainly near the coast.

Rook. A common resident, passage migrant and winter visitor. There is a fair sprinkling of rookeries in broadland, but the birds seldom attempt to feed beside the broads themselves or on marshes where there is tall vegetation. They keep to the grazing marshes, the ploughlands and the woods. Their propensity for dropping acorns in flight as they cross the river valleys to and from their roosts often results in oak trees springing up in the marshes.

Jackdaw. A common resident, passage migrant and winter visitor. It nests in derelict windmills, church towers and hollow trees and, like the rook, seldom frequents reedswamps, preferring the more open marshes and the uplands.

Magpie. Resident. Formerly extremely scarce, it became common in 1940-55, and roosted in flocks in sallow and alder carrs in winter, as many as eighty birds having been seen going in to one roost. Recently it has become uncommon.

Jay. Resident and common in the carrs. Like the rook, it is responsible for dispersing acorns over marshy ground.

Great tit, blue tit, coal tit, marsh tit, long-tailed tit. All are common residents in the area. The mixed travelling flocks of titmice which pass through the coverts and carrs of broadland during the winter months are an attractive feature of the area.

Willow tit. Resident in small numbers, tending to be local and sedentary. The nesting holes are excavated in dead grey-sallow boughs as a rule.

Bearded tit. A rather scarce resident, in this area nesting chiefly in the vicinity of Hickling Broad and Horsey Mere. Wandering flocks visit other broads in winter.

Tree creeper. Resident and common in the more mature carrs.

Wren. Resident, common and widespread; it is a regular inhabitant of all the rougher, sedge-covered marshes and in some places builds its nest quite close to the water.

Mistle thrush. Resident and common, but scarcely to be reckoned a bird of marsh country in the nesting season. It raids wild berries in the carrs in autumn and winter.

Fieldfare. Winter visitor. Large flocks come nightly to roost in alder and sallow carrs and amongst the rough herbage of the marshes. Guelder-rose berries are eaten in November.

Song thrush. Resident and passage migrant.

Redwing. Winter visitor and passage migrant. Roosting occurs in the carrs and berries of guelder-rose and wild privet are eaten in late autumn and winter. Flocks are sometimes heard singing in the trees just before departure in late March.

Blackbird. Resident and very common, its numbers being added to by the arrival of many passage migrants and winter visitors from overseas in late autumn. It frequents the carrs and rougher marshes of broadland in large numbers, especially in autumn and winter. Most of the immigrants are immature birds, the cocks having brown beaks until they are about to depart in the following spring. They are sometimes caught and eaten by bitterns here in winter.

Nightingale. It is of some interest that this species, which breeds abundantly in the sheltered river valleys of Suffolk, does not find the broads area much to its liking, although a few pairs nest in the district in most years.

Robin. Resident and common in carrs and widely distributed in the reed grounds and rough marshes throughout the winter.

Grasshopper warbler. A summer resident; not uncommon, but rather local in its distribution, frequenting particular marshes where the vegetation is very dense and yet not too tall, with a scatter of sallow bushes.

Savi's warbler. Until the middle of the nineteenth century, a summer visitor which nested in the reedswamps of the broads in small numbers. Suitable breeding territory exists for it today more especially in the *Glyceria maxima* marshes of the Yare broads, and its eventual return is regarded as by no means impossible.

Reed warbler. An abundant summer visitor and the latest of the warblers to arrive in spring. It nests chiefly amongst the 'outside' reed-beds close to the water's edge. The fluff from sallow catkins is often worked into the outer nest fabric.

Sedge warbler. Usually even more abundant in summer than the reed warbler and nesting freely in the closed reedswamps and where rough marshes are becoming invaded by bushes.

Blackcap. A common summer resident, breeding in the carrs.

Garden warbler. A summer resident, not uncommon in bushy places along the Bure valley but much scarcer in broadland habitats in the vicinity of the Yare.

Whitethroat. A common summer resident at the extreme margins of the river valleys and on the banks of fens. Family parties are often to be met with hunting for insects amongst reeds and sedges during the summer. Whitethroats caught and ate many of the large copper butterflies introduced at Surlingham a few years ago.

Lesser whitethroat. A fairly common summer resident, nesting in overgrown hedges and thickets and not seldom visiting reed and sedge marshes for insects after the young are fledged.

Willow warbler. A common and widely distributed summer visitor, nesting round the fringe of the broads area but seldom in the marshes, although it frequently uses green tracks adjoining the marshes and occasionally marsh ' walls ' for that purpose.

Chiffchaff. A common summer resident and the first of the warblers to arrive. It nests even in the wetter carrs.

Goldcrest. Resident and winter visitor. A few pairs nest in planted conifers here and there in the broads district, but it is in autumn and winter that travelling flocks of goldcrests are to be seen in the carrs, often in company with tits of various species.

Spotted flycatcher. A common summer visitor, most usually nesting on buildings.

Hedge sparrow. An abundant resident, passage migrant and winter visitor.

Meadow pipit. A common resident of the drier marshes and grassy slopes of river walls. Passage migrants and winter visitors appear in autumn.

Rock pipit. A passage migrant and winter visitor to the estuarine portion of broadland.

Pied wagtail. A common resident and partial migrant, some at least leaving in autumn to winter south of the Channel. Of those which winter in the district, a good many occupy communal roosts in reed beds.

Yellow wagtail. A common summer visitor, nesting on the grazing marshes.

Waxwing. A fairly regular winter visitor to broadland, particularly to the Yare valley, where flocks descend on ripe berries of guelder-rose bushes growing in the carrs. It has been noticed that these birds have tended to visit the same places time and again in different years.

Red-backed shrike. A few pairs nest in the area every year, more especially near the coast.

Starling. A very abundant resident, with an accession of large numbers of continental immigrants during the autumn in most years. Young birds begin to roost in many of the local reed beds in June and the numbers at these roosts increase with the arrival of migrants in autumn. The reed beds are usually deserted for woodland roosts in December. The behaviour of starlings arriving at the reed roosts varies according to the prevailing weather. On cloudy evenings, the birds come in with a great rush of wings from many directions and settle down almost at once. When the hour before sunset is bright and calm, the starlings stage a wonderful display of aerobatics. Flying at whirlwind speed, a black mass of birds rises and twists about like a giant snake of smoke; then the tail of the column is drawn up until the flock has become a cloud almost vaporous and lost to sight. Suddenly there comes a queer little spasm and a fragment of the cloud peels off and hurtles earthward; three seconds later, the cloud flings another wisp of its dark burden down to the reeds and so the spasms continue, quite rhythmically, until the last squadron of starlings has plunged through space. Occasionally the clans gather and repeat the whole performance before settling finally for the night.

Greenfinch. A common resident, passage migrant and winter visitor. It is seldom seen in the wetter parts of broadland, but flocks frequent marsh walls and river banks in autumn and winter.

Goldfinch. Resident and fairly common. Large flocks may be seen in autumn feeding on thistles along river walls; others visit alders in company with siskins and redpolls in winter.

Siskin. A winter visitor to alders in the carrs.

Linnet. Common resident, passage migrant and winter visitor, most noticeably in the coastal region. It rarely nests in the wetter marshes.

Lesser redpoll. Resident in broadland in small numbers and very inconspicuous in the nesting season. More often seen flocking to alders in winter.

Bullfinch. Resident and winter visitor. A thinly distributed species in broadland during the breeding season, nesting in carrs.

Chaffinch. Resident and very common, a large influx of immigrants from overseas adding to its numbers in autumn and winter. Considerable flocks roost in sallow bushes near broads in winter.

Brambling. A winter visitor, sometimes roosting in carrs in large numbers, but seldom visiting true broadland for feeding purposes during the day.

Yellowhammer. A common resident, frequently nesting in hedgerows round the fringes of marshland and on bush-grown banks. Flocking takes place in late autumn and the birds return to their breeding areas as a rule in February.

Corn bunting. Resident, but largely confined to within three miles of the coastline.

Reed bunting. Common in the marshes throughout the year.

House sparrow. A common resident and passage migrant.

Tree sparrow. Resident and not uncommon, but rather locally distributed. Flocks are met with in broadland wilderness of alders, sallows and poplars during the winter.

CHAPTER 13

MAMMALS

by E. A. Ellis

Unlike birds, the mammals of broadland are not often observable for any length of time, because they are most active at night and seldom come into the open when they do happen to be moving about in the daytime. People who moor boats in quiet backwaters enjoy occasional glimpses of water voles munching succulent waterside plants. On secluded waters, nowadays, coypus may be seen wallowing out in the open on a hot day, their thick, wiry tails held stiffly aloft as though it would be an indignity to get them wet. Shrill squeakings on a river bank may call attention to the frolics of pygmy shrews engaged in a follow-my-leader chase and once in a while the gentle botanist, stooping to examine low plants in a flooded fen, may find himself watching the antics of scurrying, splashing water shrews about his feet.

Those who live in the marsh country all the year round gather a richer experience of mammals gradually, through the years. They come to remember such odd incidents as the seizure of terrified, shrieking frogs by weasels and common shrews along the shores of ditches and the sudden emergence of a weasel from a mole-run to catch a blackbird from beneath. The reed-cutter in winter finds many a nest of stoat and weasel built snugly in the temporary shelter of a ' lump ' of bunched reeds. The eel-babber on summer nights is abroad in the playgrounds of otter and coypu. The marshman mowing the mixed vegetation of fens and reedswamps in July is well acquainted with the neatly woven, grassy nests of harvest mice.

Even if the mammals are not much seen, they play a very important part in the natural economy of the district. The varying abundance of small rodents and shrews is reflected in the numbers of birds of prey, especially owls, frequenting the marsh country. The disastrous flooding of thousands of acres of broadland marshes in 1938 and 1953 greatly reduced the population of small mammals in the areas affected and birds of prey suffered noticeable privation in consequence. Before the local balance was upset in this way, there occurred great ' vole years ' from time to time, when increases in the numbers of short-eared owls breeding in the district followed as a result of the increase in their food supply.

No naturalist has ever undertaken a comprehensive study of mammal populations in this region and many questions about their density and distribution in relation to drained grassy areas and undrained areas with plenty of vegetation cover cannot be answered statistically at present; but enough is known to provide some general indication of the habitats favoured by the various species and field observations have provided notes on behaviour of a special character in some instances.

ANNOTATED LIST OF MAMMALS

The HEDGEHOG avoids marshes on the whole, although specimens venture in their direction from time to time and tumble into the dykes, where they are drowned. I know of only one instance in which a hedgehog nested and brought forth young in swampy country; the nest was built under a hawthorn in the middle of a snipe-marsh.

COMMON, PYGMY and WATER SHREWS (Pl. XX) abound near the broads, the first two frequenting the ' walls ' of grazing marshes, river banks and the margins of fens while the water shrew frequents dykes, including some that are brackish, in the drained levels, and many of the reedswamps and flooded fens elsewhere. Local barn owls take toll of all three species, finding them active even when snow is lying on the ground. Water shrews living in the backwaters of the Yare Broads eat a great many freshwater snails, whose slightly bitten, empty shells are discarded by the water's edge. Many of the common shrews here are very dark in colour and in some cases almost as black-backed as the larger water shrews.

The MOLE does not inhabit the most low-lying lands liable to frequent flooding and is generally absent from typical fen and reedswamp areas; but it abounds in drained grazing marshes and their embankments and its fortress mounds are often conspicuous on slightly raised ground and under trees, especially along the fringes of valley slopes. Moles are able to swim when necessary, but their presence on river banks in areas cut off by dykes and broads from the main land mass need not have involved recent colonisation from across the water; the moles on these marsh islands are at least as likely to have been established there before artificial channels were made to connect broads with the rivers. Herons are regular mole-catchers on the grazing levels and in hard weather especially their interest in the activities of moles tends to become an obsession.

Seven kinds of bats have been noticed in the broads district, but they have been studied very little. The largest species here is the NOCTULE, which roosts in hollow trees and under bridges and may be seen careering high above the marshes with the last swallows and swifts a little before sunset. The small PIPISTRELLE is common mainly in the vicinity of buildings and is seldom seen in the more desolate stretches of marsh and water. The SEROTINE has been established in the neighbourhood of Oulton Broad for the past thirty years but has not been identified elsewhere in the district. The WATER BAT (DAUBENTON'S) is much in evidence hawking for insects low over the broads and rivers on summer nights. NATTERER'S BAT roosts in some broadland churches and may be seen catching mosquitoes over the alder and sallow carrs round about sunset. The LONG-EARED BAT is widely distributed but does not appear to be present in very large numbers here, except in the vicinity of old rambling houses and churches occasionally; emerging after darkness has fallen, it keeps very much to the wooded areas and so tends to escape notice out of doors. The BARBASTELLE has been found living close to broads of the Bure and its tributaries, in small numbers; under a cottage porch used as a roost by a barbastelle in summer (at Calthorpe Broad) recently, five hundred wings of moths, comprising thirty different species, were found.

The RABBIT, before the epidemic of myxomatosis almost exterminated it in the district in 1954, abounded chiefly on dunes, heaths and agricultural land and was never a common animal in the true marsh country, either on the extensive grazing levels or in fens and reedswamps. Near water, it inhabited marsh embankments in a good many places, but rarely sought to breed on the lower grounds liable to flooding. At the same time, many rabbits were in the habit of ranging from warrens on dry land in search of food in wet places, so that they often modified the vegetation of marginal fens both near the coast and inland, producing a turfy sward through long continued grazing. Some rough-coated 'stub' rabbits were sheltered by the alder carrs of broadland, but they were never so much in evidence here as in old forest country. When the marshes were frozen in hard winters, the rodents might have been expected to make deeper excursions into the swamps, but they showed no marked tendency to do this.

The BROWN HARE is a regular inhabitant of the drained expanses of grazing marshes. It swims readily, so that dykes and rivers are no obstacle. In the thicker cover of reed-grounds and fens it may be found taking refuge from time to time, but such habitats are not much favoured; nor is it seen very frequently in the carrs. It travels far afield in the depth of winter and has been known to cross the ice of frozen broads.

The BANK VOLE is common in the district, but does not occupy open marshes or fens, being confined to the river ' walls ', marsh embankments and hedgerows of the surrounding uplands. Melanistic specimens have been taken here. It is quite usual for bank voles to enter buildings in the marsh country at night, in company with long-tailed field mice.

The SHORT-TAILED VOLE makes runs everywhere in low-lying grassland of both drained and undrained areas. It abounds in the Yare valley fens but occurs in smaller numbers in some fens of the Bure and its tributaries; it can be found in many reed beds, most usually where there is a mixture of other plants growing with the reeds. This prolific mammal is one of the chief sources of food for many birds of prey in the marsh country; it is eaten also by herons and hunted by stoats and weasels. From time to time there are vole ' plagues ' in this district, as elsewhere; but the growth of grasses in the very fertile local marshes always keeps pace with the rodents' depredations and however great an increase may have occurred in the vole population of a fen, the vegetation remains lush. When marsh litter used to be mown in summer to provide fodder for horses and store cattle, short-tailed voles (in ' plague ' years) occasionally reduced the fodder stacks to chaff before they could be put to use.

The WATER VOLE (Pl. XX) of the broads is, in the main, a frequenter of dykes and steep-sided channels. In the broads themselves it is present but not in such numbers as to be conspicuous. It has many enemies, including the heron, bittern, various birds of prey, the stoat and the pike. Most of the water voles here are very dark in colour and wholly black specimens have been obtained from time to time; in this tendency to exhibit melanism they resemble the northern Scottish subspecies, *Arvicola amphibius reta*, but examination of their teeth has shown them to be only colour variants of *A. a. amphibius*.

The LONG-TAILED FIELD MOUSE is common and widely distributed in the district, frequenting woods, hedgerows, fields and gardens. It is not an inhabitant of wet marshes, but does live in carrs where alders and sallows are growing in swamps. The YELLOW-NECKED MOUSE, found in woods and gardens only a few miles away in Suffolk, has yet to be discovered in broadland.

The HARVEST MOUSE in east Norfolk is still fairly common in cornfields, although it has become much scarcer on farms in recent years. It is a regular inhabitant of most of the fens supporting tall vegetation round the broads and is often abundant in association with the purple small-reed, reed canary-grass, reed and great pond sedge. Its summer nests of shredded and interwoven leaves are made of these plants. In winter, the mice collect and eat the fluffy seeds of the reed and often seek temporary refuge in bunches of reeds stacked on ronds and river banks between January and April.

The BROWN RAT forages along the riversides and banks of some broads and the estuary of Breydon, feeding in part on tide refuse; it also eats freshwater mussels, snails, frogs, nestling birds, the young of small mammals and the seeds of many wild plants. At times of flood, waterside rats move to higher ground, sometimes in embarrassingly large numbers. They venture little into tracts of fen and reedswamp, except when the water table happens to become exceptionally low in droughty summers.

The RED SQUIRREL occurs sparingly in the district, where it is confined to the drier woodlands. It is not present in any of the fen carrs dominated by alder or sallow nowadays, but it was what might be termed a marginal visitor to some of these valley woods until about forty years ago. The GREY SQUIRREL has never gained a footing in this area.

One of the most interesting changes in the natural economy of the broads in recent years has been brought about by the accidental introduction of the COYPU (Pl. XXI), a large South American rodent closely allied to porcupines and guinea-pigs. This aquatic mammal, superficially resembling a giant rat, was brought to Norfolk from the Argentine in 1929 and bred in captivity for its valuable 'nutria' fur. In 1937 a few of the animals escaped from their wired enclosures and succeeded in discovering suitable habitats for breeding along the margins of local rivers. They multiplied and spread quickly to all the broads, which provided them with almost inexhaustible supplies of food in the form of aquatic and marsh vegetation.

Coypus grow to about the size of otters and specimens taken from the broads have weighed up to 25 lb. They are dark brown above and lighter beneath and have blunt noses, very large orange-coloured incisor teeth, webbed hind feet and scaly, rat-like tails. The females suckle their young from teats situated high along the sides, both in and out of the water. Breeding goes on throughout the year and from two to three litters of from three to eleven young (commonly five) are produced in the course of twelve months. It is usual for a good many to be born in the inclement months of January and February, with the result that in hard winters the offspring are to be found dead in the marshes where both they and some of the older animals perish through eating frozen vegetation.

The nest platforms constructed in places where the vegetation is tall much resemble those built by swans. They are made of reed and sedge, sometimes with the addition of slender twigs cut from sallow and wild currant bushes in the carrs. The sites chosen are commonly in beds of reed, lesser reed-mace and saw sedge; it is usual to find tussock-sedges and stools of trees used as nest foundations. Since coypus have become established also in the grazing marshes, where there is little natural cover, they have adopted the habit of nesting in holes excavated in dyke banks.

The animals make well-worn tracks leading from the waterside into the marshes and along these, their slug-shaped, striated droppings are much in evidence, together with discarded fragments of gnawed plants. During the early years of colonisation, little burrowing was seen, although the animals often took shelter in erosion hollows formed by wave-wash and under roots of overturned willows. More recently, however, since the population has ' exploded ', burrowing has become extensive on the drained levels and in winter it occurs even in hedge-banks when frost drives the animals towards the upland fields.

Coypus are normally nocturnal feeders and sleep by day on small platforms built in reed beds, in couches gnawed out of sedge-tussocks or at the roots of bushes, or in burrows. A warm summer day will sometimes bring them forth to frolic in quiet waters. On such occasions they may be seen floating with their tails stiffly erect, or wallowing for pure pleasure, like hippopotamuses in an East African river. They tend to remain mute during the day, even when taking part in a communal water frolic. At night, however, they utter mournful cries at intervals, especially when there is moonlight. There is much individual variation in pitch and it is a weird experience to hear the calm of the night on the water broken by what seem to be the voices of lost souls of various ages and sexes scattered over a vast expanse of swamp and brooding mist. Monster coypus disturbed while feeding at the water's edge utter diabolically low growls, long drawn out; rivals growl in the same way when they meet. A mother will croon softly to her young in gentle, high-pitched tones, when she is at peace with the world.

Coypus have made a tremendous impact upon the vegetation of

the broads, by selective feeding. In the early years the overall effect was not greatly damaging; indeed, by helping to keep channels open the animals helped to maintain habitat variety by deflecting the process of stagnation and plant succession. The outer fringes of reed beds were destroyed, but at the same time, water was let into the farther parts of the beds and had the effect of improving the quality of many acres of fen reeds. Beds of reed-mace and saw-sedge would be eaten out almost completely, but often the coypus would then forsake the exploited area and concentrate their efforts elsewhere, so that there was a chance for regeneration to take place. Unfortunately this holds good no longer, because of the greatly increased density of the population. Many of the characteristic plants of the broads seem now to be threatened with almost total destruction unless coypus can be cleared from the marshes. The cowbane (*Cicuta virosa*), despite its poisonous nature, has been all but eliminated from broads where it was plentiful up to 1950; similarly, the great water dock (*Rumex hydrolapathum*) has almost disappeared from large tracts of marsh land where it abounded until recently.

The character of the marshes has been altered in a spectacular way in many places. Reed beds have been cut back so as to increase the water area of some of the smaller broads three-fold in the last twenty years. Some large patches of fen have been converted into expanses of black mud and shallow water, dotted about with tufts of purple loosestrife. Land altered in this way near Surlingham Broad has become a new nesting site for black-headed gulls and common terns recently, while ducks and waders welcome the creation of these 'coypu-lows', as they provide excellent feeding places. On some of the firmer stretches of fen, the destruction of herbaceous plants has been followed by a spread of grasses such as the creeping bent, rough meadow-grass and red fescue, which form a coypu-grazed turf. Sometimes great numbers of reed-mace seedlings will colonise shallow mud exposed as the result of clearance by coypus; but the animals usually return to the attack as soon as the colonists have grown to a height of a foot or so. The yellow flag, which has floating seeds, often spreads rapidly over the cleared flats; but again there follows a mass onslaught on both leaves and rhizomes. Purple loosestrife is very coypu-resistant and some of the new lows are covered by vast quantities of the magenta-coloured flower-spikes in summer; the plants were never seen in such profusion until coypus came to the broads. The colonisation of fens by sallow bushes has been halted by these animals to a marked extent in some areas. Not only are the young bushes grazed, but large sallows, osiers and even white willows are killed. Their roots are gnawed persistently until they are almost free of soil, so that the trees are blown over very easily. They are then barked, especially in winter. Most of the ivy on riverside trees has been killed in recent years through barking by coypus.

On marsh banks and along the sides of ditches, nettles, bur-marigolds and hemp-nettles are replacing great willowherb, hemp agrimony and other species more vulnerable to attack by the new enemy, and at lower levels, water forget-me-not, brooklime and water starwort are gaining ground because coypus show a preference for their usual competitors.

In addition to consuming wild plants, coypus wander increasingly from the waterside to make inroads on crops of sugar beet, kale and cereals. In winter, especially, they tend to travel long distances in search of food, if the marshes are frozen. Although almost wholly vegetarian, they have been proved to break open and devour fresh-water mussels in their Norfolk haunts, the molluscs attacked being *Anodonta cygnea*, *A. anatina* and *Unio pictorum*.

Coypus have few enemies of significance in this country, apart from Man. Young ones have been found dead with tooth and beak wounds inflicted by stoats, herons and bitterns on occasion. Marsh-harriers and tawny owls attack them once in a while. Foxes have been known to prey on them but there are very few foxes in the broads district. Carrion-crows may be seen in close attendance on coypus when the latter are digging out rhizomes and shoots of marsh plants; the crows pick up many unconsidered trifles. Many other birds, including mallard, moorhens and water-rails, are to be seen feeding amicably with coypus in the swamps.

Generally, coypus are extremely healthy creatures. Their fur is sometimes infested with lice (*Pitrufquenia coypus*), but by no means commonly, and common sheep ticks have been found attacking them at times.

Nineteen sixty-three saw a great decline in the coypu population in Norfolk, as the result of the very severe winter and a great increase in trapping.

The FOX used to be almost unknown in the vicinity of the broads and in any case, so far as East Anglia is concerned, it is almost wholly an introduced species, put down for hunting. Since the coming of myxomatosis in 1954, foxes have become more widely dispersed and some of them have moved into the broads district.

The BADGER appears to have been not uncommon here a few

Plate XXI Coypu (*Myocastor coypus*). An old male on a river bank

Plate XXII *Above*, ditching tools
Below, reed-cutting

centuries ago; it is now extremely rare but probably not quite extinct; no set has been discovered in the district very recently.

The OTTER is thoroughly at home in every local river and throughout the broads and surrounding marshlands, but although widely distributed, the total population is not thought to be very large at the present time. It is a creature of mystery to many people and, like the 'abominable snowman', known to them only by its footprints in the snow. One can have otters as near neighbours for a number of years without ever catching a glimpse of one, although their tracks may be discovered and their whistling calls heard in the swamps from time to time. Dog otters travel about a great deal and tend to use certain paths with great regularity; at least one 'otter's roadway' near one of the broads in the Yare valley is known to have been in use continuously for the past fifty years. The animals have their lairs or 'holts' under overturned trees, in clumps of saw sedge and between tussock sedges. Once in a while family parties of cubs are surprised at play in a quiet backwater and those who enjoy the gentle sport of babbing for eels on a summer night are sometimes entertained by glimpses of otters swimming and diving upwind of their boats.

Broadland otters catch not only fish, frogs, molluscs and earthworms; they also seize and devour wildfowl, especially in hard weather. When broads and dykes are frozen and snow lies on the marshes, their tracks can be followed for miles. In the neighbourhood of Horsey Mere, Major Anthony Buxton has recorded the discovery of numerous slides made by otters at play in the snow.

The STOAT is a regular inhabitant of the carrs and reedswamps, where it hunts water voles, moorhens, water rails and the various passerine birds which have winter roosts in the marshes. It nests in the crowns of sedge tussocks, under tree roots and occasionally in holes several feet above ground, in tree trunks. Fishes and frogs are eaten at times: the remains of three eels were found in a stoat's nest at Wheatfen Broad a few years ago. In winter, the animals are in the habit of making temporary nests in riverside reed-stacks; these are lined with plumes cut from the reed-tops, together with fur and feathers stripped from victims of their hunting. Stoats swim well, but are defeated by soft mud; this was illustrated clearly on one occasion when one of the animals was seen to pursue a moorhen across a patch of mud exposed beside a fen channel at low tide; the intended victim got away and a very muddy stoat struggled back to the reedy shore. The percentage of stoats acquiring ermine coloration here in winter is very small.

The WEASEL thrives everywhere in the marsh country, where it preys on field voles and moles to a large extent. Birds on the ground are sometimes seized by weasels lurking in mole runs. Nesting sites include hollow, rotten trunks of old alders and sallows in the carrs, the nest being placed a few feet off the ground, out of the reach of flood water; the animals are extremely secretive, however, and their breeding quarters are seldom discovered. As in the case of stoats, the young are led forth in packs and may be met with on marsh banks occasionally, running with their heads close together, attended by the small mother, on a trial hunting expedition. Weasels take to the water readily but are not such regular climbers as stoats. Like the latter, they often make winter nests in reed stacks, lining them with reed fluff and the fur of moles and voles.

There are a very few records of seals and porpoises travelling up broadland rivers. The GREY ATLANTIC SEAL has once reached the estuary of Breydon and the COMMON SEAL, which breeds off the Norfolk coast, has penetrated the river Yare as far inland as Surlingham on three occasions in the past three hundred years (one about the middle of the seventeenth century, recorded by Sir Thomas Browne and the others in 1947 and 1956).

There are no deer breeding in the area today, but the bones of red deer are fairly commonly found in the post-glacial peat deposits and river muds.

Activities of Man

CHAPTER 14

MAN IN BROADLAND

by R. R. Clarke

In few regions does the human settlement depend more on the natural features of the area than in broadlands for the story of Man in this part of East Anglia is largely the story of his reactions to a powerful and compelling physical environment. Despite his acquisition in recent centuries of new and potent means of subduing his surroundings, much of broadland still remains untamed. Throughout the human occupation of the district, even comparatively small fluctuations in the relative levels of land and water have wrought drastic changes in the life of the local population. Inundation by the sea, flooding by inland waters and the erosion of the coastline have been recurring perils for the inhabitants. In such a dynamic environment, the precarious balance of man and nature has been frequently disturbed by changes in the distribution of land and water. Drainage and communications, the land available for cultivation and pasture, the location of settlements, ports and fortifications have all been influenced by the physical configuration of the area, its natural vegetation and the animal life dependent on it. The combination of these factors together with the changes of climate to which the district has been subject, have in each period presented man with a varied environment. The action he has taken in any particular period to subdue and exploit its resources has depended partly on the size of the social group and its technical equipment and partly on the relative merits and demerits of adjacent districts. The early part of the story reveals man as the victim of his environment, but later, with the acquisition of superior tools, the master of his surroundings. His increasing domination of his environment is seen in the embanking of the waterways, the drainage of the marshes, the relative stabilisation of the coastline in recent years, and the expansion not only in the number and size of his settlements but in the spread of effective occupation from the uplands to the marshes themselves.

The earlier chapters of this book have revealed the extent of modern knowledge of the physical features of the broads area in past ages. They have set the stage against which human drama was played but, as their authors would be the first to admit, only the bare framework has yet been erected and much research will be necessary before the precise nature of the environment can be clearly reconstructed for each of the periods with which this chapter attempts to deal. Any explanation of human activities here in past ages must therefore be regarded as tentative until a comprehensive study of archaeology and history in the area has been made on the lines pursued with such success in the fenland. The inadequacy of our present knowledge is due partly to the lack of interest broadland has aroused until recently in geologists, palaeobotanists and archaeologists but even more to the dearth of those portable antiquities which, in the fens, have been made so effectively to write its story. Owing to differences in soil, the broads area has not been subject to that degree of modern tillage or intensive drainage which in fenland has yielded such a rich harvest of antiquities, though relics of the remote human past in the broads area probably lie beneath its swamps where excavations would be difficult and expensive.

The valleys of the Yare, Bure, Waveney and their tributaries radiating fanwise from Yarmouth, dissect the marshland and now act as a barrier to communication, though in the past these waterways helped unify the area. Understanding of the human settlement of the broads district is, however, incomplete without consideration of the intervening and encompassing areas of upland. Hence for the purposes of this survey broadland will be regarded as a rectangular area of east Norfolk and north-east Suffolk some twenty miles from east to west and twenty-four from north to south, running inland from the coast at Waxham to the upper Bure at Burgh-next-Aylsham, thence south through Norwich to Shelton and so due east to Pakefield, whence the coastline completes the circuit of some five hundred square miles.

Since the separation of Britain from the Continent by the enlargement of the North Sea during the Mesolithic or Middle Stone Age, broadland has occupied a significant geographical position. Lowestoft Ness is the eastern extremity of England, and so this region looking out to the North Sea is an obvious landfall for the invader or refugee from the opposing coasts of Denmark, Germany, Holland, Belgium or France. The immediate coastal fringe might attract some settlers from overseas, but most of the successive prehistoric and protohistoric arrivals from the Continent would appear to have used the outfalls near Yarmouth of the rivers Bure, Yare and Waveney. By these waterways easy penetration to the interior of Norfolk or northern Suffolk was available until a suitable site for settlement was located. Most of the invaders, so far as present knowledge suggests, passed upstream to settle in the upper reaches of the three rivers or their tributaries where gravel slopes bore light vegetation, or they spread over the uplands of east Norfolk where the woodland was not too thick for clearance nor the loamy soil too heavy for primitive agriculture. The extent of the marshland and its relative wetness and salinity varied with the progress of the submergence of the land but in general these water-logged areas held no attractions for the prospective settler until drainage and embankment rendered building practicable, and even then they were unable to compete with the adjacent uplands. The long tentacles of marshland intersecting and almost surrounding some areas of higher ground impeded land communications between the uplands and only served to emphasise the importance of water communications which even now have not been entirely superseded for economic purposes by road and rail. The significance of the rivers as routes into the interior for invaders and traders in prehistoric and historic times is vital, yet they never acquired the importance of the rivers flowing through the fenland into the Wash as corridors to the inhabited areas. The reason for this contrast lies in the nature of the hinterland. Behind broadland, apart from the amenable loam of the Norwich region and the gravel heaths to the north, there lies central Norfolk, the formerly forested boulder-clay country, with heavy soils difficult to cultivate even when cleared and so unattractive to most settlers before Late Saxon times. The fens, on the other hand, led to the relatively open chalk ridge of west Norfolk and north-west Suffolk and the sandy Breckland, with light easily-worked soils favoured by primitive agriculturists. The economically attractive character of the hinterland of the fens thus ensured its importance as a thoroughfare apart from its own potentialities when drained, while the somewhat intractable character of the areas abutting on broadland and its own lack of attraction for settlers rendered its communication system of secondary importance. Poor land routes to southern England, due to the difficulty of traversing the clay country of central Norfolk and Suffolk, led to the isolation of broadland from many of the cultural influences which exerted so powerful an effect on the borders of the fenland. For permanent habitation early man sought dry, well-drained soils suited to his agricultural needs, within easy reach of an adequate water supply. In broadland settlement was thus restricted in prehistoric, Roman and Early Saxon times to the margins of the valleys until more efficient farming equipment and improved means of clearing woodland in the Late Saxon Age led to the exploitation of the loam and clay uplands and the creation there of village communities. Throughout most periods of history until the seventeenth and eighteenth centuries, the actual marshes were of course unsuitable for human habitation until they were drained and the rivers embanked, though some of the islands of firmer soil amid the swamps had, by their isolation, attracted religious communities as at St. Benet's Abbey, Horning. Human settlement in east Norfolk has thus depended mainly on the valley slopes and adjacent uplands, where farming, at first extensive and later intensive, provided the mainstay of existence. The drainage of the marshes was, however, economically important in extending considerably the area for pasturing sheep and cattle, thus completing a more balanced system of agriculture. It must not be concluded that the rivers or the undrained marshes were of no value economically. From prehistoric times they probably supplemented the resources of primitive agriculture by a plentiful yield of fish and fowl. This exploitation of the wild life of the region, albeit of diminishing importance from an economic point of view, has continued to the present day. Another contribution to the economy of the region in medieval and later times has been the excellent grazing and mowing provided by the drained marshes. Until the twentieth century peat has been extensively cut for fuel while the estuarine clay has been converted into bricks or pottery, or utilised for embanking. Sedges and rushes have been used as litter for cattle and the latter was favoured as a floor covering in houses while reeds provided thatching for houses, farm buildings and ricks.

A consideration of the scattered traces of human activity in our district in the Old Stone Age is irrelevant to a study of Man in broadland, as this area only assumed its general physical characteristics after the waning of the last glaciation which corresponded with the end of that cultural period. The subsequent rise in sea-level from the waters liberated by the melting ice sheets then led to the formation of the North Sea, the separation of England from the Continent and the gradual creation of the coastline of what is now Norfolk. The Middle Stone Age, when these momentous events took place, is conventionally dated about 8000–3400 B.C. During that long period, as the climate ameliorated to a phase of greater warmth than today, the soils left by the Ice Ages became colonised by the birch and pine type of light woodland, followed during damper conditions by the denser growth of oak, elm, lime and similar trees. Human existence, as in the Old Stone Age, was based on food-gathering, hunting, fishing and fowling and consequently Man was nomadic, with, at the most, seasonal settlements of a few flimsy huts close to the haunts of the fauna on which he lived. These sites are now identified by the small worked flints called microliths which formed part of composite tools and by the waste material resulting from their manufacture. Sandy or light soils free from heavy tree growth were favoured and in broadland the temporary halting places of these hunters are probably indicated by the discovery of flint tools on the valley slopes just above modern marsh level at Markshall, Salhouse and on Oultney Common, Bungay, with a further site at Hellesdon inside the modern boundary of Norwich. The location of these sites suggests that similar remains may well lie on the surface of the glacial sands and gravels where these are overlain by clay and peat deposits in the valleys, just as similar sites have been found on sandhills in the fens well below modern sea-level.

The New Stone Age or Neolithic period, about 3400–1700 B.C., saw important developments in Norfolk. The arrival of newcomers from the south of England and ultimately from France, bringing with them a knowledge of crop growing and the domestication of animals, resulted in the first attempts, though on a limited scale, to clear lightly forested land for farming. The need for heavy flint axes for tree-felling and carpentry led to a demand for suitable flint in large quantities satisfied by the digging of numerous mines in the chalk. Alongside the newcomers, collectively termed the Neolithic A culture, with their temporary arable plots, their mining activities and their long barrows, dwelt descendants of the Middle Stone Age hunters, perhaps combining hunting with occasional crop-raising, for flint sickles are found on their settlement sites. The chief visible remains of the New Stone Age in Norfolk lie in Breckland and on the chalk ridge of west Norfolk. Broadland has fewer and less spectacular monuments to show to indicate the arrival of the newcomers. To them may probably be attributed the pits sunk in the chalk to extract flint at Whitlingham. From this local flint were probably knapped the hoards of flint axes found at Trowse Newton, Burgh St. Margaret and Lound Run. At the last site roughly trimmed axes were being ground on a block of sandstone to give them a keen cutting edge. Some indications of long range trade in valuable commodities like tough stone for the manufacture of axes are beginning to emerge. An axe from Salhouse and an axe-hammer from Caistor-by-Norwich have been identified as Borrowdale tuff from Langdale in the Lake District, two of a group of axes from this factory which were traded to East Anglia, while an axe found at Thurlton has been identified as made from stone obtained from south-west Wales. Long barrows, communal burial grounds of the New Stone Age, are rare in East Anglia but a long mound on Broome Heath, Ditchingham near Bungay, appears to be of this type and its Neolithic date is suggested by the numerous sherds lying on its surface as a result of the activities of rabbits.

During the Neolithic period the valleys of east Norfolk were filled by brackish water which deposited the Lower Clay detected by borings. In the Bure valley this clay has been identified as far inland as Horning, but nowhere has archaeological material been found in such a relationship with this deposit as to provide a more exact date or indicate if this submergence is contemporary with that which deposited buttery clay in the southern fens at approximately 3000 B.C. Towards the close of the Neolithic Age about 2000 B.C., emigrants from the Rhineland and Holland, known from their characteristic pots as Bell Beaker folk, invaded East Anglia. Traces of them have been detected in broadland at Chedgrave, Rollesby and Stalham. Other newcomers arrived from north-west Germany and one of them probably brought a stone axe-hammer of material derived from Schleswig-Holstein. From the intrusive Bell Beaker culture evolved in Britain the Necked Beaker culture which is well represented in broadland by highly decorated pots from Bergh Apton, Halvergate, Norwich, Rackheath, Sutton and Trowse. Just outside the city boundary of Norwich in the parish of Arminghall, air photography revealed and excavation confirmed the existence of an impressive timber circle or temple, which was used by a group of people allied to the Beaker folk. The eight gigantic oak trees which composed the sanctuary were sunk seven feet into the gravel and probably towered many feet above ground level. Around were two ditches defining a massive bank which probably served for the congregation. The size of the trees utilised in this 'Henge-monument' serves to emphasise the luxuriant nature of the forest then existing in the neighbourhood.

The change from a stone- to a metal-using economy was of necessity slow, especially in East Anglia where the abundance of cheap flint for tool-making provided little incentive to change to the more expensive bronze implements. The earliest of these axes were imported into the area in small numbers from Ireland during the Early Bronze Age (about 1700–1500 B.C.) but were rare. It was only during the ensuing Middle Bronze Age (1500–1100 B.C.) that axes, daggers, swords and spear-heads were commonly made of metal and not until the Late Bronze Age (about 1100–500 B.C.) that the use of bronze became really widespread and technical skill adequate for the fine circular bronze shield found at Sutton and now in the Norwich Castle Museum. Itinerant metal founders were now operating in Norfolk and a mould for casting axes has been found in Norwich while hoards of scrap metal collected for recasting have been found at Gorleston, Horstead, Ingham and Somerleyton as well as at four sites within the confines of the city of Norwich. Many burials of the Early and Middle Bronze Ages took place in round barrows. The few which now survive are usually on uncultivated heathland in the southern part of the area, such as Belton Common in Lothingland and Broome Heath, but the former presence of many others on the gravel heaths north of Norwich, in the area round the Henge-monument at Arminghall and on light soils near Thurton is attested by records and air-photography. By the Late Bronze Age the custom of interring the cremated remains of the dead in large urns placed in the ground without a prominent mound had become common. Cremations of this period have been found at Bergh Apton and elsewhere in the region.

The beginning of the Iron Age in East Anglia is now conventionally dated to about 500 B.C. but there seems little evidence at present for the use of iron tools and weapons until considerably later in the period which terminated with the Roman conquest of south-east England in A.D. 43. The arrival in the fifth century B.C. of peasant farmers from the Rhineland and their settlement in Breckland and west and north Norfolk is adequately confirmed but evidence for their presence in broadland is conspicuous by its absence. The reasons for this are at present uncertain. It may be due to the failure of archæological fieldwork to recognise the settlement sites of this phase of the Iron Age or it may be that some of the relics attributed to the last phase of the Late Bronze Age are contemporary with the arrival in other parts of East Anglia of the first Iron Age invaders. The scanty indications of human activity in broadland at this time may, however, be attributed to other more fundamental causes. There may have been a genuine recession of human settlement due to climatic and geographical changes. The increased rainfall during this period may have stimulated the growth of dense vegetation on the clay soils of the upland not only in Flegg where there are few traces of any earlier occupation but also in those areas where there is evidence for settlement in the Bronze Age. The increased rainfall would also have led to a higher water-table in the marshes. Furthermore, during this period, probably during the first century B.C., there began that acceleration of the long process of the submergence of the land relative to sea-level which resulted in the extensive deposit of the upper clay in all the valleys of broadland. This indicates the presence of open estuarine conditions as far inland as Horning and Strumpshaw and of fen and swamp in the upper reaches of the rivers. Before these conditions attained their maximum, the decapitated human head of a deformed man was thrown in the waters at Runham where the skull was found in 1954.

Whatever the cause, the sparseness of relics of the Iron Age at present known from this area is indisputable. Pottery from Aylsham, Arminghall, Markshall and Norwich indicates that the valleys of the Bure, Yare and Tas on the western limits of our area had been colonised by at least the first century B.C. A bronze cauldron fastened originally with iron rivets and later repaired with bronze found in Lound Run, Lothingland, suggests a settlement on the slopes of that attractive valley. From the early years of the first century A.D. the tribe of the Iceni of Norfolk and north-west Suffolk minted coins of gold and silver, isolated specimens of which have been found near Acle, at Irstead and Oxnead and at Thorpe-next-Norwich.

The principal evidence for the Iron Age in Norfolk comes from the fenland margins, from Breckland and the west Norfolk ridge. It was in this area that military adventurers from the Seine-Marne district of France arrived in the third and second centuries B.C. to establish a hegemony over the peasant cultivators they found there. Socially the arrival of this new ruling class was important for the whole of northern East Anglia, for it provided the royal dynasty of the Iceni which culminated in the dramatic figure of Queen Boudicca in the middle of the first century A.D.

The evidence for the Roman Age in broadland is more ample than for all previous periods of its human history, and has received vital additions from the excavations carried out at Caister-by-Yarmouth for the Ministry of Public Building Works and primarily by Mr. Charles Green. The more numerous material traces of human activity in this period reflect not only the expansion of population in areas occupied in previous periods but the colonisation of districts such as Flegg where the heavy forest cover had largely deterred former cultivators. In the silt areas of the fenland extensive traces of peasant agriculture in the Roman period have been detected, but nothing similar is known from the clay areas of the broads district. The cultivated areas of the fens lay just above contemporary water level while the similar soils in broadland lying at most two or three feet above O.D. if not actually submerged were too subject to the incursions of saline water for farming to be successful. The precise water level in the area in the Roman period is unknown and may not have been constant during its four centuries but though it probably did not vary from modern level by more than a few feet, the presence of estuarine conditions in the area west of Yarmouth may be safely assumed.

The Romano-British peasant cultivators in broadland, farming much as their Iron Age forebears would have done in west Norfolk, dwelt round the slopes of the upland. Indications of their presence have been detected in the Bure valley and its tributaries at South Walsham, Ingham, Neatishead, Coltishall, Horstead, Stalham and in the parishes of Brampton, Buxton and Oxnead, where some industrial activity in the form of pottery making is also known. In the Yare valley settlements have been discovered at Brundall and Thorpe-next-Norwich and probably at Reedham, while air-photography has revealed the outline of a farmyard at Cantley. In the Waveney valley most of the known Roman sites occur to the west of our area, but inside it settlements existed at Ditchingham, Kirby Cane and Geldeston. In the wooded areas between the Waveney and Yare valleys Roman finds are scarce and some of these, like the kiln at Hedenham, are due to the presence of clay for pot-making and wood fuel for firing it; charcoal burners still operated in this area as recently as about 1920. Traces of iron-working in the first century A.D. have been noted at Ranworth.

Peasant agriculture was the economic background of the district in Roman times but superimposed on this was a new phenomenon—town life, represented in broadland at Caistor-by-Norwich and Caister-by-Yarmouth. On present evidence the former came into existence first as a sprawling open township on the east bank of the Tas four miles south of Norwich. It was founded about A.D. 70 and only acquired its still formidable walls about A.D. 200 when the central area of some thirty-five acres was enclosed. It is generally accepted that its Roman name was 'Venta Icenorum' and that this town at the northern end of the highway from Colchester was the cantonal capital, chief market and administrative centre of the tribal area of the Iceni. Between 1929 and 1935 excavations revealed its market place, two temples, the public baths, several houses, its fortifications and industrial features such as pottery kilns, a glass furnace and a bronze founder's workshop. The selection of the Norwich area for the foundation of this town is a matter for surprise in view of the concentration of population in west Norfolk not only in the latter part of the Iron Age but also in the Roman period. The creation of an administrative centre so far east implies that the economic centre of gravity of East Anglia was moving away from the open lands of the west of Norfolk and Suffolk and that the forested clay areas of the central part of the county were being opened up even if only on a limited scale. There may also be some historical reason such as the former presence in the Norwich area of an Iron Age tribal headquarters which may have influenced the Roman government in its selection of this site, but if so, no evidence has yet been found to prove it.

In any case the existence of the Roman town at Caistor-by-Norwich must be considered in relation to its port at Caister-by-Yarmouth, an equally surprising foundation when the previous unattractiveness of Flegg is taken into account. From the recent excavations there it is clear that the settlement, of which sporadic traces have been recorded by archæologists since the days of Sir Henry Spelman and Sir Thomas Browne, was a Roman walled town of some ten acres. From its geographical position with a well-protected harbour on the estuary, this town was clearly a port. But a port presupposes an adequate hinterland for the supply and distribution of some of the commodities which kept its shipping occupied, and in this case the nature and extent of the hinterland is far from clear. The rivers of east Norfolk form an obvious feeder system for this east coast port as they did in medieval and later days for Yarmouth but it is difficult to visualise how such a relatively poverty-stricken area could have sustained so grandiose a conception. It is, however, possible to suggest a land route which may help to explain the dilemma. From near Wayford Bridge, Smallburgh, a Roman road runs westward and has been traced with a fair degree of accuracy for most of the way across Norfolk to Upwell whence it continues to the pottery manufacturing area around Castor-on-Nene. Its eastern terminus is unknown but may possibly have been Caister-by-Yarmouth. If so, this road would provide a route to the industrial areas of the Roman midlands. Apart from coastal trade, this port, the most important between Colchester and the Humber, doubtless saw its wharves stacked with merchandise from the Low Countries, mill-stones from the Rhine and glazed Samian pottery from central France.

This town came into existence on rising ground north of the present Caister-Acle road in the first half of the second century A.D., being protected initially by a timber palisade, replaced later in the century by a flint and brick wall, some ten feet thick, backed by a rampart. So far, only a few of the internal buildings have been examined but a vast structure inside the south gate by which traffic from the harbour entered, has been plausibly identified as a seamen's hotel or lodging house. It was erected about A.D. 175 and with various additions continued in use until the fourth century.

Apart from the stretch of Roman road already mentioned between the Ant and the Bure, little enough is known of Roman roads within the broadland area. The road from Caistor-by-Norwich southwards towards Colchester is well-defined but its other land communications are uncertain. A road ran north-eastwards towards the Yare near Surlingham but its route is uncertain and its further course unknown, though it may lead eventually to Caister-by-Yarmouth. South-eastwards a road probably ran through Poringland and Brooke to cross the Waveney at Wainford Mills and on in the direction of Halesworth. Most of these highways were probably constructed as part of the programme of pacification after the revolt of Queen Boudicca in A.D. 60, but the road to Caister-by-Yarmouth can hardly be earlier than the early second century. The bloody retribution which fell on East Anglia after A.D. 60 left a trail of burnt homesteads and wasted farmlands. The resultant famine and depopulation impeded the spread of Roman material culture for half a century and East Anglia only acquired the outward symbols of Romanisation in the elaboration of town-life, in the construction of well-made villas and the raising of the standard of living from the early years of the second century.

By the third century the concealment of numerous coin hoards illustrates vividly the economic insecurity of the times and this was soon matched by a military threat when raiders from the opposite shores of the North Sea known collectively as Saxons began to arrive. This menace was met by the construction of a chain of coastal fortresses round the south-east shores of Britain, usually located by a sheltered roadstead for a naval squadron to intercept the seaborne raiders and garrisoned by cavalry regiments to liquidate those who escaped the navy. The tidal lagoon of Breydon Water provided an ideal harbour for this purpose and on the high ground at its south-western end the fortress of 'Gariannonum' now called Burgh Castle was erected in the late third century. Its bastioned outer walls still largely survive after 1700 years as testimony to the efficiency of the Roman military engineers who erected them. These massive walls of flint and brick form perhaps the most imposing monument to the past endeavours of Man in broadland.

Exactly when these Anglo-Saxon raids first gave place to settlement is not known, nor is the ultimate fate of the Roman coastal defences at Burgh Castle and Brancaster, but the presence of Romano-Saxon pottery at several sites in the area suggests the settlement of some Teutonic folk from at least the end of the third century, doubtless with the approval of the Roman government. This approval must also have been given to other Teutonic settlers or ' foederati ' in the late fourth century, but hardly extended to those who followed them from Schleswig, north-west Germany and Holland. The predominantly Anglian character of these invaders is shown by the pottery which survives from their graveyards of the fifth and sixth centuries A.D. The cremated remains of their dead accompanied by brooches, combs, beads and other articles of personal adornment or, more rarely, burials by inhumation are almost the only material evidence at present available for assessing the human occupation of broadland in the early part of the Dark Ages. The small villages of squalid huts of no architectural pretensions in which they dwelt in other parts of East Anglia have not yet been identified in our area but an isolated hut has been detected on the edge of the marshland at Postwick. However the location of their graveyards gives an adequate idea of the type of country they favoured in the initial phase of settlement. They established themselves on sandy or gravelly patches on the valley slopes and doubtless tilled the lighter soils in their vicinity.

No cemeteries are yet known in the Bure valley or its tributaries within the limits of our area. In the Yare valley one has been recorded at Brundall; two occur close together at Markshall and Caistor-by-Norwich on opposite sides of the Roman town of ' Venta Icenorum ' while another has been found just outside the later medieval walls of Norwich. There also seems to have been a graveyard of this date outside the walls of the Roman coastguard fortress at Burgh Castle and others at Earsham and Stow Park, south-west of Bungay, in the Waveney valley. It may be assumed that the initial groups of these invaders on their way to seek fresh homes passed through the river mouth at Yarmouth in rowing ships of the type found in Ashby Dell in the last century which probably dates from the Dark Ages.

Place-names ending in *-ing* and *-ingham* are usually considered to indicate that the settlements to which they are attached were founded at much the same date as the pagan cemeteries of the fifth and sixth centuries. A few names like *Horning*, and many like *Burling-*

Plate XXIII Old reed-thatched church at Horsey. Barn owls, kestrels, jackdaws and other birds regularly nested in the tower, beside and beneath the bell, until the louvres were closed with wire netting in about 1952

Plate XXIV *Left*, external view of a typical Norfolk windpump showing the sail feathering gear
Below, the wherry *Albion*

ham, and *Raveningham* are found in the valleys and on the uplands of broadland, but as none coincides with the site of any known pagan graveyard, it is probable that they are of slightly later date, possibly seventh or eighth century. Some archæological evidence of occupation in this period has been found in the excavations at Caister-by-Yarmouth. Here the irregular huts of an Anglian village were discovered to have been built in the main street of the Roman town and in open spaces between its ruined buildings. Outside the town wall and ditches lay an extensive inhumation cemetery in use from the seventh to the early ninth centuries. Among its early graves were at least a dozen 'pseudo ship burials' where the dead had been covered with timbering cut from a ship's side, a poor man's version of the royal ship burial of Sutton Hoo.

Across the estuary at Burgh Castle there is historical and archæological evidence for the establishment of his missionary headquarters in 636 by the Irish monk Fursey who seconded the efforts of Felix of Burgundy in converting the kingdom of the East Angles to Christianity. There had been two false starts before this became the accepted religion of the East Anglian monarchs in 631 when Sigbert ascended the throne. Few traces have been detected of any ecclesiastical buildings as early as this, probably owing to the perishable materials with which they would have been constructed, and to destruction by the Vikings, but the post-holes and painted wall-plaster of some of Fursey's monastic buildings at Burgh Castle have been discovered recently.

The period from about A.D. 850 to the Norman Conquest in 1066 is termed the Late Saxon or Viking Age, and saw the most momentous developments in broadland. For during these two centuries there must have come into existence many of the present village communities whose presence is confirmed in the Domesday record together with some which passed out of existence in the Middle Ages. From about A.D. 850 its coasts were harried by seaborne invaders, mainly Danes, but including a sprinkling of adventurers from all along the eastern shores of the North Sea. The success of their destructive raids was due to the element of surprise given by their sea power, to the mobility resulting from the employment of captured horses on land, and to their superior armament, but above all to the divisions among the Anglo-Saxons which prevented any effective resistance to their inroads. Raiding rapidly gave place to colonisation and the bulk of the Danish settlements in the area were probably made between A.D. 880 and 917 when their ascendancy was checked by the reconquest of East Anglia by the Anglo-Saxon monarchy. A concentrated Danish settlement took place in the Flegg Hundreds (itself a Danish name), where numerous names like *Hemsby*, *Filby*, *Mautby*, *Clippesby* and *Billockby* indicate villages founded in areas probably only scantily inhabited prior to this time. Other settlers penetrated farther inland and probably added a considerable Danish element to the population of the scattered villages which from at least the ninth century began to grow into Norwich. This name first appears as 'Northwic' on coins minted there in the early tenth century, and its subsequent growth as the chief urban centre in Norfolk dates from this period, though until after the Norman Conquest it was closely rivalled by Thetford. The origins of Yarmouth are wrapped in obscurity, but a small town was certainly in existence here by the middle of the eleventh century and a cremation cemetery found at Runham Vauxhall shows that part of the site was probably inhabited at the latest by early Anglo-Saxon times. The town of Yarmouth was on an island site until the closure in the middle of the fourteenth century of the northern channel between it and Caister, called Grubb's Haven, converted it into a peninsula. The tidal range in Breydon Water and the salinity of its confluent rivers were probably restricted by the blocking of this channel and by the tendency of the Yarmouth spit to grow southwards. This growth reached its maximum in the fourteenth century when the river mouth was opposite Corton.

Evidence obtained from the site of the South Denes Power Station at Great Yarmouth suggests that from Saxo-Norman times to the late thirteenth century the land stood some ten feet higher in relation to the sea than it does now. This uplift in Late Saxon times would render intelligible the selection of a marshland site at Horning for the foundation at some uncertain date of St. Benet's Abbey (Pl. XXV); this was re-endowed by King Canute in the early eleventh century but no buildings of this date are known and the visible structures are all medieval. The submergence of the land in the late thirteenth century probably accounts for the record of river embanking in 1274 close to this abbey for only in the heightening of the river banks from this date lay any security against periodic flooding.

An excellent detailed picture of east Norfolk in 1086 is furnished by the Domesday Survey, though as a source of information, it is limited by its failure to include property of no taxable value. The Flegg Hundreds and the loam region of east Norfolk appear as the most intensely cultivated regions in the whole of Norfolk owing to their fertile and easily-worked soil and the dense population which they supported. The mixed character of the farming is shown by the combination of well-tilled arable with a wide extent of meadow land in both the Flegg and the Norwich area which together had more than the rest of the county. The absence of woodland of any size in the area is due to its clearance for cultivation, probably by the Danes, and points to the need for an alternative fuel supply. Many sheep were kept in the meadow lands but for part of the year they were folded on the arable fields, thus providing manure to sustain the fertility of the soil. The lack of winter feed for cattle with its consequent necessity for annual slaughter led to a great demand for salt for the preservation of the meat. This is reflected in the numerous salt pans listed for east Norfolk in the Domesday record. Most of the Flegg villages, especially Caister which is credited with forty-five salt pans, had several. A site at marsh level on Ashtree Farm by Acle New Road, partly excavated in 1948, possibly represents one of these salt pans. Cantley, North Burlingham, Sutton and South Walsham were also taxed on the revenue from salt pans, but it should not be assumed that these were necessarily located within the modern boundaries of those parishes and therefore that the waterways in their vicinity were strongly saline. The fallacy of this argument is well demonstrated in north Norfolk where parishes far from a stream of any sort are credited with the possession of salt pans. Salt-making probably continued in parts of broadland throughout medieval times due to the demands of the herring industry, and on Cobholm Island even in the late eighteenth century.

The presumed salt pan by Ashtree Farm on Acle New Road yielded early medieval pottery and indicates that some at least of the great triangle of marshland between Yarmouth, Acle and Reedham was relatively dry for part of the year. This desolate area is at present partitioned among numerous parishes, most of which are situated at some distance, and in the case of Postwick as much as twelve miles away. Parishes with detached portions of marshland are Acle, Beighton, Burgh St. Margaret, Burlingham St. Andrew, Cantley, Chedgrave, Freethorpe, Loddon, Moulton St. Mary, Postwick, Raveningham, Runham, Stockton, Toft Monks, and South Walsham. It is not known when this allotment of marsh took place but it may be suggested that the area represented a communal summer pasture for the sheep and cattle of these upland parishes, possibly as early as the eleventh century. This is more likely than the suggestion that it results from a combined effort at marsh reclamation. Little seems to be recorded about the economy of these marshes in medieval times and even the records of a wealthy monastery like St. Benet's throw little light on contemporary activities in the other marshland areas of the broads district.

Stress has already been laid on the relatively dense population of the Norwich and Flegg areas in the eleventh century and in this context it should be remembered that East Anglia was at Domesday the most thickly populated province in Britain. The exhaustion of timber resources through clearance of the area led to the widespread cutting of peat for fuel for the large local market and thus created the peat pits which became the broads. The stratigraphical evidence for assigning the origin of these sheets of water to deep excavations for peat has been set out in an earlier chapter and documents suggest that this intensive exploitation had ended before the early years of the fifteenth century. No definite evidence is yet available to indicate when this considerable economic activity and engineering enterprise began but the evidence already cited for the relative prosperity of parts of broadland at the time of the Domesday Survey suggests that this demand for peat as fuel may date back at least to the Norman Conquest if not to the Late Saxon Age. It has even been suggested that the dense settlement of Danes in Flegg may have first led to this exploitation of the local peat deposits. Shallow excavations for clay beyond the south-western boundary of Hickling Broad in Potter Heigham parish probably provided the raw material for potteries which flourished there from the twelfth century onwards and gave their name to the village.

The increased population in Late Saxon and Early Medieval times required more effective land communications between the areas of upland and led to the construction or rebuilding of bridges. The repair of the Weybridge over the Bure near Acle is recorded in 1101, while Wayford Bridge over the Ant near Stalham was in existence as early as 1363 when it was known as 'Wardeforthebrigge'. But in medieval times land communications were of secondary importance in comparison with those by water. The ferrying of cattle to the grazing marshes, the transport of litter and fuel, the conveyance of building materials and the products of the local woollen industry alike depended on water transport. The use of stone imported mainly from Northamptonshire for church building is directly related to ease of conveyance by water and the sites of some churches, like Reedham, owe their location more to this than to the proximity of their congregations. The woollen products of the Norwich region, destined for export, were mainly transported by water to Yarmouth

Plate XXV *Above*, houses and wherries on the Yare. From a watercolour by John Crome

Below, St. Benet's Abbey in 1845. From a picture by Richenda Cunningham

Plate XXVI *Above*, view from the tower of Ranworth Church showing the broad and drained marshes in the background
Below, Rockland Broad with reed boat

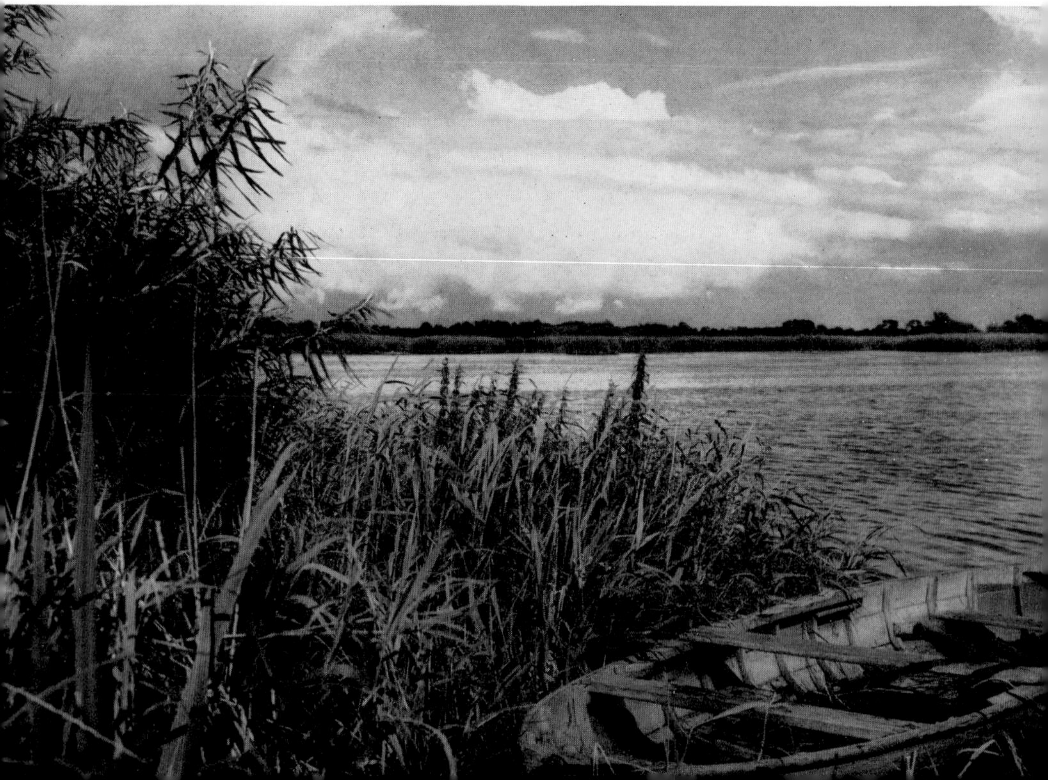

which became a staple wool port in 1353 when it exported more worsted cloths than any other English port. The medieval growth of Yarmouth was due not only to its geographical position, which made it the obvious entrepôt for the woollen exports of its wealthy hinterland in the Norwich area, but also to its flourishing herring industry. The annual herring fair at Yarmouth was an international trade meeting which augmented its wealth and provided the resources for building in the thirteenth and fourteenth centuries its protecting walls and towers and numerous monasteries. But the heyday of Yarmouth's prosperity was the late sixteenth and early seventeenth centuries when the arrival of Dutch immigrants, the growth of the herring industry and the stabilisation of the harbour mouth all combined to render it wealthy and led to large-scale rebuilding though retaining its medieval layout with narrow ' rows ' separating tenements.

Beneath South Quay at Yarmouth in 1952 were found the remains of a clinker-built ship, fifty feet or more in length, dated to medieval times by its contents. This ship probably served in the coasting trade from Yarmouth. Little is known for certain about the types of boat which traversed the broadland rivers in the Middle Ages but probably the keel, which survived till the late nineteenth century, was the principal transport craft during this period, supplemented from the late sixteenth century by the wherry (Pl. XXV) which eventually superseded it. The range of these craft depended on their draught, and on the limitations imposed by low bridges and in the upper reaches by mills. For the conveyance of a few individuals along narrow waterways smaller craft doubtless existed. Primitive types like the dug-out canoe dredged from the River Ant below Wayford Bridge, and now preserved in Norwich Museum, may have been in use in medieval times.

The tortuous natural waterways were by-passed by the construction of artificial cuts but few of these are earlier than the nineteenth century though canals were dug as early as the early fifteenth century to transport building materials for Caister Castle from the adjacent Bure. The connection between the earliest records of river embanking in the late thirteenth century and the accelerating subsidence of the land has already been noted. The necessity for it is shown by such disasters as the flood one night in the winter of 1287 vividly recorded in the chronicle of John of Oxnead, monk of St. Benet's. The dunes at Horsey were breached and the sea waters rushed in to inundate several villages including Hickling, one hundred and eighty persons perishing, many trapped in their beds. This loss of human life, ruination of marsh pastures and destruction of fish lent an impetus to the construction of adequate defences. By the early sixteenth century the aid of the Dutch seems to have been sought. A graveslab in Haddiscoe Church commemorates the wife of Peter Peterson, a 'dike-reeve' (1525). A fellow countryman was responsible for the successful stabilisation of the harbour mouth at Yarmouth in the late sixteenth century after its vagaries had defeated previous engineers.

The 56,000 acres of marshland behind the slender line of sandhills at Horsey are constantly menaced by the sea which broke through the defences in 1607–8, 1655, 1792, 1805, 1897 and 1938. Since the disaster of 1938 and the tidal surge of 1953 the coastal defences have been greatly improved but as many of these marshes lie only just above sea-level and some below, anxiety for their safety will persist. The coastline of broadland has been eroded, though probably not at any uniform rate, and its area diminished by many thousand acres since the beginning of the Middle Ages. Eccles and Little Waxham churches have been destroyed by the sea and their parishes much reduced in extent, while the hamlet of Marketsthorpe near Eccles has disappeared completely. In recent years erosion has been severe at Caister though the dune formations near Winterton Ness indicate accretion during the last century.

The organisation of the country on military lines after the Norman conquest of 1066 is reflected in the erection of castles to control the main concentrations of population and principal communication centres. The timber-built castle on its artificial mound dominated the town of Norwich, that at Bungay controlled the main crossing of the Waveney while the walls of the Roman fortress at Burgh Castle were incorporated as a bailey to a motte constructed at the south end of the enclosure. It is only towards the close of the Middle Ages in the fourteenth or fifteenth centuries, when considerations of comfort began to outweigh the needs of protection, that fortified manor houses like Claxton Castle were erected in the river valleys. But a fortress like Caister Castle, which may be regarded as a functional descendant of Burgh Castle, was erected as late as 1435 to a Rhenish design for its owner, Sir John Fastolff.

The century after 1550 saw the widespread erection of manor houses in which the desire for comfort and elegance of living were paramount. These were financed out of the profits of the woollen trade and the increased revenues from agricultural improvement. They are too numerous to mention individually, but the mansion of the Pastons at Oxnead and others at Waxham, Salhouse, Rollesby, Ludham and Ingham may be taken as representative.

More widespread than fortifications in our area in the Middle Ages were the communities of the religious—ranging from great land-owning establishments like St. Benet's Abbey to small hospitals for the sick and needy like those at Great Hautbois, Herringby and West Somerton. Most of these institutions were founded between 1100 and 1300. Apart from the concentration of monastic buildings in Norwich and a lesser one in Yarmouth, they are evenly scattered along the river valleys and especially by important road junctions. Among the principal monasteries may be noted the pre-Conquest foundation of St. Benet's at Horning and later ones at Hickling, Ingham, Langley, Bungay, Gorleston and Herringfleet.

The other material manifestation of the religious spirit of the Middle Ages which has left its mark even more noticeably than in the monasteries was the erection of numerous village churches. The churches between Loddon and the river Yare are exceedingly rich in architectural features of the Norman period, but their very survival is an indication of declining wealth in the succeeding centuries. Elsewhere in the broadland region the wealth produced by the woollen trade led to costly and elegant rebuilding in the Decorated and Perpendicular styles. The Decorated work at Ingham, Belaugh and Stokesby in the fourteenth century is matched by the Perpendicular expansion at Worstead, Martham, Bungay, Beccles, and Winterton. This wealth is also noticeable in the painted and carved rood screens for which the district is famous. The finest surviving examples in this area are at Ranworth, Barton Turf, Worstead and Fritton.

No abrupt change separated medieval from modern broadland. The monasteries fell into decay, their lead and stones were pillaged for secular purposes: the peace was broken by Kett's Rebellion which for a brief moment focused the attention of Europe on Norfolk; and the train-bands in 1587–8 prepared to defend East Anglia should the Spanish Armada have achieved its purpose. A weak monarchy whose impotence is visible in every page of the Paston Letters gave place to a strong centralised despotism; but apart from these events the life of broadland and its inhabitants flowed on as placidly as its waterways. In attempting to outline the story of Man in broadland from the sixteenth century to the present day it will be convenient to focus attention in turn on the marshland and broads, the encompassing uplands and finally on the roads and rivers forming the communication system of the area and the channels for its trade.

It has already been suggested that some of the broadland marshes were used as summer pasture during the Middle Ages. This is partly confirmed by the demand of Kett's men in 1549 that 'redegrounde and meadowe-grounde may be at such price as they were in the first yere of Kyng Henry the VII'. Certainly by the early eighteenth century the marshes between Norwich, Beccles and Yarmouth were providing grazing for about forty thousand lean Scots cattle each year, as well as horses and sheep, as noted by Defoe in 1722. The cattle fed eagerly in those lush pastures from May to Christmas and grew 'monstrously fat' before they went as beef to the local and London markets. Yet in 1782 Marshall made a tour of part of the Yarmouth marshes and asserted that 'until about twenty years ago this valuable tract lay principally under water except in a dry summer' and recorded that he rode to his horse's knees in water for the first mile out from Halvergate. At the close of the eighteenth and during the early years of the nineteenth century, the drainage of marshes higher up the valleys was authorised by enclosure acts. Between 1799 and 1807 these were passed for Cantley, Catfield, Fishley, Hassingham, Hickling, Ludham, Potter Heigham, South Walsham, Sutton and Upton, and considerable improvements were effected in these areas. But despite the labours of many internal drainage boards organised to construct and maintain drains, sluices and mills much of this drainage did not achieve the anticipated results. The main responsibility for the drainage of the area now rests with the East Suffolk and Norfolk River Board, legal successors of the sixteenth century Commissioners of Sewers, who were primarily charged with the defence of the area against the incursions of the sea.

The marshes are intersected by dykes which serve to separate the pastures, as well as drain the land and provide channels for navigation. Until recent years the initial excavation and subsequent periodical cleaning of the dykes in the marshes was done entirely by hand (Pl. XXII), but has now been largely superseded by mechanical methods, owing to the rise in the cost of labour. To construct a marsh dyke by the old methods the surface was first flayed with a heart-shaped spade or hodder and then dug with a 'heaving-tool'—a spade about six inches wide at the toe. For each foot of depth the dyke would be narrowed about seven inches so that the sides were well battered. A wooden spade shod with iron (a fly) was used for soft subsoil and the 'shod-up scoop' for even softer material. This is a wooden shovel, shod at the end, about one foot across and leathered up at the butt to hold the semi-fluid mud. If water was reached, the dyke was dug in sections between dams and the water thrown out with an unshod water scoop. For maximum efficiency dykes must be ' drawn ' and cleansed annually, the work being done from September onwards by the tenant of the marsh. The vegetation is cut with a long-handled short-bladed scythe or ' maig ' and pulled out with a rake or crome, A crome is like a rake or long fork with four prongs curled over. fitted to a handle about eight feet long. If in bad order the edges of the dyke have first to be cut down with a shore cutter—a broad knife on a long shaft, a stack knife often being employed for this purpose. Mud is thrown out with a dydle—often a curved iron frame carrying a stout net, mounted on a long haft.

Despite all efforts, vegetation encroaches on the channel and ' bottom finding ' or ' bottomfying ' has to be carried out from time to time. This is an expensive operation and usually the landlord's liability. Each section of the dyke is blocked up at either end with boards, the water thrown out and bottom and sides dug out.

The multitude of shallow drains flow into dykes which carry the surface water into the mill-dyke or drain. The mill or draining pump is situated at the junction of this dyke with the main river. Sometimes a mill may drain only a small area, but often it has to deal with the water of about a thousand acres of marsh, called a ' level '. As most of the marshes lie below river and often sea-level, the water must be lifted generally about six feet by the mill from the main drain to the river.

It is not known when windmills (Pl. XXIV) were first erected for drainage purposes in the broads area and it is doubtful if any existing specimens are earlier than the early eighteenth century. Oby Mill on the Bure bears the date 1753 and Marshall records that most of the mills in the Halvergate Marshes were erected about 1760–80, while Faden's Map of 1797 shows just over thirty drainage windmills in the marsh area between Acle, Yarmouth and Reedham, but it is uncertain if all are marked. Most of the surviving mills have brick towers generally tarred externally, with a small vertical fan-tail in the side opposite the four main sails to keep them facing the wind. The sails were cloth-covered at first, but movable wooden vanes or shutters were introduced in the early nineteenth century; these could be opened or shut at will and the mill started or stopped. A weight allowed some adjustment of the vanes according to the strength of the wind, as many mills had been destroyed by igniting through driving too fast in a high wind. Lightning and excessive wind pressure were also responsible for the destruction of many mills. Before automatic winding gear was installed in the mid-eighteenth century, the cap of the mill was turned by hand. The sails used to drive paddle wheels to lift the water in the mill sump, but these gave place to turbines, the first to be erected in England being in a mill east of Kendal Dyke, near Heigham Sound. Between the wars of 1914–18 and 1939–45 windmills were gradually superseded in broadland by steam pumping stations and these in turn are now rapidly giving place to electric pumps. In 1948 there was opened at Breydon a big electrically powered water pumping plant with two pumps, each capable of drawing fifty tons of water a minute, with two smaller pumps at Haddiscoe and a third at Berney Arms. Here also at Berney Arms a marsh-mill has now been preserved in working order by the Ministry of Public Building and Works, and is open to visitors as an important example of nineteenth-century archæology.

During the nineteenth century many of the drained marshes were converted into arable, and corn crops were taken off the levels near Ingham and Palling. Now, with the exception of a few acres near Horsey and Yarmouth, this arable has reverted to pasture. The broadland marshes are now used principally for grazing though some rough pasture is also of value for mowing. There are about forty thousand acres of grazing marshes and their value varies considerably with the locality. The best areas are the clay lands of the Acle-Reedham-Yarmouth level and the marshes bordering the Yare. In 1938 their chief economic use was for the summer fattening of mature bullocks, though dairy cattle and horses and, nearer the uplands, some sheep were also grazed. Since then the number of dairy cattle has tended to increase. The main type of cattle brought to these marshes were Irish stores, usually bought at Norwich Cattle Market, and in earlier days at St. Faith's Fair to the north of Norwich. The beasts are turned out to graze on the marshes in April or May and removed for sale in October or November. While on the marshes the grazing stock were under the care of a marshman, who might look after as much as a thousand acres, dealing with stock belonging to various owners. The number of marshmen has declined steadily in this century and in 1938 only twenty of them were left.

Though grazing has been for long the principal economic asset of these marshes, it is by no means the only one. The medieval or even earlier practice of deep excavations in the peat for fuel has already been given as the cause of the formation of the broads, but the demand for peat or turf, as it is called in the area, did not cease with the abandonment of this particular method of extracting it. It gave place to widespread shallow excavations in the middle sectors of most of the broadland valleys and produced the characteristic turf-ponds. The industry was well established in the late eighteenth century when Marshall in his tour of 1782 recorded the prevailing prices for it, which included the cost of transport by water and a sum ' for Profit and Hazard—great quantities are sometimes swept away by the floods '. The extent of this superficial peat-cutting in the nineteenth century can be gauged from the area between Barton Broad and Catfield as shown in the Map Appendix (map 20). By 1881 Woodward noted that little peat was then obtained but the practice persisted into this century at least in the Bure valley in the neighbourhood of Horning Ferry.

The extensive reedswamps which in some areas lie between the marshes and the rivers or broads, are also of economic importance. The chief areas are along the river Ant from Sutton Broad to Irstead, beside the Bure from the south end of Wroxham Broad to St. Benet's Abbey and in the Surlingham-Rockland area in the Yare valley, while smaller stretches adjoin Hickling, Horsey and Martham Broads. The demand for reeds for thatching houses and ricks has led to a revival of the industry in recent years. The reed beds are usually cut during the winter in alternate years. They are then loaded on reed-boats for transport to a staithe where they are stacked. Reed merchants operate at Salhouse and Horning, while at Rockland St. Mary there was for some years a small factory for the mechanical production of reed matting as a foundation for plaster walls. The cultivation of other plants is referred to in chapter 4.

The basis of the present economy of broadland depends on the widespread appreciation of its scenery which attracts tourists to its waterways in increasing numbers. Some come to fish, others to sail or cruise by motor-launch and the presence of this seasonal influx has stimulated the erection of hotels and shops as well as the building of pleasure boats. This important industry now flourishes in various centres, especially at Brundall, Coltishall, Potter Heigham, Thorpe next Norwich, Wroxham and Oulton Broad, and its products are exported to many parts of the world.

Since the advent of tourist traffic in the late nineteenth century when the broads were ' discovered ', there has been a decline in what was formerly a characteristic broadland and especially Breydon industry—wildfowling. Most of the regular wildfowlers have died or taken to more settled occupations, just as did many of their Middle Stone Age food-gathering forebears on the arrival of the first farmers. The decoying of wildfowl, widespread in the late eighteenth and nineteenth centuries, is now also at an end. Fritton, Flixton, Mautby and Waxham Decoys, Decoy Broad at Woodbastwick, Decoy Farm at Hemsby, Decoy Carrs at Acle and Reedham and Decoy Woods at Hemsby, Rollesby and Winterton, among others, bear witness to the former extent of this practice.

The growth of urban communities such as Yarmouth and Lowestoft on the perimeter of broadland has created a demand for the supply of water drawn from the broads and rivers. The former town draws water from Ormesby Broad and the Bure at Horning, while the Fritton Decoy valley known in its upper reaches as Lound Run has been converted into a series of reservoirs for Lowestoft.

Apart from the three main concentrations of population in Norwich, Yarmouth and Lowestoft, the density of population in the rest of broadland varies considerably, being low in the true marshland and high in the arable areas of the adjacent upland. It is not surprising, therefore, to find practically no buildings on the marshes apart from a few inns, mills, marshmen's cottages, farm sheds and boathouses. A few warehouses associated with the staithes constructed in the heyday of wherry transport in the nineteenth century still survive (Pl. xxv). Almost the only recent development has been the erection of bungalows of varying degrees of permanence close to the river banks, chiefly in the neighbourhood of Horning, Potter Heigham, and Wroxham. Apart from red brick, the chief material used in the construction of the eighteenth and nineteenth century buildings on the marshes was clay lump, noted for its qualities of keeping the building cool in summer and warm in winter.

The upland of our area presents many local variations in soil type including boulder clay, loam, and gravel, but in general the soil is an easy working medium loam which has been conducive to intensive arable farming from medieval times onwards. While broadland proper consisted in 1938 of 75 per cent grassland (15 per cent ronds or reedswamps, 6·4 per cent heathland, 1·2 per cent arable, 1 per cent woodland, 1 per cent houses), the adjacent Flegg Hundreds had no less than 63·3 per cent of their area devoted to arable farming. The agricultural efficiency of the inhabitants of the Fleggs was noted appraisingly by Marshall in 1782. Much of east Norfolk had been enclosed before 1800, and further enclosure of the remaining common fields took place before the middle of the nineteenth century. In the present century the east Norfolk uplands are primarily noted as a winter bullock-fattening area, but root crops like mangolds and swedes are important, though they have been reduced in recent years

Plate XXVII Hickling Broad by moonlight

Plate XXVIII The Broads overflow their banks. Flooded fields near Beccles on the Suffolk-Norfolk border

in favour of sugar beet. In the early days of the sugar beet industry east Norfolk provided much of the material for operating the factory at Cantley, first opened in 1912, and financed mainly by Dutch capital and operated by Dutch labour. A further important economic development in recent years has been the growth of the soft fruit industry, of which black-currant cultivation is the mainstay. This has led to the establishment of canning factories at North Walsham, Wroxham and Yarmouth.

The villages in the upland are generally areas of concentrated human settlement, but scattered farmsteads occur on the fringe of upland overlooking the adjacent marshes on which the balance of their farming often depends. Building materials are various, but brick predominates.

In recent times, as in medieval, the waterways of broadland have been the main lines of communication, not only for local traffic, but for the transport of seaborne products from the port of Yarmouth to the interior and corn for export on the return journey. Though commerce has been little affected by the recent growing up of the broads and adjacent channels, it has been restricted by the parallel process of silting in the main waterways, which has limited drastically the size of vessels. In the seventeenth century the Yare only took boats of twenty to thirty tons, but through continuous dredging can now accommodate those of ten times greater tonnage. The development of seaborne coastal trade in that century, especially the transport of coal in the import of which Yarmouth was second among provincial towns, led to a demand for the improvement of the navigation of the broadland rivers. By an act of 1698 duties were levied on coal entering Yarmouth to maintain the Haven and deepen the Yare, but though the former was attended to assiduously the latter was neglected. In the early nineteenth century various proposals for improving the navigation to Norwich were made, but it was only in 1832, despite opposition from Yarmouth and other vested interests, that a canal called the New Cut was made from the Yare at Reedham to the Waveney near Haddiscoe railway station, whereby the route for river craft plying to Lowestoft was greatly shortened. The Waveney river had never had an opening to the sea through Oulton Broad and Lake Lothing in historic times until the barrier between Lake Lothing and the sea was pierced in 1831; at the same time a lock was constructed between the Lake and Oulton Broad. In 1825–6 the Ant above Wayford Bridge was canalised with locks at Dilham, Witton and North Walsham, and the Bure above Coltishall was improved in the late eighteenth century with locks at Coltishall, Buxton, Oxnead, Burgh and Aylsham, which is forty-four miles by water from Yarmouth. The enclosure movement of the late eighteenth and early nineteenth centuries rendered possible the construction of numerous boat dykes and staithes for conveying goods to and from the nearest villages. Faden's map of 1797 marks staithes on the Thurne at Ludham, Thurne and West Somerton; on the Bure at Tunstall and Upton; on the Waveney at Burgh St. Peter and Geldeston; while on the Yare, which was more important than any of these, there were staithes at Norton, Hardley, Langley, Cantley and Buckenham. Besides the import of coal and timber up the Yare, which even now constitutes the principal traffic of the river, other materials were carried in the late eighteenth and early nineteenth centuries, the great age of wherry transport. Chalk was carried from Whitlingham to Burgh Castle for the manufacture of Portland cement. Boulder clay was conveyed for use as marl in the adjacent arable areas, while the products of the Surlingham and Rockland brickyards travelled by water. Wherries continued in use as trading craft until the 1930's (Pl. XXIV) when the competition of rail and road eliminated them. An attempt to revive the wherry for trading purposes was made in 1949 by the Norfolk Wherry Trust formed for this object.

The evolution of the road system of the broads area since medieval times has not been studied in detail, but it was doubtless modified locally by the enclosure movement. By 1800 it was substantially as at present, with a few notable exceptions. The improved drainage of the Acle-Yarmouth marshes in the late eighteenth century and the need for improved communication between Norwich and Yarmouth led in 1831 to the construction across these levels of the Acle New Road with a branch to Halvergate. This was considerably shorter than the old road through Caister, but even part of the latter was of no great antiquity, for the act for constructing the Caister-Yarmouth section was only passed in 1712. Before this, most road traffic from Yarmouth to Norwich passed through Haddiscoe and Loddon. In addition to the bridges on which the road system of this marshy area pivoted at Yarmouth, St. Olave's, Acle, Potter Heigham, Ludham, Wroxham and Wayford, the unbridged river crossings or ferries were of considerable local importance, some carrying passengers only, others vehicles, while some were primarily for transporting cattle to and from the marshes. Several of the ferries are now inactive owing to dilapidation which occurred during the war of 1939–45. In the nineteenth century they operated at Yarmouth, Stokesby and Horning on the Bure and at Reedham, Cantley, Buckenham, Coldham Hall, Surlingham and Whitlingham on the Yare.

The construction of the Norwich-Yarmouth railway line in 1844 dealt a severe blow to the prosperity of river-borne commerce. Owing to the importance of Norwich and Yarmouth the railway-lines focus on these two centres, but display a lack of planning explained by the independent origin of the several lines. In the twentieth century the rapid expansion of transport in heavy lorries has eliminated from the local waterways all transport vessels except sea-going craft with bulky cargoes.

CHAPTER 15

NATIVE RIVER CRAFT OF THE BROADS

by H. Bolingbroke

The *Norfolk Wherry* and its predecessor, the *Keel*, were the commercial river carriers of east Norfolk until power-driven craft superseded them. Their cargoes included grain, coal, timber, bricks, manure, marsh litter, ice and more latterly, sugar-beet. These vessels, in their time, contributed much to the prosperity of Norwich in former days when they formed an important trade link with the port of Yarmouth. Vessels of deeper draught have been enabled to navigate the Yare up to Norwich only through the mechanical dredging undertaken during the past half-century or so. The villages of broadland were able to send produce by water to the towns and to receive essential supplies of fuel and building materials by the same means.

The *Keel* was a clinker-built craft having a mast stepped amidships in a tabernacle fixed to the keelson and unsupported by any deck beams. She carried a primitive square sail, with reef-points at the foot. This was hoisted by a winch at the stern, while another winch, in the bows, was used for lowering the mast. The sail was trimmed by ropes made fast to each end of a yard on which it was set; the free ends led aft to the helmsman (Pl. xxv). Sailing was good in a fair wind, but in an adverse one it became necessary to depend on the use of a quant and the help of the tide for making progress. The quant, a long pole, was lowered on to the river-bed, the top of the shaft being placed against the shoulder; the user then pushed, almost on all fours, working his way along the plankway alongside the cargo-hold to the stern, where the quant was withdrawn. The hold was amidships and without hatches and forward of it was a small cabin, entered from the starboard side.

The last of the Norfolk keels was sunk opposite Postwick Grove to help strengthen a bank of the river Yare and in 1912 this vessel was partly excavated so that measurements could be taken and models constructed, one for the Science Museum in London and another for the Bridewell Museum in Norwich. This keel was 55 feet long,

13 feet 8 inches broad and 4 feet deep and could carry a load of about thirty tons.

The Norfolk sailing wherries (Pl. XXIV) were a class of trading vessels peculiar to the broads district. They were clinker-built and double-ended, i.e. pointed at both ends. The single mast was pivoted well forward on a tabernacle and by means of a fore-stay, which was the only standing rigging, one man could raise or lower it easily; this was made possible by the mast being balanced by the weight of one and a half to two tons of lead fixed to the base. There was one high-peaked sail, hoisted by means of a winch placed in front of the mast. The greater part of the tarred hull was taken up by one long hold for cargo, which was protected from the weather by a number of hatch-covers. The capacity of the hold could be increased when desired by the addition of ' shifting right-ups ', placed above the coaming. A cabin in the stern, large enough for a crew of two, was painted in gaudy colours, usually with the roof red, doors blue and panels yellow. Aft of the cabin was a small well from which the wherryman could work the tiller and at the same time tend the main sheet. The mast was a very stout and heavy spar of spruce, surmounted by a metal vane from which flew a streamer of red bunting to indicate the wind's direction. Mastheads were painted brightly, distinctive coloured bands being used by different owners. Quanting was carried out from narrow plankways running along either side of the boat.

To improve their sailing qualities, many wherries were equipped with false keels which could be detached in shallow waters. When these keels were removed, only a four-foot depth of water was needed for navigation, with a full load. The sail was controlled by a single halyard, roved in two sizes of rope and led in an ingenious way so that it hoisted first the throat and then the peak. The advantage of this method of hoisting lay in the fact that the sail could be brought into service in two parts. The peak could be lowered or 'scandalised' when gybing in boisterous weather might otherwise dismast the vessel. The special halyard device allowed the sail to swing over in two separate instalments: first the peak and then the lower half, so relieving the strain on the mast. In order to avoid reefing, some wherrymen merely lowered the peak when they were in a hurry.

The large black sail, placed far forward and spread by a heavy gaff, gave the wherry a peculiar advantage in negotiating the winding rivers; given reasonable room, the boat could beat against a head wind in a remarkable fashion, although some assistance from the quant might be necessary here and there. A quadrant of white paint on either side of the bow showed up at night; wherries carried no lights when sailing after sundown.

These vessels varied a good deal in size; most of those trading on the Norwich river were forty tonners while those using the Bure carried about twenty-five tons. The largest ever built was the *Wonder*, of eighty tons burthen; she used to sail out to steamers lying in Yarmouth roads, supplying them with coal and returning with parts of their cargoes. The *Wonder* was in service in this way in 1881, at a time when it was often found necessary to lighten the steamers at sea before they could cross the bar at the mouth of the river Yare. The smallest wherry on record was a five-tonner called the *Cabbage*; she took garden produce from Ludham down the Bure to Yarmouth vegetable market.

Many wherrymen owned the craft which they sailed and this gave them the privilege of choosing what cargoes they should carry. A certain amount of smuggling used to go on in the broads district. Contraband brought to village staithes or secreted in drainage mills and reed-stacks could be picked up and taken farther inland very conveniently by wherry.

Races for wherries were a feature of 'water frolics', the forerunners of modern regattas, on most of the broads and at certain points on the rivers. In these races, it was customary for the wherries to be lined up with their sails down; then, at the firing of the starting-gun, the crew of two on each boat would work feverishly to hoist the sail, cast off the moorings and get away. Close finishes were frequent in these races. It was common for brass bands to attend these frolics and for winning wherries to be greeted with 'See the Conquering Hero Comes' at the moment of victory. A special flag, with a cup painted on it, was flown at the masthead of the winner when she sailed away after the frolic had ended. Although these craft were not designed for sea work, a number of them competed at marine regattas held off Great Yarmouth, Gorleston and Lowestoft between 1883 and 1901. During that period, some owners of trading wherries built vessels specially designed for racing in summer and carrying freight in winter. One wherry had her hold fitted with a track along the centre of the floor, on which a small truck of ballast could be run fore and aft to trim her for different courses. In later years, as the number of wherries declined, regatta committees found it increasingly difficult to induce crews to enter their boats for races, since the prize money to be set against loss of earnings tended to become insufficient to warrant the interruption of trading. At broadland regattas, a wherry was used as a committee boat on almost every occasion, and the officials would partake of a sumptuous meal spread on a long table in the centre of the hold, the floor of which was strewn with freshly cut rushes.

It has been estimated that about three hundred wherries were in use on east Norfolk rivers and broads in the middle part of the nineteenth century. Nearly all heavy goods were carried by these vessels until the introduction of rail transport in this area. The decline in wherry trading dates from the opening up of railways. In due course, further competition came from iron lighters towed up and down the rivers by tugs, and from road transport by motor lorries. A very few trading wherries still sailed on the broads up to the commencement of World War Two; but they had all gone out of commission by the time hostilities ceased. Afterwards, the Norfolk Wherry Trust reconditioned one of these vessels, the *Albion* (Pl. XXIV), and has since subsidised her as a part-time trader, so that visitors to the broads may still see one example of a wherry in local service. The hulks of other wherries, denuded of masts, have been adapted for use as towed lighters, or have been fitted with engines, while a few have been converted into pleasure-wherries. There are also specially built pleasure wherries which perpetuate the hull design and rig of the former trading craft.

BROADLAND PUNTS

Open, double-ended punts, propelled either by a quant or by oars, are in common use on the broads. They are light and narrow, with very little freeboard, and can be used along narrow, shallow waterways, enabling marshmen to cut and load reed in places otherwise difficult of access. A typical example of the open marsh punt is sixteen feet long and four feet broad, with a slightly curved bottom, clinker-built with three ' strakes ' or planks and a dozen ribs on either side. There are no fixed thwarts or seats and a small box or stool is provided for the use of a rower. When out of use, this stool is stored under a short, sunken deck in the stern. The freeboard is kept as low as possible to minimise the effect of strong winds encountered on the open broads. In addition to mooring ropes, the punt is equipped with a small stake attached to a line on each side. On landing at a reed-bed, the marshman can moor the punt quickly by means of one of these stakes. When first built, these boats are usually painted grey; later in life, they are apt to be tarred inside and out. At the old-time water frolics, there were often rowing and ' shoving ' races for marsh punts. Marshmen were, and still are, great experts at quanting their boats at a remarkable speed. The open punts were not used only for marsh work in former times, but also for fetching goods and provisions where families lived in places apt to be isolated by the flooding of low-lying lands in winter. They were also brought into service for wildfowling. A modified version of the old Norfolk punt can be seen at most riverside and broadland staithes today. It is furnished with an extra line of planking, which gives it more freeboard, and greater rigidity is provided by fixed seats. This type of boat is commonly hired out to anglers and in some instances it has a special ' well ' in the bottom, for keeping fish alive.

The Hickling punt, designed for wildfowling, is decked fore and aft and has the maximum beam just forward of the mid-section, where formerly the weight of a punt-gun had to be supported. The early punts of this type were rowed and quanted. Now that they do not carry heavy swivel-guns, many are equipped with a sail and a small plate and rudder. There has also been a slight increase in their dimensions, from 18 feet to 19 feet 9 inches in length and from 4 feet to 4 feet 6 inches in breadth. Since 1926, fast racing punts have been evolved from the Hickling-type punt, for recreation on the broads. It is still considered essential in their design that they should be ' suited to the purpose of being quanted, rowed or sailed to fowl '.

The gun punts used by wildfowlers on the estuary of Breydon are strongly built, flat-bottomed, 18 to 20 feet long and 4 feet in breadth. The sides are single-planked, the planks being flared outwards slightly at either end and covered with a gently sloping deck. These craft are capable of being sailed, rowed, quanted or sculled. They are light and fast and their slightness of freeboard reduces wind resistance to a minimum. The extensive decking provides dry cover for a shoulder-gun, spare clothing, ammunition and provisions. Heavy swivel-guns were mounted on these punts in the hey-day of wildfowling. The swivel rest was a stout iron pin in a socket drilled into a block of hard wood, which was either fixed, or allowed to slide in a short run on the bottom of the boat, the recoil being checked by a powerful spring when the gun was fired. It was the practice of some fowlers to screw ice plates on either side of the punt at the bow end as a protection when they went on the estuary in hard weather. These plates were of thin brass or copper, two or three feet long and some four inches wide. When the ice was still thicker, some of the punts were equipped with runners, so that after they had been drawn up on the ice covering the mudflats, they could be pushed along with a short, iron-shod pole to within shooting distance of the quarry. In open weather, the punt-gunner made a near approach to wildfowl by assuming a prone position and propelling the boat forward with small hand paddles similar to table tennis racquets.

A. H. Patterson recorded that for a few years, punt races were popular events at Breydon water frolics and usually attracted a score or more boats. These competitions took the form of sailing matches and the sail adopted was a standing lug with a loose foot.

REED LIGHTERS

Large, flat-bottomed boats, tarred inside and out, are in common use on the broads for carrying reed, sedge and marsh litter to the staithes. These are classified variously as whole, three-quarter and half-load boats. Two cart-loads of reeds can be stacked in a whole-load boat, which is usually some twenty-five feet long and eight to nine feet across. Most of these lighters are completely open boats, with no cross-beams which would interfere with loading and unloading. To compensate for the lack of any tie-beam, large numbers of rib timbers are used in their construction, so that the sides may keep their shape. The ribs are two inches square and about fifteen inches apart. The sides are planked with three-quarter-inch strakes and the total depth of a lighter seldom exceeds eighteen inches. It is customary to bale water out of these boats with wooden scoops. Propulsion is by quant most of the time, but tholes are provided for rowing in the bows when the load stands so high that quanting becomes difficult.

QUANTS

A good light quant is a precious part of the equipment of all the native river craft of the broads. It is a long, supple pole with a prong jutting out at the lower end to prevent it from sinking into the mud. Unlike a Thames punt pole, it is not trailed along after a stroke, but lifted out of the water and swung forwards. Most of the steering is done before and during the stroke and less after it. The timber used for quants is usually larch or deal.

Appendices

Bibliography

Index

APPENDIX A: MAPS

by J. M. Lambert and J. N. Jennings

SECTION I

KEY MAPS OF THE EAST NORFOLK RIVER VALLEYS AND THEIR BROADS

The first six figures of this map appendix have been reduced from slightly simplified tracings made directly from the 1946–8 Provisional Edition of the 1 : 25,000 Ordnance Survey maps. Although the latter are based on earlier surveys and do not show the present limits of the open water, they nevertheless serve to indicate the relative positions of the broads in their respective valleys. The outlines of many of the broads are now rather different from those given here, and, in addition, all the shallow peat cuttings shown as rectilinear areas of open water between and around the broads themselves have now grown up again to fen.

For reasons of space, it has only been possible to illustrate the middle reaches of the three main broadland valleys, the Bure, the Yare and the Waveney (maps 1–3), and of the two chief tributaries, the Ant and Thurne (maps 4 and 5). Although this covers the great majority of the broads, a few outlying sheets of water are consequently not represented in these figures. For instance, the big downstream side-valley broads of the Ormesby-Rollesby-Filby series of the Bure and of Fritton Lake of the Waveney have had to be omitted, though the former series is covered by the inclusion of a separate map on the same scale at the end of this section (map 6).

The close stippling on the maps indicates the extent of the undrained parts of the fenland: this encompasses all regions which are served by high-level dykes freely open to the river system, with the addition of certain areas round land-locked broads of independent water level and a few other swampy places. In contrast, the stretches of alluvium which have been embanked and belong to the low-level system have been left blank, even though some of these are no longer pumped and have now become derelict. To simplify the general picture, some of the numerous minor dykes intersecting the fenland have been omitted, and, except for the twenty-five-foot contour line, no detail is shown beyond the limits of the alluvium in the valleys.

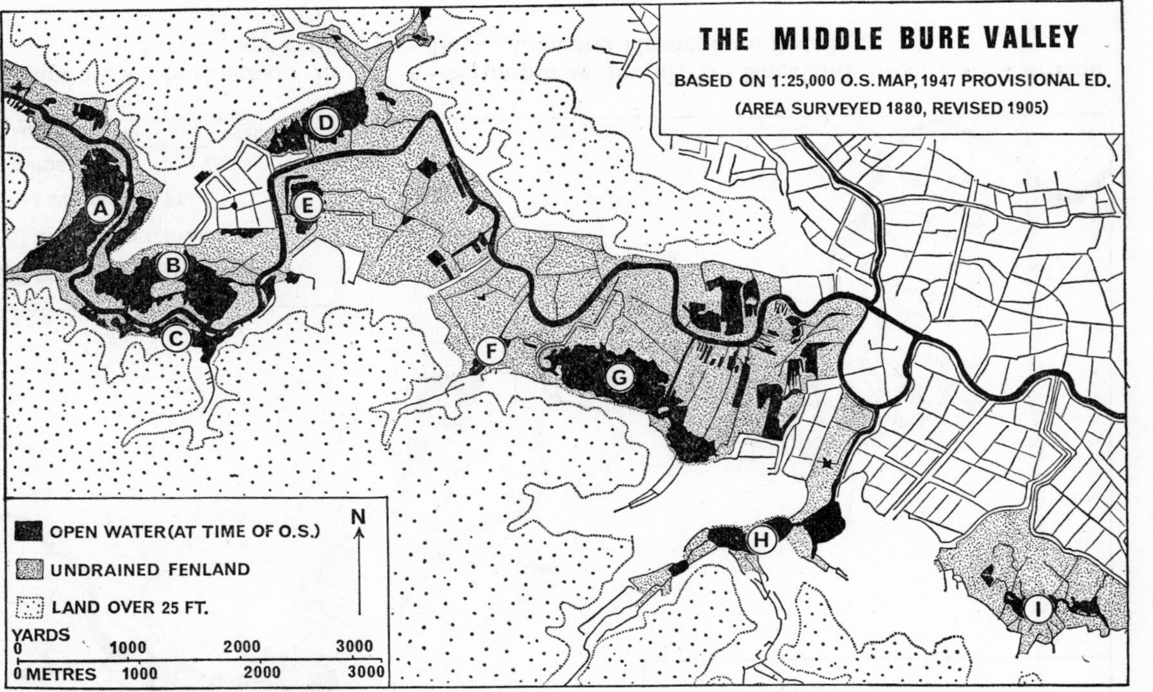

Map I. A—Wroxham Broad; B—Hoveton Great Broad; C—Salhouse Broad; D—Hoveton Little Broad; E—Decoy Broad; F—Cockshoot Broad; G—Ranworth Broad; H—South Walsham Broad; I—Upton Broad. N.B. Belaugh Broad (farther upstream), Burntfen Broad (to the north-east of Hoveton Little Broad) and the Ormesby-Rollesby-Filby series (some distance farther downstream) are not shown on the map

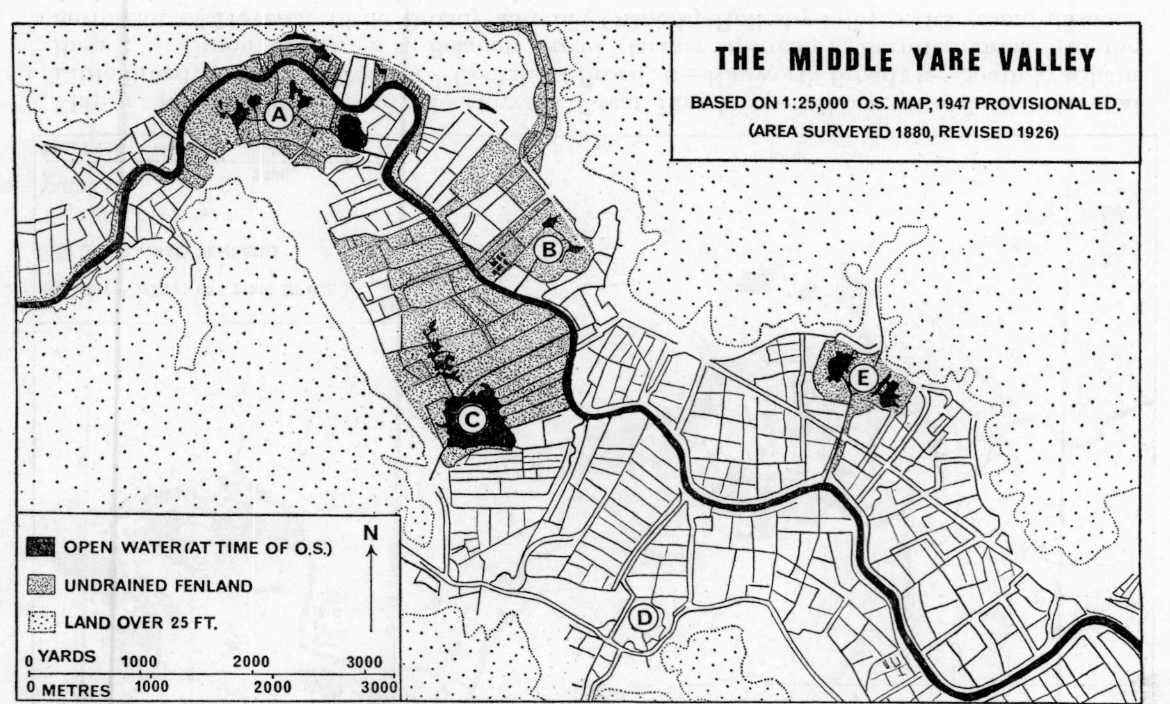

Map 2. A—Surlingham Broad; B—Strumpshaw Broad; C—Rockland Broad; D—Carleton Broad (now extinct); E—Buckenham and Hassingham Broads

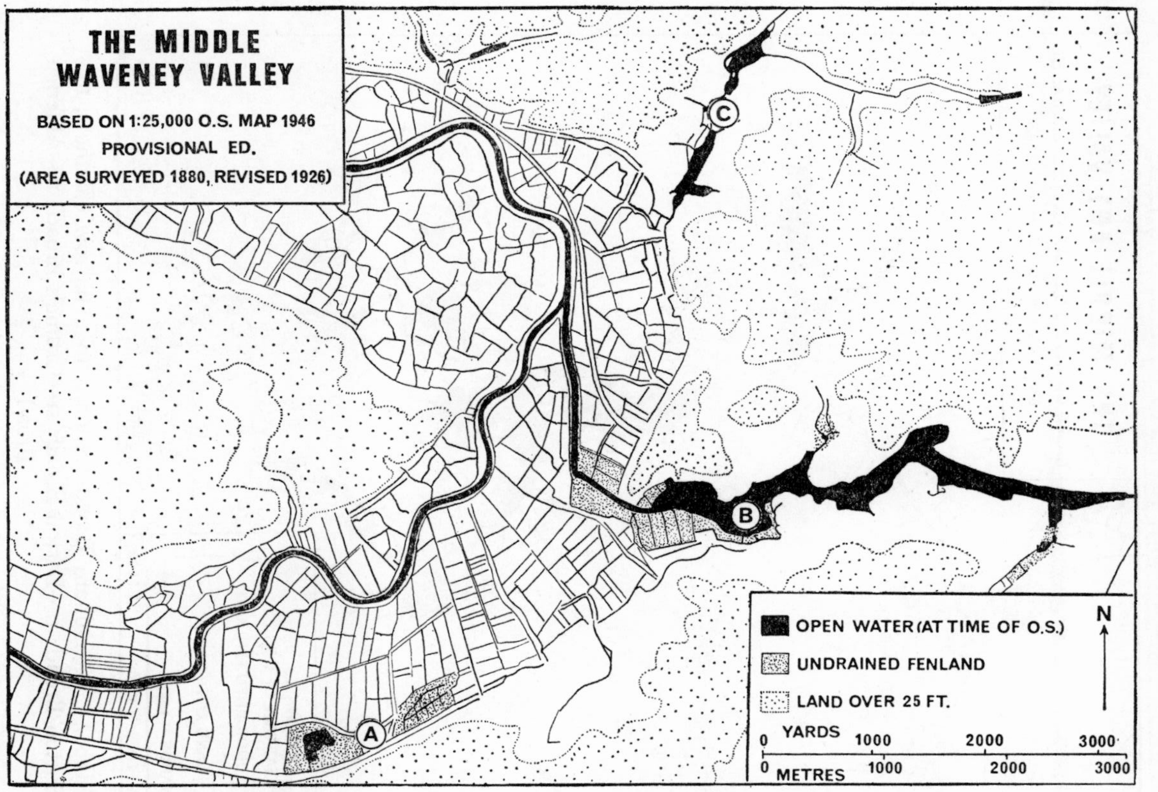

Map 3. A—The two Barnby Broads (one now extinct); B—Oulton Broad and Lake Lothing; C—Flixton Decoy. N.B. Fritton Lake (farther downstream) is not shown on the map

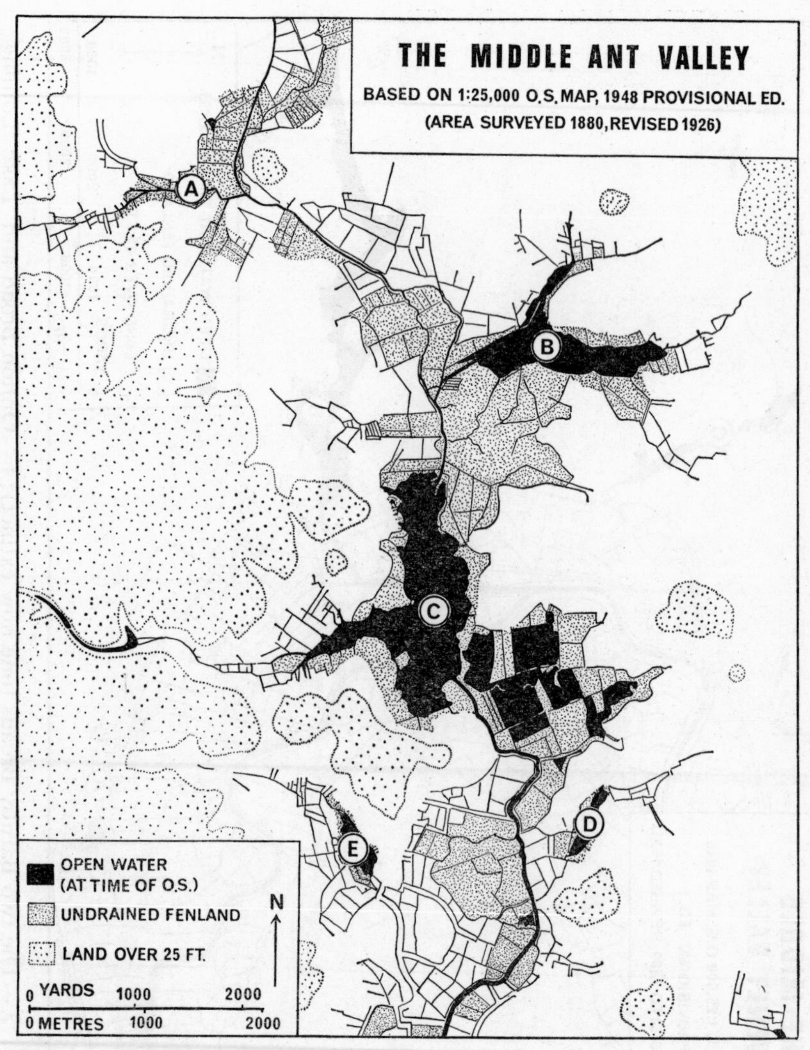

Map 4. A—Dilham Broad (reduced to a narrow channel); B—Sutton Broad; C—Barton Broad; D—Crome's Broad; E—Alderfen Broad

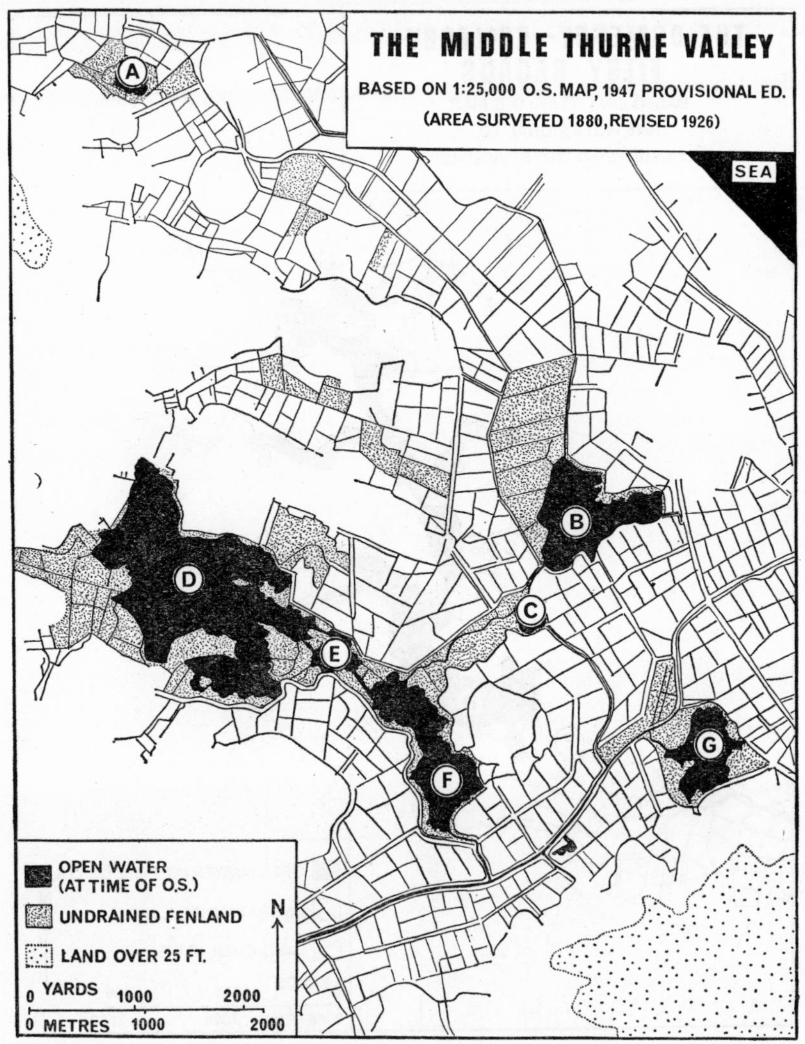

Map 5. A—Calthorpe Broad; B—Horsey Mere; C—Blackfleet Broad; D—Hickling Broad; E—Whiteslea; F—Heigham Sounds; G—Martham Broad. N.B. Womack Water (farther downstream) is not shown on the map

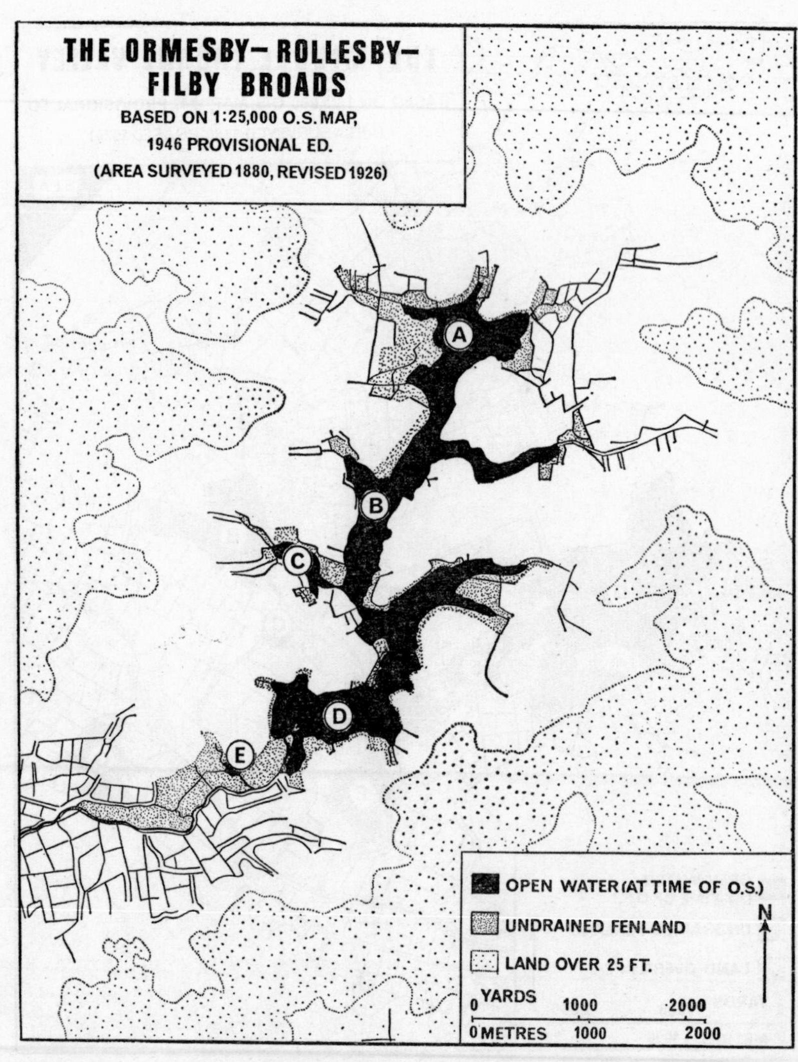

Map 6. A—Ormesby Broad; B—Rollesby Broad; C—Lily Broad; D—Filby Broad; E—Little Broad

N.B. In certain of the tithe maps, it was not always possible to distinguish lines representing dykes from those marking parcel limits without dykes. In such cases, the relevant boundaries have been drawn in the maps concerned as broken lines

SECTION II

SPECIAL FEATURES AND OVERGROWTH OF INDIVIDUAL BROADS

The series of maps set out in the following pages illustrate both the conformation of various individual broads and the extent of recent changes in the outline of their open water up to 1945–6. Three maps are given for each broad, with a time interval of roughly forty years between the first and second, and of roughly sixty years between the second and third. To bring all maps to a comparable basis, they have been standardised in each case against ruling points on the latest edition of the relevant six-inch Ordnance Survey map.

The maps for 1838–49 are reduced from large-scale plans which were produced for each parish by the Tithe Redemption Commission during the survey of Britain which followed the Tithe Commutation Act of 1836. They were made by a number of different surveyors, and vary somewhat in scale (from about 1 : 800 to about 1 : 2100) and in accuracy; but they nevertheless constitute the first complete and comprehensive series of maps which are generally reliable in detail. The Ordnance Survey maps of the same period, at a scale of 1 in. to 1 mile, are too small to approach the accuracy of the Tithe maps in the detailed outline of the open water, and the earlier large-scale Enclosure maps (dated between 1779 and 1819) are in many cases not extant, so that a complete series of these is not available for all the broadland parishes; moreover, the usefulness of these as a basis for comparison is diminished by their greater range in time than that of the Tithe surveys.

The maps for 1880–5 are reduced from slightly simplified tracings made directly from the 1st Edition of the 6-inch Ordnance Survey maps. These are preferred for the present purpose to the 2nd Edition maps, made just over twenty years later, since only a few of the changes in open water which must have taken place between the two editions appear to have been incorporated in the 2nd Edition revisions.

The maps for 1945 and 1946 are based on tracings made from Air Ministry vertical air photographs: an excellent series of these, in complete stereoscopic cover, on a scale of approximately 1 : 10,000, is available for the whole of broadland. In making the tracings from the prints, it was necessary for practical reasons to regard the limits of the open water as coincident with the outer edge of the continuous reedswamp. It is probable, however, that reedswamp areas were estimated as open water in the Tithe and Ordnance ground surveys; and therefore, although the differences involved are probably not great, allowance for this must nevertheless be made in any detailed comparison of open water outlines at different periods.

It must be clearly stated, moreover, that the 1945–6 outlines do not necessarily reflect the present status of many of the broads. The great increase in the naturalised coypu population during the last decade (see chapter 13, p. 225) resulted in such a wholesale destruction of the marginal vegetation that much of the encroaching reedswamp, fen, and even carr has been eliminated in places. No maps are yet available to show the present position, but general observation leaves no doubt that the area of open water in most of the broads is now much greater than that shown in the 1945–6 maps.

Altogether, between forty and fifty different broads occur in the river valleys, if parts of subdivided basins known under different individual names are reckoned in the total. It is obviously neither necessary nor possible to give separate map series here for all these broads, and a representative selection from each of the five broadland valleys has therefore been made. Those which are figured have been chosen to give as wide a range of different types as possible, and include by-passed and side-valley, tidal and land-locked, large and small, deep and shallow broads. Several of the maps, moreover, have been included to illustrate specific points discussed in chapter 3, and should be looked at in close conjunction with the text of this chapter.

In the arrangement of maps, the broads of the three chief valleys—the Bure, the Yare and the Waveney—have been given first, followed by those of the secondary valleys—the Ant and Thurne; and in each case they have been placed as nearly as possible in order down the valleys. Each map series is accompanied by a brief description of the most interesting features of the area depicted.

The broads actually illustrated are as follows:

The general key to the maps in the following pages is given below:

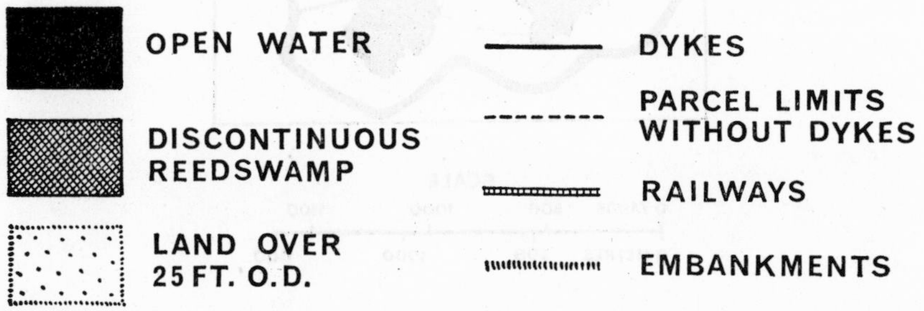

OPEN WATER

DISCONTINUOUS REEDSWAMP

LAND OVER 25 FT. O.D.

DYKES

PARCEL LIMITS WITHOUT DYKES

RAILWAYS

EMBANKMENTS

Map 7. Hoveton Great Broad (Bure Valley)

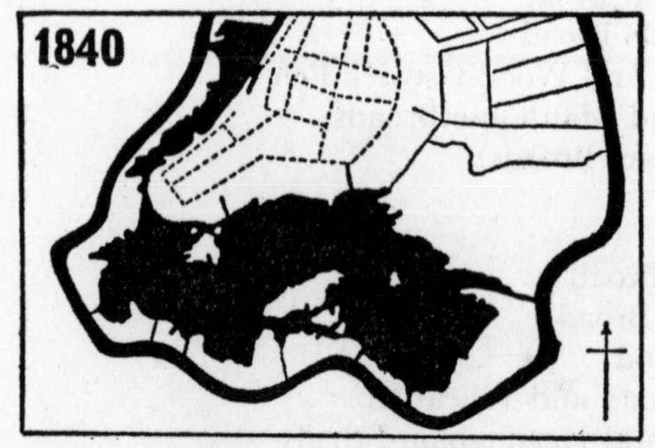

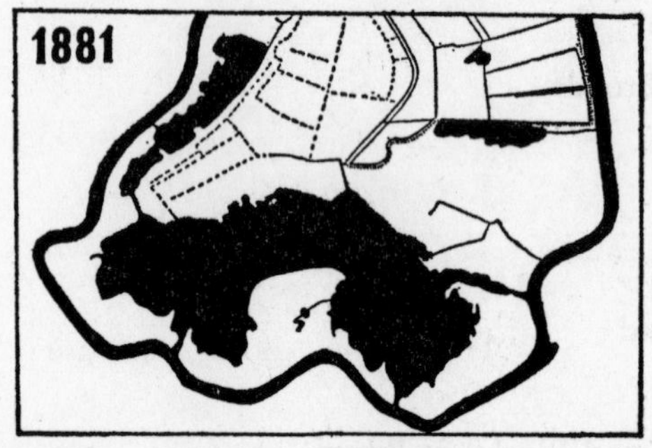

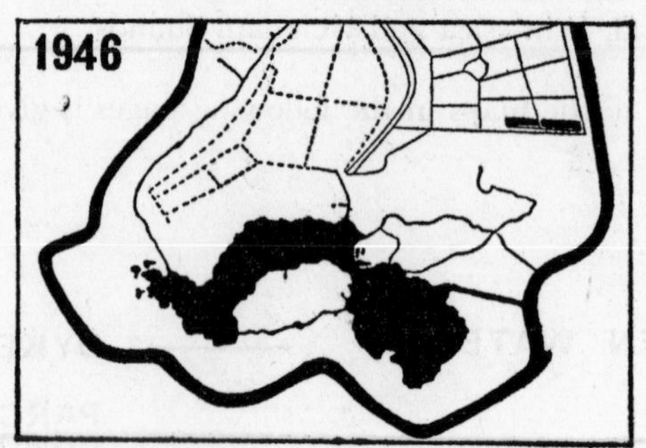

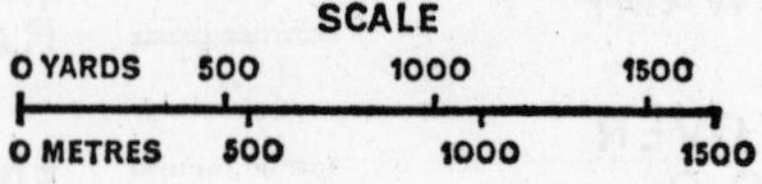

HOVETON GREAT BROAD

This is a very typical by-passed broad, lying within the concavity of a big meander of the Bure. The Great Broad itself consists of a roughly C-shaped sheet of water, connected with an overgrown northern limb known as Hudson's Bay.

Since the broad lies fairly well upstream, the clay wedge between the basin of the broad and the river is quite narrow, and only a relatively thin strip of the original alluvium has been left as a rond [1] between the broad and the river. The broad was originally connected with the river by a number of short dykes or 'gatways' cutting across the rond, but all except one of these are now overgrown.

Two lines of bores made across the centre of the broad have shown that the original limits of the basin corresponded very closely with the outline of open water shown on the 1840 map, so that very little overgrowth had taken place, at least along the section lines, before that date. The basin of the broad is typically steep-sided, and only moderately deep, the greatest depth recorded in the bores being approximately ten feet below the surrounding undisturbed alluvium.

Encroachment of vegetation has taken place from all directions during the last century, and the southern complex of separate islands has become merged into a single island (Larkbush), which is now only separated from the rond by a narrow dyke. The remaining open water is now filled with mud to within about four feet of the surface and, since the broad is closed to navigation, there has been little disturbance of the mud or erosion of the surrounding reedswamp by the wash of power craft. The encroachment of vegetation has therefore continued more or less unchecked until the recent depredations by the coypu, and the original sharp edges of the broad are completely obscured. Much of this vegetation had already progressed to carr by 1946 and, although the reedswamp and fen have been damaged by coypu activities, there is still a good range of primary communities to be found around the broad.

Hoveton Great Broad now forms part of the Bure Marshes National Nature Reserve by agreement with the owner in 1958, and the area can be visited by permit.

[1] The term 'rond' is here, and subsequently, used to designate the whole stretch of fenland which lies between a by-passed broad and the adjacent river. The local usage of the term, however, seems to vary: it is sometimes employed in a more restricted sense to apply only to the narrow strip of vegetation between a river or broad and its embankments (in regions where the latter occur).

Map 8. Hoveton Little Broad
(Bure Valley)

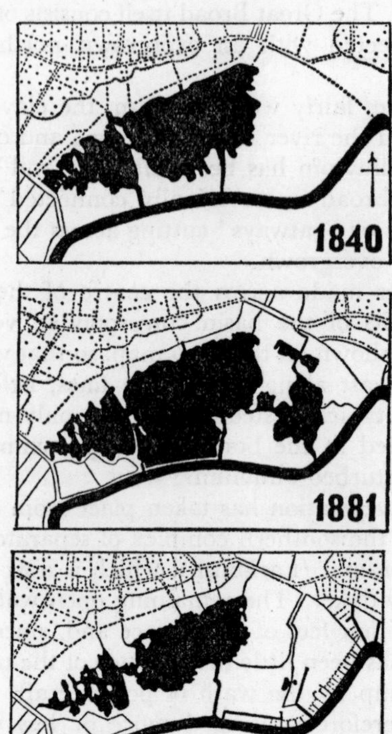

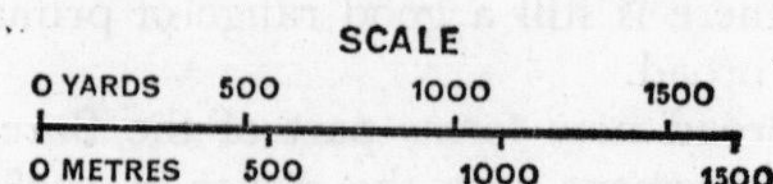

HOVETON LITTLE BROAD

Unlike the Great Broad, Hoveton Little Broad is situated on the convex side of a river meander, with its landward side close against the steeply rising upland. Since it is farther downstream than the Great Broad, the clay flange underlying the rond is here a little wider, and the basin of the broad lies slightly farther from the river.

The broad shows a distinct division into a western (inner) and an eastern (outer) part, separated by a peninsula of compact alluvium cut through by a narrow channel. This peninsula, composed of peat at the landward end, and of peat and clay towards the river, is undisturbed and steep-sided, and obviously represents a former balk left between the two parts of the basin when the latter were excavated. Suggestions of other balks or ridges can also be seen in the roughly parallel arrangement of shorter peninsulas and islands in the western part of the broad.

Borings made in both the inner and outer broads have shown that the original depth of the basin—between eight and eleven feet—was very comparable to that of the Great Broad, though there has been greater accumulation of mud in the inner part (to within two or three feet of the water surface) than in the outer (to within about four feet).

The comparison of open water areas in the map series is complicated by the extensive cutting of surface peat which has taken place in the area during the last century. From stratigraphical evidence, a great deal of the solid fenland to the south and east of the broad appears to have been dug to a depth of about three feet, and the maps indicate that much of it took place between 1840 and 1881. During this period, the whole of the rond between the outer broad and the river was cut over except for a very narrow strip, and additional open water areas were also produced in the fens to the east of the broad; but, by 1946, both regions had grown up again to reedbed and fen. This turf-cutting, as well as enlarging the area of the outer broad, must also have affected the rate of vegetational encroachment on the original deep basin. Most of the overgrowth of the latter, as distinct from the growing up of the shallow cuttings, has therefore taken place along the more undisturbed northern margin and at the western end; much of this area has now progressed to carr, which has been less susceptible to coypu attack than the younger vegetation on the southern side.

Both the inner and outer broads formerly had separate connections with the river, but now the east dyke alone remains. The inner broad is private, but the outer part, often called Black Horse Broad, was opened to restricted use by the public in 1949.

Map 9. Decoy Broad and Woodbastwick Fen (Bure Valley)

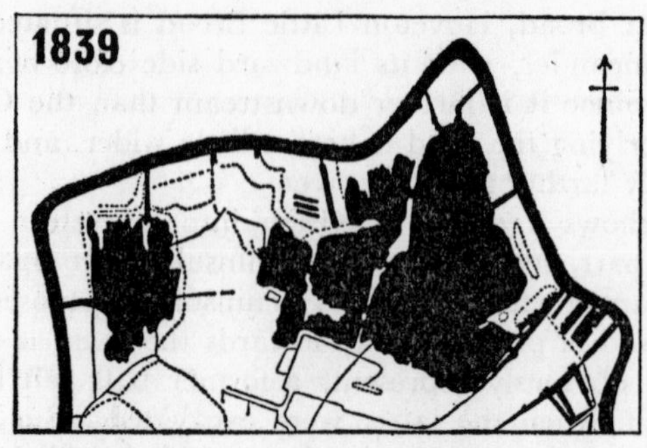

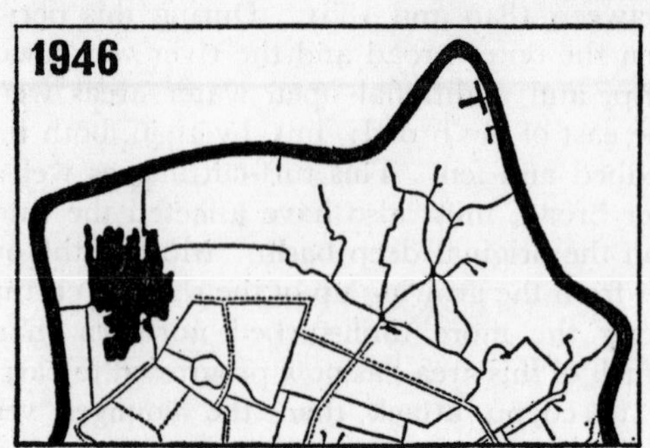

SCALE

O YARDS 500 1000 1500

O METRES 500 1000 1500

DECOY BROAD and WOODBASTWICK FEN

Decoy Broad, lying to the west side of Woodbastwick Fen, occupies a rather asymmetrical position in the big stretch of fenland encompassed by the river meander in this region. The eastern part of the fen was occupied during the last century by a huge, rather irregular turf-pond known as 'Broad Waters': but this had completely disappeared by 1946, with the exception of a network of dykes which have been kept open. Many other smaller, more rectilinear turf-ponds can also be seen scattered over the fenland in the 1839 and 1881 maps, but these were similarly impermanent. In contrast, Decoy Broad has changed only insignificantly in outline during the same period, and borings have moreover indicated that the original maximum extent of its open water was almost identical with that shown on the 1839 map.

The area therefore offers excellent contrasts in the rate of overgrowth of deep and shallow water. 'Broad Waters' was only about three feet deep, whereas Decoy Broad possesses one of the deepest basins in the Bure valley, reaching down in parts to over fourteen feet below the level of the surrounding fenland. The muds which are filling up the basin are still over six feet below the water surface in many places, with the result that very little primary reedswamp and fen vegetation has been able to encroach on the open water round the margins of the broad, except in a few parts of the somewhat shallower south end.

The north edge of the basin of Decoy Broad shows some particularly good examples of steep-sided parallel peninsulas of the original alluvium projecting into the open water, with deep inlets of open water between. Certain of the peninsulas have been shown to extend outwards as under-water ridges of solid peat running well towards the centre of the basin, and in one or two cases the lines of individual ridges can be picked up again by small projections at the south end of the broad. As in the case of Hoveton Great Broad, these peninsulas and ridges almost certainly represent the remains of former balks or strips of peat left *in situ* during the excavation of the basin.

In the absence of much primary marginal vegetation, the greater part of Decoy Broad is directly bordered by tall carr growing on the solid alluvium which surrounds its basin, and this sheet of water is therefore rather different scenically from more typically overgrown broads. The broad is part of the Bure Marshes National Nature Reserve and is not normally open to navigation, though it can be entered in small boats by permission.

Map 10. Ranworth and Malthouse Broads (Bure Valley)

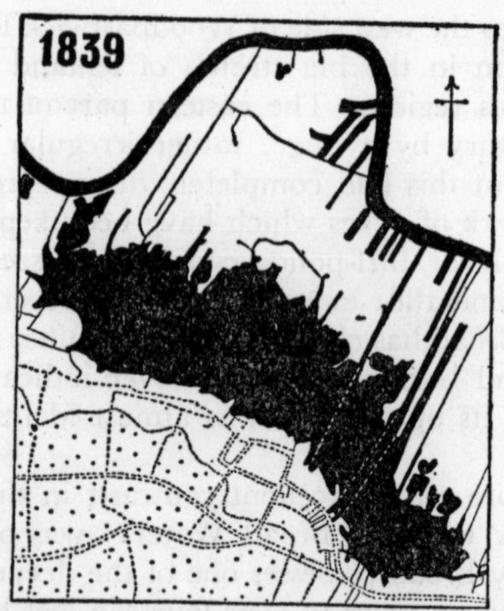

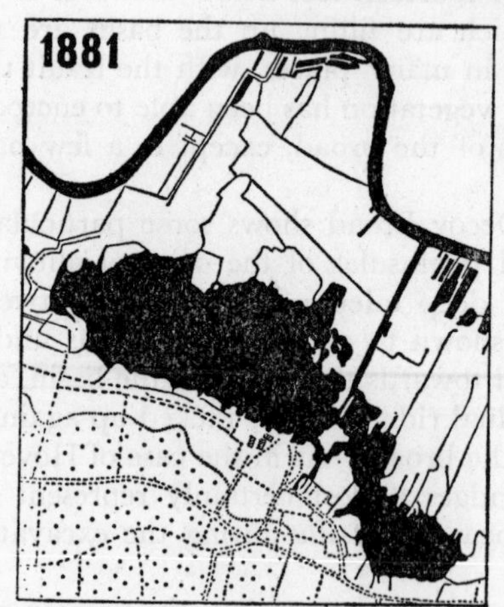

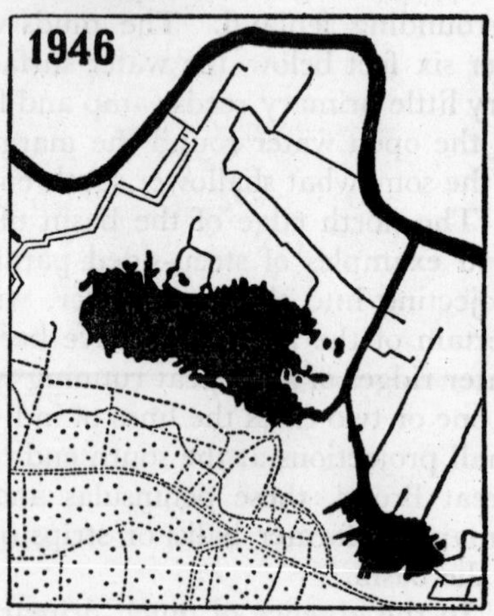

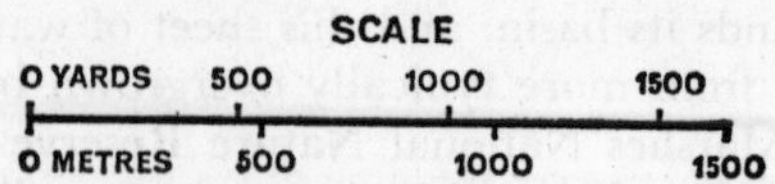

RANWORTH BROAD

This broad, like the preceding ones, is by-passed in type, but it lies some distance farther down the valley. The rond is correspondingly much wider, and the broad lies well back from the river. It was originally connected with the river by several long dykes of varying width running across the rond, but these are now all overgrown and closed except for one —Ranworth Dam—which has been widened and dredged as a sailing channel.

The Ranworth basin is easily the largest in the Bure valley, and, although it has become much overgrown, the remaining open water still considerably exceeds the others in area. The broad once formed a continuous sheet of water, with its original maximum limits approximately equivalent to the outline in the 1839 map: but it has subsequently been divided into an inner and outer part by overgrowth of vegetation, encouraged in the vicinity of Ranworth Dam by deliberate piling to make the separation.

The basin of the broad is of moderate depth, averaging between ten and twelve feet, with the muds now reaching in general to within three to six feet of the water surface. It has thus reached a stage in its infilling at which conditions are ripe for a rapid overgrowth of marginal vegetation; this is partly expressed in the great diminution in area between 1881 and 1946, though coypu attack has recently caused the vegetation to recede again.

In the first two maps of the series, rectilinear peat cuttings can be seen in the rond, sometimes extending from the margin of the broad itself. The 1839 map also shows peninsulas projecting into the open water, though their outlines are rather obscured in the 1946 map by marginal overgrowth. As in Decoy Broad, these peninsulas have been shown to consist of solid, undisturbed alluvium, often continued outwards as underwater ridges, and to have deep inlets between them, distinct from the shallow cuttings.

An interesting feature of the 1839 map is the three parcel lines drawn across the open water. It is significant that the peninsulas of solid peat, and the shallow cuttings in the rond, both run approximately parallel with these lines: this gives support to the idea of a former strip-parcelling of the whole area, and strip-excavation of peat, both deep and shallow, in relation to these parcels.

The outer part of Ranworth Broad, sometimes known as Malthouse Broad, is open to pleasure cruisers. Ranworth Inner Broad, which is part of the Bure Marshes National Nature Reserve, can be entered in rowing-boats during the summer by permission, but is closed between September and March.

Map 11. South Walsham Broads (Bure Valley)

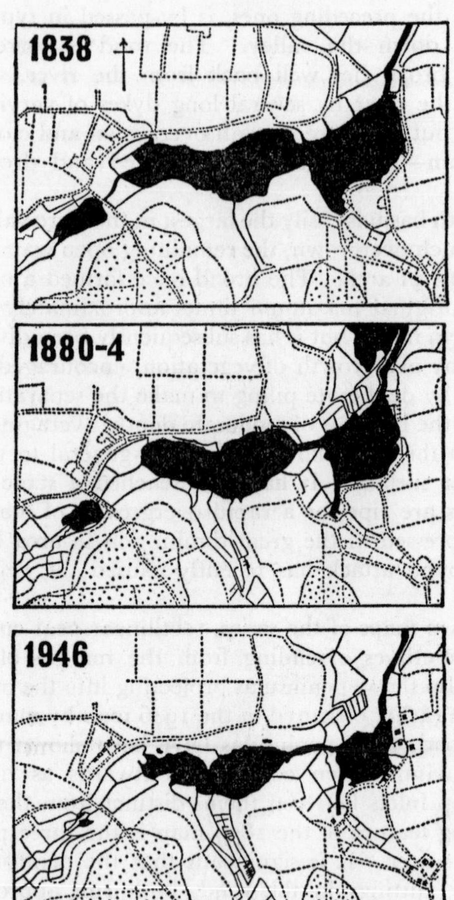

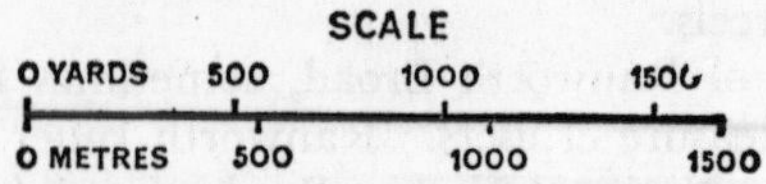

SOUTH WALSHAM BROAD

In contrast to the examples so far given, South Walsham is a typical side-valley broad, and possesses the elongate shape characteristic of this type. It lies in a small tributary valley fairly well back from the main river, but is in open connection with the latter by the long South Walsham Fleet Dyke, so that this broad, unlike most other side-valley broads, is still part of the navigable system of waterways.

The clay deposit in the main valley extends across practically its whole width in this region, and has been shown to reach the upland a little east of the Fleet Dyke. The clay, however, only just enters the mouth of the tributary valley, and the broad lies beyond its limits in normal fashion. The Fleet Dyke itself forms a rough boundary between the downriver stretch of drained grazing levels, lying on the clay, and the undrained fenland above, where the clay cover is less complete. Much surface peat-cutting took place during the last century in the undrained fens to the west of the dyke, and part of one extensive shallow turf-pond can be seen at the top of the 1880–4 map.

Like Ranworth Broad, the South Walsham basin once held a continuous sheet of open water, which has been divided up by vegetational overgrowth during the last century into an inner and outer broad, connected only by a narrow channel. No information is available as to the original maximum limits or depth of the basin, but it is probable that the small overgrown pool at the south-west end of the broad also originally formed part of the same sheet of water. Some distance farther up the tributary valley, well off the maps, lies another small lake, sometimes called Panxworth Broad, but this was almost certainly formed as a separate entity.

The outer broad is open to holiday traffic, but the inner broad is private.

Map 12. Surlingham Broad (Yare Valley)

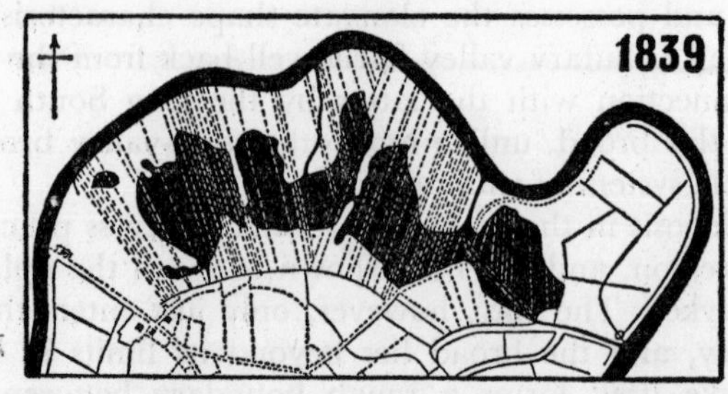

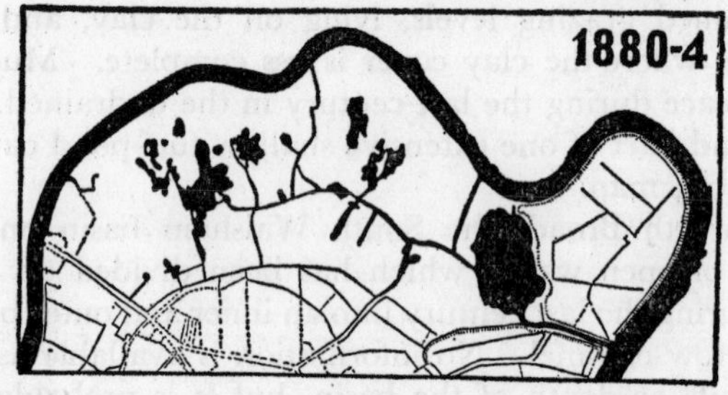

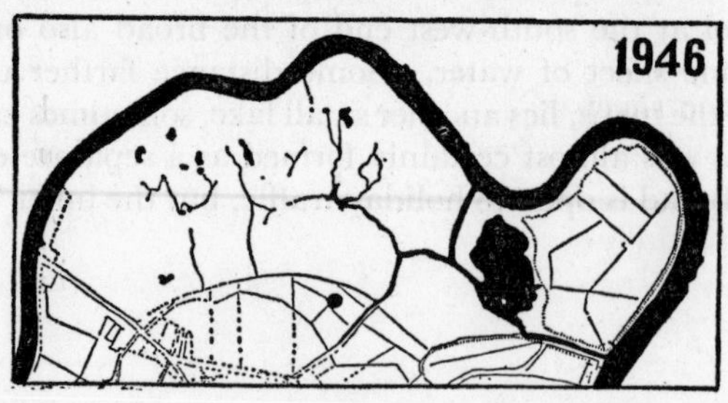

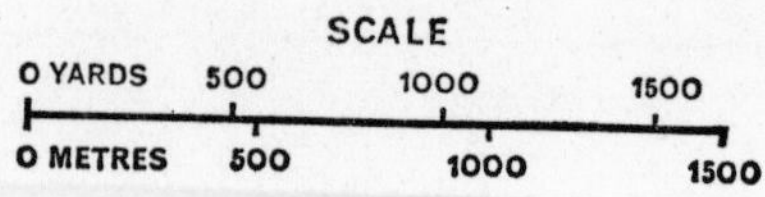

SURLINGHAM BROAD

This by-passed broad is the most upstream broad in the Yare valley, and lies fairly close to the river channel. Except for a small area at the eastern end, and a few channels and pulk-holes, the open water is now almost obliterated.

The original basin of the broad was considerably bigger than the outline of open water shown on the 1839 map, and stretched westwards to the road leading to Surlingham Ferry and southwards to the extreme edge of the upland now marked by the most landward dyke. The basin is fairly deep, with its bottom lying between ten and fourteen feet below the fenland surface, and dropping in at least one place to over seventeen feet. Though muds have accumulated within it to fairly near the surface, the actual overgrowth by vegetation has been mainly brought about by a free-floating mat of rond-grass (*Glyceria maxima*), which rises and falls with the tide and is to some extent independent of the level of the mud for its encroachment.

One of the most interesting features of the 1839 map is the parcelling up of the whole area—open water as well as the fens around—into sets of narrow parallel strips, representing former separate holdings, and strongly suggesting that the whole area was once solid fenland. This map also shows particularly well-marked examples of peninsulas dividing up the basin, and it is noteworthy that they run strictly parallel with the parcel lines. Like those described for other broads in the preceding pages, borings have shown that the peninsulas are virtually vertical-sided and consist of solid, undisturbed peat, or peat and clay: and many similar, though less complete, ridges have also been found projecting from the floor of the basin.

To the east of the broad lies an area which was previously embanked and drained, but which has now reverted to waterlogged fen. The clay horizon extends only partway across this area, and the dereliction of the latter forms a good example of the difficulties accompanying permanent drainage in the middle reaches of the valleys where there is only an incomplete clay cover.

Surlingham Broad has recently been acquired by the Norfolk Naturalists' Trust. There is free access from the river to the eastern sheet of water, and the narrow channel running west into the overgrown part of the basin is navigable by rowing-boat.

Map 13. Strumpshaw Broad (Yare Valley)

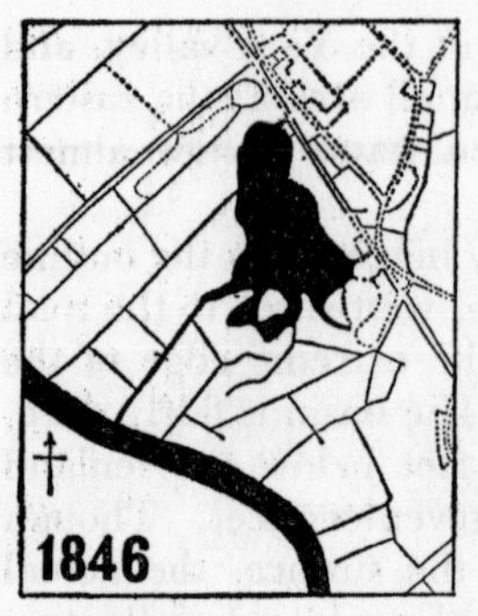

Map 14. Carleton Broad (Yare Valley)

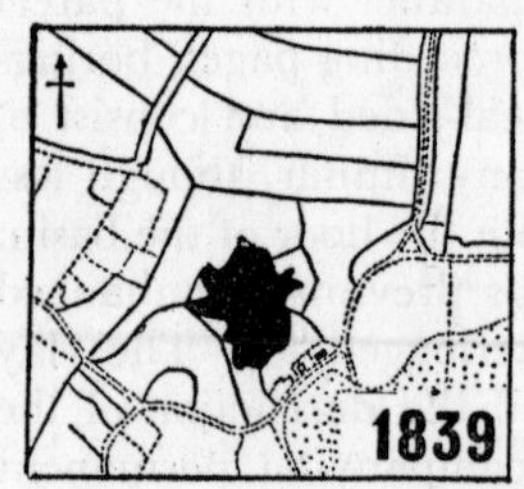

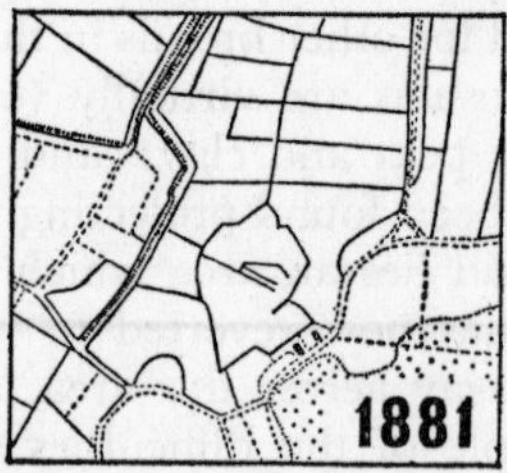

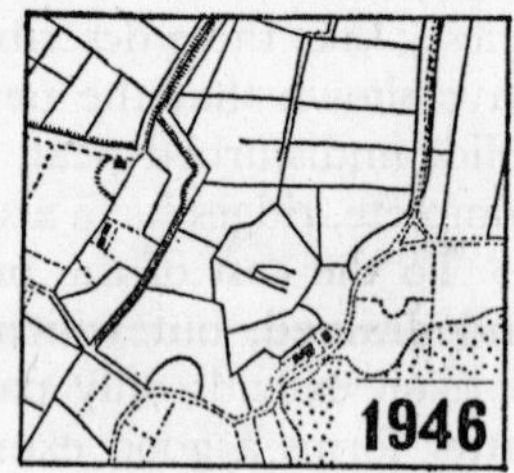

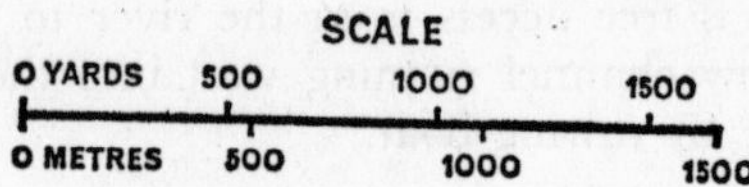

STRUMPSHAW BROAD

Strumpshaw Broad lies farther back from the river than Surlingham Broad, and, although it was never as big as the latter, the actual limits of the basin are somewhat greater than the open water outline shown on the Tithe map. The original broad, in fact, cut some distance into the clay flange on the riverward side, so that the clay is here sharply truncated.

The basin itself is of average depth, with the transition between the solid underlying peat and the muds which fill the basin occurring between ten and twelve feet below the fenland surface. The usual ridges of peat, buried in the mud, have been found running across the floor of the basin to make it shallower in places.

Like most of Surlingham Broad, the open water was almost completely obliterated in 1946. The two remaining pools of water are in open connection with the river, and floating rafts of sweet-grass have again formed the main agent of overgrowth.

Some of the fenland lying on the clay between the broad and the river has been embanked and drained in the past, but has now reverted to rough fen.

CARLETON BROAD

This diminutive broad, which originally occupied a shallow basin well back from the river at the mouth of a small tributary valley of the Yare, is now extinct. It was incorporated into the low-level drainage system of the adjacent grazing marshes during the last century, and the small tributary stream of upland drainage water which originally flowed down the side valley and fed the broad has been diverted to the west and embanked to form an independent high-level unit.

The water table now lies between one and two feet below the surface of the muds which had previously accumulated in the basin of the broad, and the site is occupied by carr, standing out among the flat pastures round it. In many places, the trees have directly colonised the exposed surface of the muds without an intervening reedswamp and fen phase.

Map 15. Rockland Broad and Wheatfen (Yare Valley)

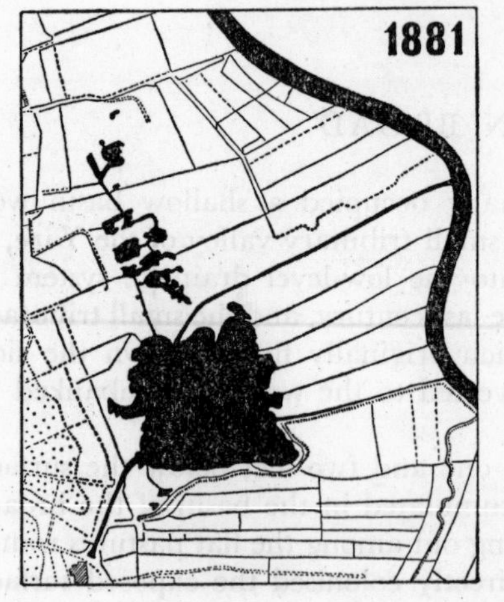

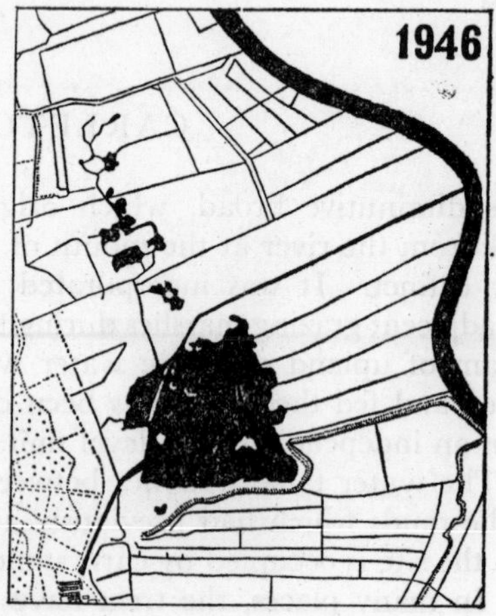

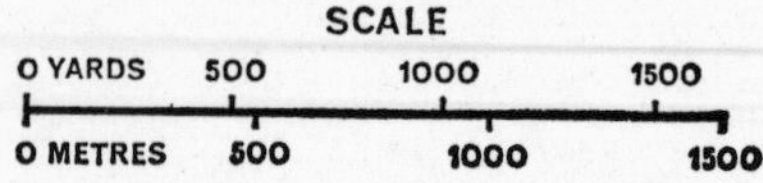

ROCKLAND BROAD and WHEATFEN

Rockland Broad is now the largest stretch of open water remaining in the Yare valley. It occupies the south end of a still larger basin, of which the other end has completely grown up to leave only the twisting channels and small pools of the Wheatfen chain of waterways to the north of the broad. The Rockland part of the basin is fairly deep; it reaches down to between eleven and fourteen feet, though muds have accumulated within it to within four to five feet of the mean tidal level of the water. The overgrown Wheatfen part is somewhat shallower, averaging about nine feet at the northern end.

The original extent of the whole basin was very approximately equal to that of Surlingham, and it appears to have been similarly divided into a number of separate units by bars of undisturbed peat. The most northern and shallowest of these sections was already grown up by the time of the 1839–40 map, so that the balk which divided it from the rest was masked and does not show on the map: but a very clear balk, cut by a central channel, can be seen a little farther south, and it is significant that this is parallel with parcel lines which run across the open water in the same map. Submerged ridges of peat which have been found in other parts of the basin also doubtless represent the remains of further balks.

The basin is also characterised by the presence of a number of steep-sided islands of solid peat surrounded by deep muds. In the open expanse of Rockland, the tops of these islands lie for the most part just below the surface of the water, but they are marked by great reedbeds which stand isolated in the middle of the open water. The islands shown in series to the north side of the broad in the 1946 map are of a rather different nature: they mark a line of disused wherries which were sunk in an abortive attempt to improve the tidal scour in the main sailing channel to Rockland Staithe, and which subsequently became colonised and almost obscured by reedswamp vegetation.

Rockland Broad is connected with the river by a series of dykes, of which two are wide and open to navigation. The Wheatfen waterways are private.

Map 16. Buckenham and Hassingham Broads (Yare Valley)

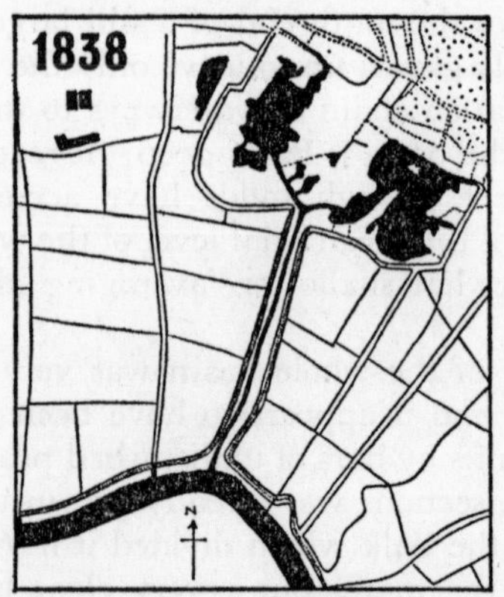

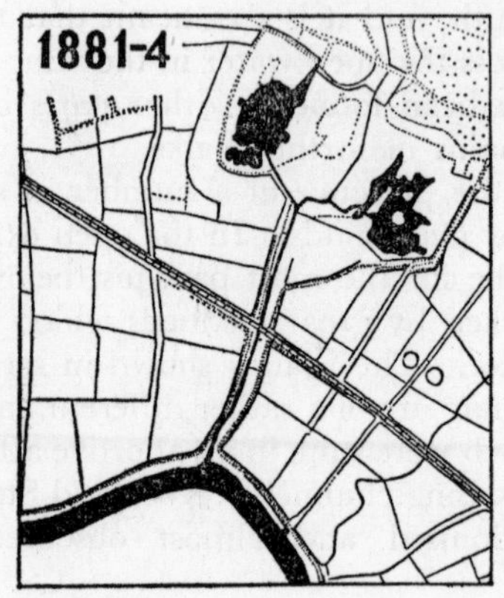

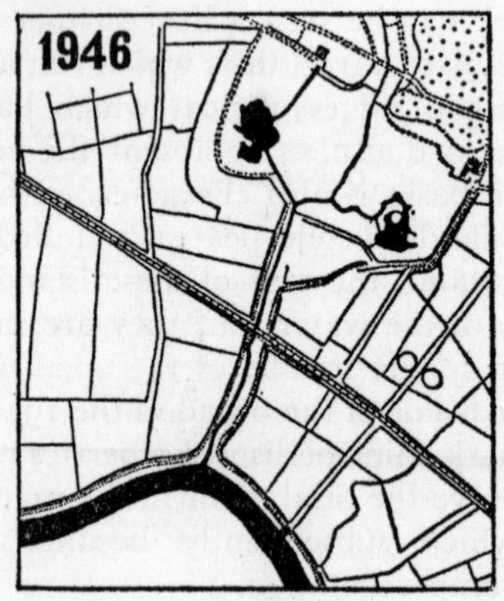

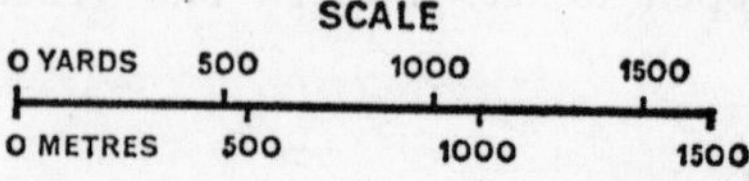

BUCKENHAM and HASSINGHAM BROADS

The two small interconnected sheets of water now known independently as Buckenham and Hassingham Broads represent respectively the north-west and south-east remnants of a formerly more extensive series of adjacent open water areas. Numerous intersecting lines of bores have shown that they originally formed part of an elaborate system of excavations, of varying depth, separated from one another by steep-sided solid balks. Most of the slightly shallower central sections of the system had already grown up by 1838, leaving only small isolated pools between the two main broads; these intermediate pools had been obliterated and the two residual sheets of water much reduced in size by the time of the 1881–4 survey; and by 1946, Buckenham and Hassingham Broads themselves had diminished to less than a third of their original maximum extent.

The broads were freely open to the river, and belonged to the high-level system plied by trading wherries, until the dyke exit was closed by a sluice in the middle of the last century to protect the adjacent low-level grazing marshes from flooding. The original sluice was recently replaced by a new and more effective mechanism, and there is now practically no tidal rise and fall in the broads. As a result of this isolation from tidal movement, the present vegetation round Buckenham and Hassingham is somewhat different in character from that of the strongly tidal upstream Yare valley broads: instead of the great floating masses of rond-grass (*Glyceria maxima*) round Surlingham, Strumpshaw and parts of Rockland, the reedswamp is here dominated by the lesser reedmace (*Typha angustifolia*), while the fen sedge (*Carex acutiformis*), saw sedge (*Cladium mariscus*), and fen rush (*Juncus subnodulosus*) occur widely in the primary fen.

The erection of the sluice has also effected a slight general lowering of the average water level in the system, and approximately one to two feet of the surrounding peat surface has consequently wasted away. Though the original excavations must have been up to ten or eleven feet deep in parts, the bottoms of the Buckenham and Hassingham basins now lie between seven and nine feet below the present level of the adjacent fenland, and there is only about two to three feet of free water above the muds filling the basins. The residual open water of Buckenham Broad is kept fairly open by artificial clearing, but the secluded Hassingham Broad was becoming rapidly overgrown by reedswamp until the advent of the coypu. Both broads are private

Map 17. The Barnby Broads (Waveney Valley)

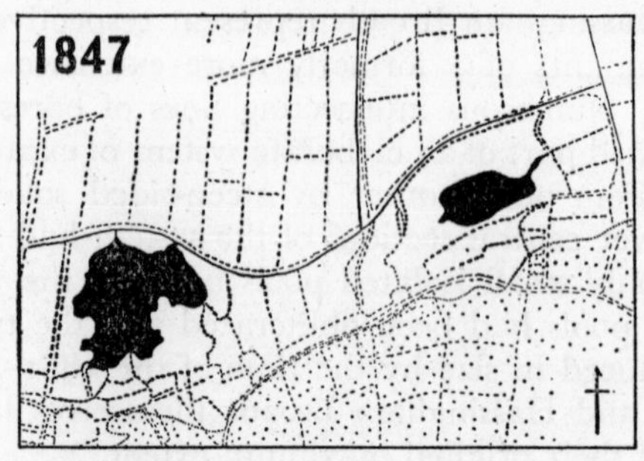

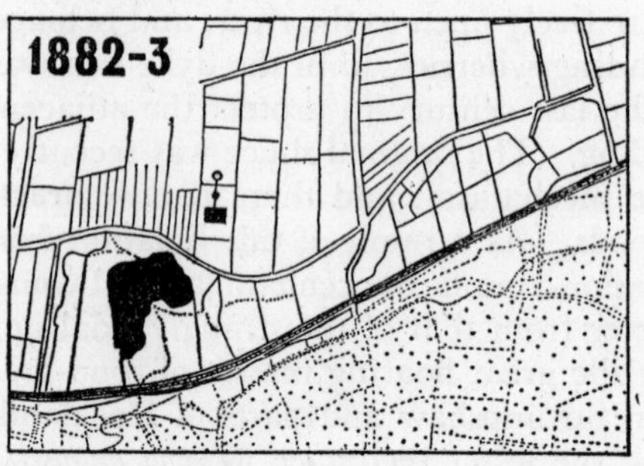

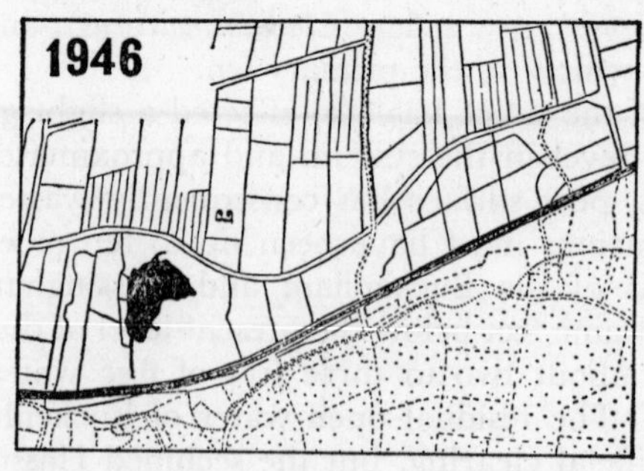

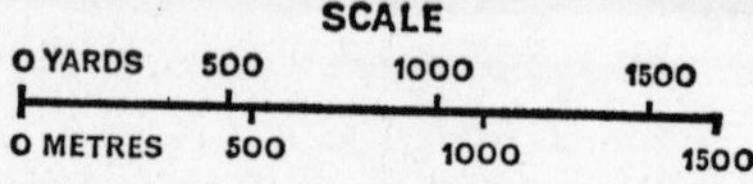

THE BARNBY BROADS

The two original small Barnby Broads, lying just over half a mile apart with their basins separated by a continuous stretch of solid fenland, form the only examples of the by-passed type of broad in the Waveney valley. The eastern of the two broads—Barnby Old Broad—had become extinct by the latter part of the last century, but the western broad still exists as a small pool of open water, very much reduced from its original maximum extent.

The two basins lie roughly a mile back from the river, from which they are separated by drained grazing marshes underlain by clay. The map series shows that neither of the broads had a direct connection with the river within the last century, and, unlike other land-locked broads in similar positions, such as Upton Broad in the Bure valley, there is no evidence from the pattern of the drains that such a direct connection ever existed.

In the remaining western broad, the level of its water, mainly derived from drainage from the adjoining upland, is artificially controlled by sluices. Some wastage of the surface peat has obviously taken place around the broad as well as in the adjacent grazing marshes, so that, as in the case of Buckenham and Hassingham Broads, the former level of solid peat was somewhat higher and the original total depth of the excavation forming the broad correspondingly greater. The bottom of the basin is irregular, with the usual steep-sided ridges of peat within it. In its deepest parts, it now reaches down to some eight feet below the level of the surrounding wasted peat, and is filled with mud to within one to two feet of the present water surface. The broad is private, and reedswamp encroachment has been checked to some extent by artificial clearance, so that, although the broad is so shallow, an appreciable area of open water still remains.

The site of the former eastern broad is entirely occupied by fen and carr, intersected by artificial dykes. The basin here is only five or six feet deep, so that the original broad was shallower than its neighbour. In many ways, the area closely resembles the extinct and drained Carleton Broad of the Yare valley, with brushwood peat similarly directly overlying compacted muds in places, so that it is probable that the final stages in the extinction of this broad were brought about in the same way by deliberate lowering of the water level.

Map 18. Fritton Lake (Waveney Valley).

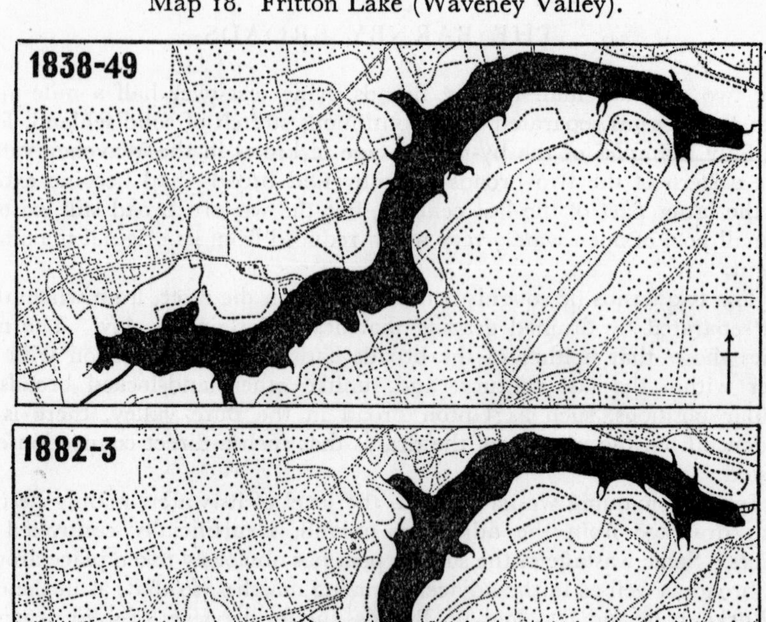

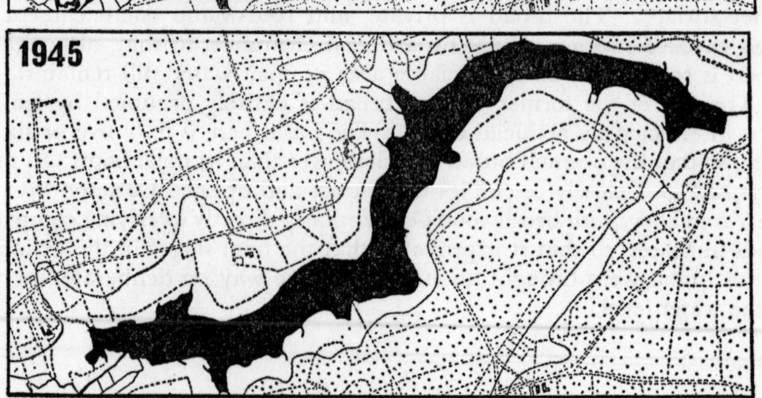

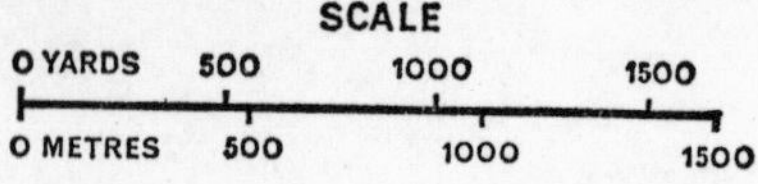

FRITTON LAKE

At first sight, the long, sinuous stretch of Fritton Lake appears to have a very different character from that of the other broads. Instead of a wide, shallow sheet of water set in flat, peaty fenland, the waters of Fritton are deep and narrow, and for the most part lap directly on to well-wooded, steeply-rising, gravelly valley slopes. The outline of the lake follows the valley contours closely, and superficially there seems little to suggest that the lake is indeed of the same nature and origin as the more typical broads.

At the lower end of the lake, however, the whole valley is filled with the usual sequence of solid peat and clay, and here there are the same sharp, truncated edges to the lake basin as have been found round the other broads. Above the lake, the valley was similarly filled with solid alluvial deposits until they were recently cut away to form a series of water reservoirs. Moreover, although only a very few, small, isolated patches of solid peat remain along the sides of the lake, the muds in the centre of the basin are directly underlain by peat in typical fashion. On this and other evidence, there seems no doubt that Fritton Lake is a normal side-valley broad, made by the cutting out of peat across the whole valley width so that its lateral margins are formed by the slopes of the valley sides themselves.

The special features of the present lake may be correlated with the great depth of the original excavation which formed it. In contrast to the usual ten to twelve foot depth of the great majority of broads, the basin here reaches down, at least in parts, to more than seventeen feet below the level of the wasted, but otherwise undisturbed, alluvium at the lower end. In consequence, the muds which have accumulated within it are still some ten feet below the present water surface, and practically no primary vegetation has been able to encroach on the deep open water. Only a very narrow, interrupted, scanty zone of reedswamp occupies the steep, gravelly, lake margins, and the outline of the open water has remained essentially unchanged since the broad was formed.

The present broad, which is used as a pleasure lake for boating and fishing, is land-locked. There is a narrow stream emerging from its lower end and connecting it with the Waveney, but this is closed by sluices.

Fritton Lake is often alternatively known as Fritton Decoy, from its former extensive use in the decoying of wildfowl. The decoys are easily seen in the maps as short curved inlets round the margin of the broad.

Map 19. Sutton Broad (Ant Valley)

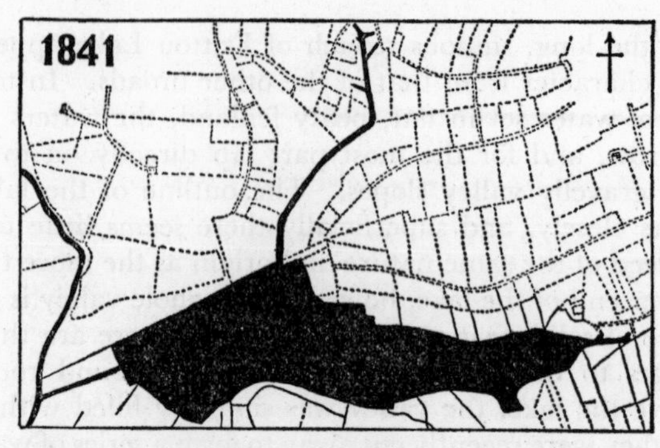

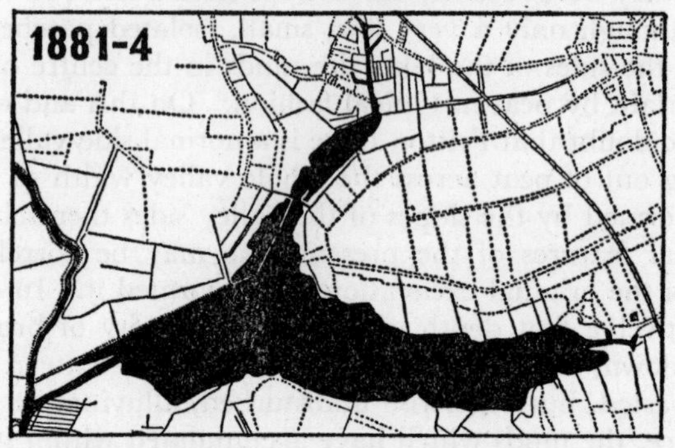

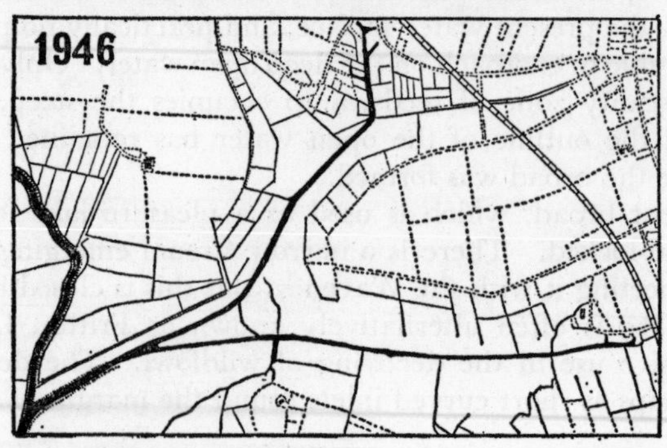

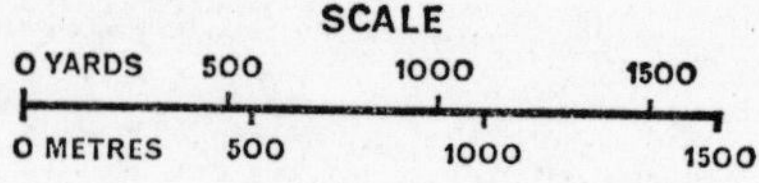

SUTTON BROAD

Sutton Broad, which, with its Stalham fork, occupies almost a side-valley position well up the main valley of the Ant, forms an excellent contrast to Fritton Lake of the Waveney. Whereas the tributary Fritton valley, lying well to the south-east of broadland, is deep with steeply rising sides, the Sutton-Stalham indentation, to the north-west of the system, is relatively shallow and bordered by only very gentle upland slopes. The basin of the broad itself is similarly shallow, and nowhere appears to be more than about six to seven feet deep. Towards the sides and end of the indentation, the bottom of the basin coincides with the valley floor itself, but farther towards the centre, the muds of the broad rest on solid peat.

The very obvious straight line forming the north-west limit of the open water in the 1841 map is the site of the Sutton-Stalham parish boundary. Borings have shown, however, that the buried muds of the broad extend some distance beyond this line, so that the original basin must have been somewhat larger than the 1841 outline. It is significant that the parish boundary itself was found to be marked by a ridge of residual solid peat standing up from the floor of the basin. Between 1841 and the 1881–4 survey, the broad was enlarged in the Stalham direction by shallow surface cuttings, and the second map of the series shows the narrow staddles of peat which were left in places between these cuttings and the main Stalham channel. The original basin of the broad and the adjacent shallow cuttings are now completely overgrown by reedswamp and fen, except for two narrow channels leading respectively to Sutton and Stalham staithes and kept open for the passage of craft.

Sutton Broad is therefore a good example of a broad with a relatively shallow basin which had become almost extinct by natural overgrowth by 1946. The broad itself now exists as such only in name, though the remaining narrow channels connect freely with the river and are open to holiday traffic.

Map 20. Barton Broad (Ant Valley)

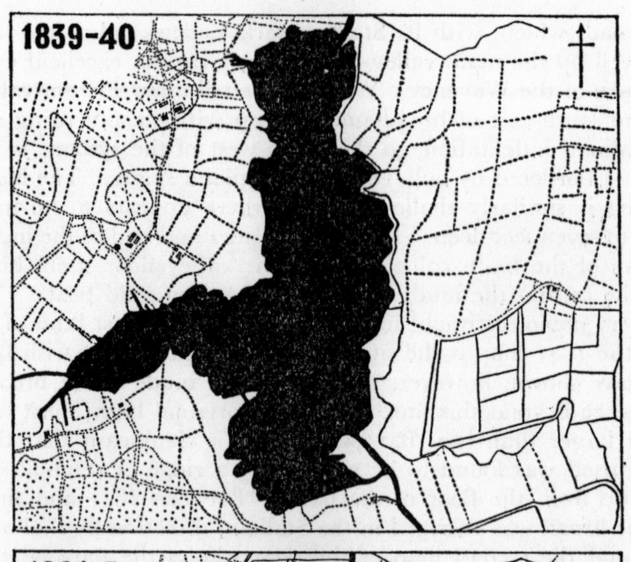

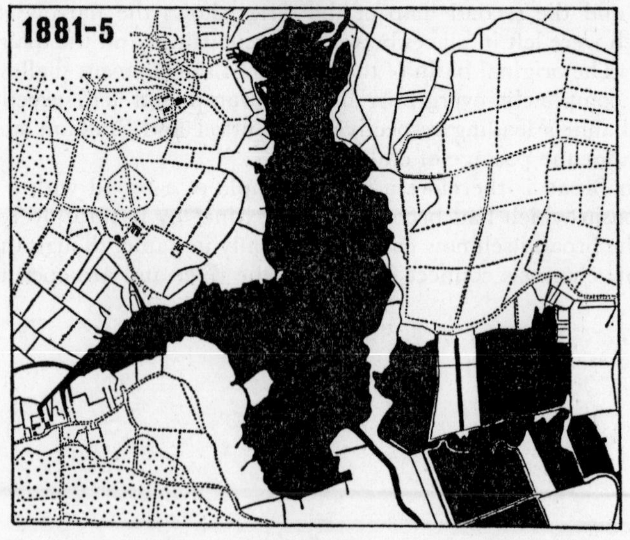

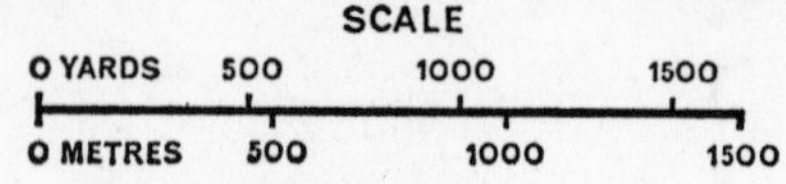

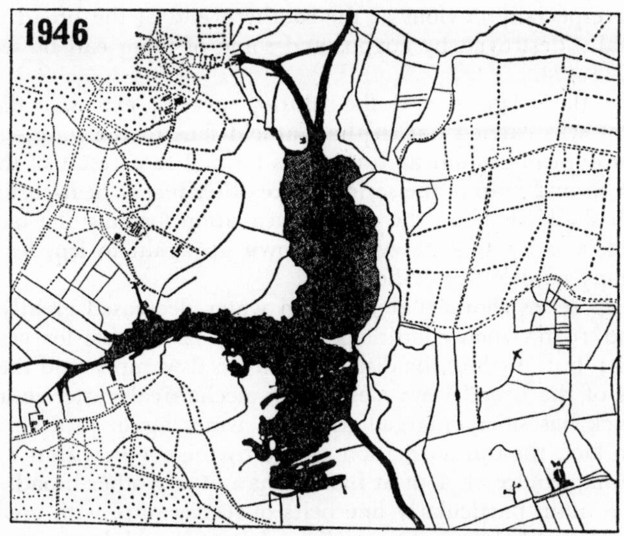

BARTON BROAD

Barton Broad, which is one of the largest and most popular sheets of water in broadland, has at first sight a rather anomalous position in relation to the river in whose valley it lies. Whereas the other broads are either by-passed by their associated rivers, or occupy small tributary valleys or indentations on the upland, Barton straddles the present course of the Ant so that the main river flows directly through it. This difference in position, however, is not a fundamental one, since the river has been artificially diverted into and out of the broad at some time in the past. The old channel of the Ant, which has been revealed by boring, lies overgrown and buried in the fens to the east of the broad, with its course only indicated by the line of the Barton-Catfield parish boundary; the sinuous dyke, following this line, is easily identified in Catfield Fen, south-east of the broad. The broad was therefore formerly by-passed by the river in typical manner, and its present position in the line of the main stream is secondary in origin.

The broad, which is shared between the parishes of Barton Turf and Irstead, lies in a basin of only moderate depth, reaching down to about nine feet in places. A special feature of the basin is the large number of shallowly-submerged remains of ridges of solid peat which lie in parallel series across the floor of the broad, with their direction changing slightly at the Barton-Irstead boundary. Parts of these ridges bear isolated patches of reedswamp, and their ends are often clothed with fingers of alder fen. They were especially obvious at the southern end of the broad until they were partially destroyed by coypu, and some of them can be seen in the 1946 map.

Between the 1839–40 and the 1881–5 surveys, extensive digging for surface peat was carried out in the Catfield fens to the south-east of the broad: the typical rectilinear turf-ponds formed as a result of this can be seen in the second map of the series. Like other recent peat-cuttings, these were much shallower than the earlier excavation forming the basin of the broad itself, and by 1946, they had grown up again to fen, leaving only a few swampy pools or ' pulk-holes '.

The map series shows that the open water decreased greatly between 1881–5 and 1946, when conditions were very favourable for vegetational overgrowth; but much of the discontinuous reedswamp round the east and west edges of the broad were cleared by mechanical cutter in 1949, and coypu attack has since enlarged the open water again to a very marked extent. In fact, the transformation caused by the coypu within a few short years is perhaps more obvious at Barton than in any other broad. Whereas it used to contain particularly fine belts of reedswamp, with great beds of true bulrush or ' bolder ' (*Schoenoplectus lacustris*) and lesser reedmace or ' gladden ' (*Typha angustifolia*), interspersed with extensive sheets of white and yellow water-lilies (*Nymphaea alba* and *Nuphar lutea*), these have now practically disappeared; moreover, the primary fen has also been seriously affected, and the edge of the carr itself is beginning to disintegrate in places, particularly Heron's Carr to the south-west of the broad.

In contrast to this large-scale disruption of the primary vegetation, the triangle of fen at the north end of the broad, separating the dyke to Barton Staithe from the main river channel entering the broad, is much less affected; but this patch of vegetation has been deliberately encouraged to grow up rapidly during the last sixty to seventy years by artificial piling and deposition of dredgings, and is therefore much more stable and less susceptible to coypu attack.

The larger part of the broad and surrounding fen and carr are the property of the Norfolk Naturalists' Trust, but the broad itself is freely open to pleasure boats.

Map 21. Alderfen Broad (Ant Valley)

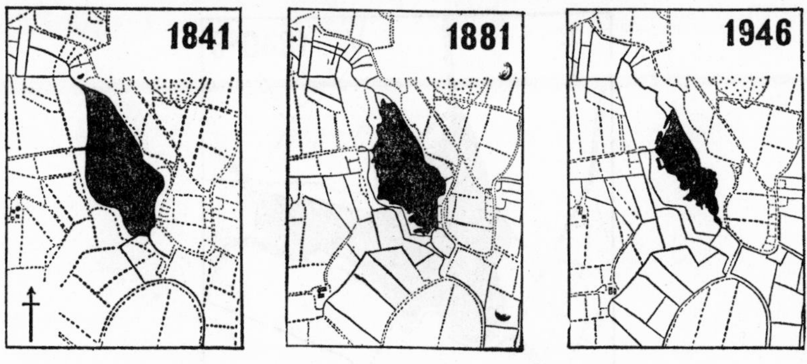

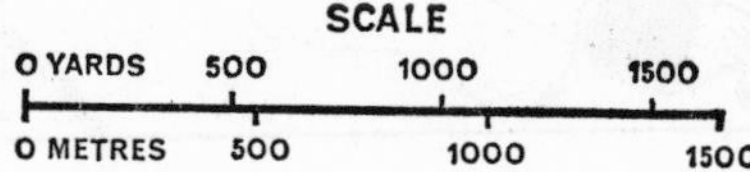

ALDERFEN BROAD

Lying in a small downstream tributary valley well back from the river, Alderfen Broad is a typical side-valley broad. It is separated from the Ant by drained grazing marshes, and, although an open connection between the broad and the river probably existed at some time in the past, Alderfen is now land-locked and sealed off from the high-level system by sluices.

The broad lies in a relatively shallow basin of a maximum depth of some seven feet, with muds filling the basin to about one to two feet below the present water surface. Borings have shown that the open water originally extended much farther upstream and in parts filled almost the whole width of the valley. The broad has therefore decreased greatly in size since it was formed; by 1946, its present area was less than half that of a century ago.

Like Barton, Alderfen Broad belongs to the Norfolk Naturalists' Trust. It is a well-known breeding ground for black-headed gulls.

Map 22. Horsey Mere and Blackfleet Broad (Thurne Valley)

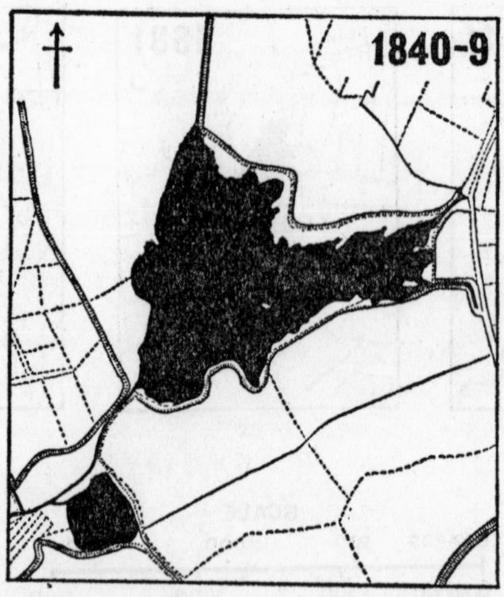

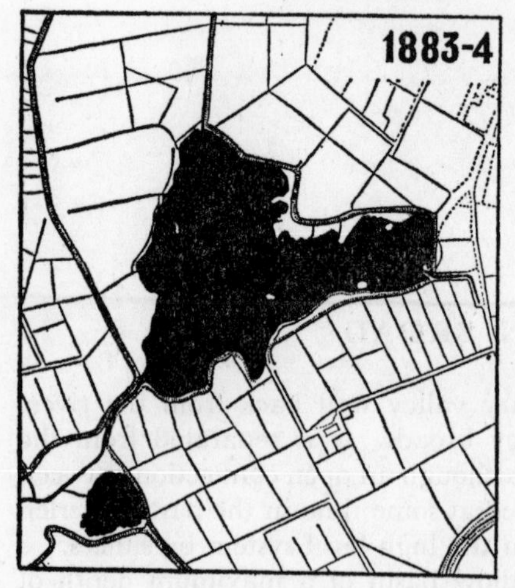

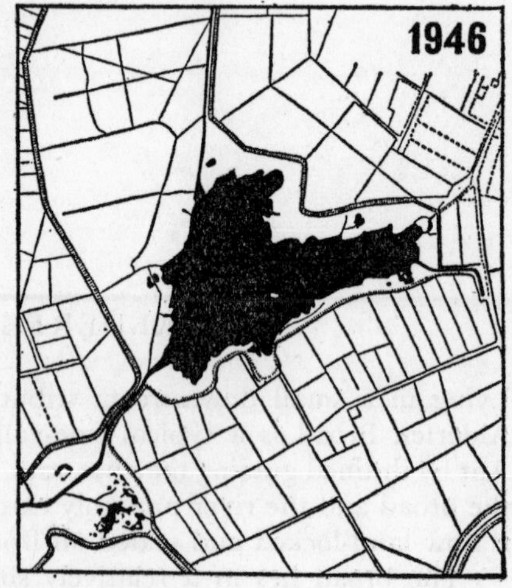

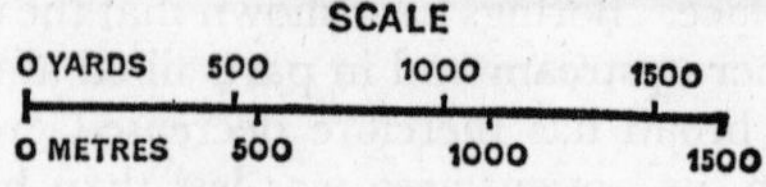

HORSEY MERE and BLACKFLEET BROAD

Horsey Mere lies in the centre of a vast, low-lying stretch of alluvial land separated only from the sea by a narrow barrier of sand-dunes. Sub-soil seepage from the sea makes Horsey the most brackish of all the Norfolk Broads, though the other broads in the vicinity—Martham Broad and the Hickling-Whiteslea-Heigham complex—have also a slight tendency to saltness.

The relationship of broad and river in this region is by no means clear, since the original hydrographic pattern has been greatly modified by extensive artificial disturbance of the natural drainage system at various times in the past. Parts of the original channel of the Thurne itself have become disused and supplanted by artificial cuts, while a former exit of the Hundred Stream—a tributary of the Thurne—to the sea south-east of Horsey was closed before the nineteenth century. To complicate the picture further, this exit itself may have been secondary in origin, by erosion and break-through of a low divide separating the river system from the sea.

Water draining from the alluvial land to the north of Horsey now enters the Mere by the Waxham Cut, and eventually reaches the lower part of the Thurne via the twisting Meadow Dyke and Heigham Sounds (map 5). Since the whole length of the connection is unimpeded by sluices or other barriers, Horsey Mere forms part of the high-level system, and the surface of its water stands two or three feet above the level of the surrounding drained and wasted grazing marshes. The roughly triangular sheet of water is closely embanked on two of its three sides, but on the west, where the embankment is farther away, the broad is bounded by a wide stretch of wet fen intersected by dykes which are open to the broad.

The basin of Horsey is only five to six feet deep, and its floor is formed partly by peat and partly by estuarine clay. The decrease in size of the broad between 1883–4 and 1946 is less great than might be expected in such a shallow basin, but frequent artificial clearing of the encroaching vegetation has almost certainly been largely responsible for this. Horsey Mere has now been taken over by the National Trust under special agreement, but is open to pleasure boats.

To the south-west of Horsey Mere lies the small Blackfleet Broad, which occupies a by-passed position relative to Meadow Dyke and is connected with the latter by a narrow channel. This broad was almost obliterated by growth of reedswamp by 1946.

Map 23. Hickling Broad, Whiteslea and Heigham Sounds (Thurne Valley)

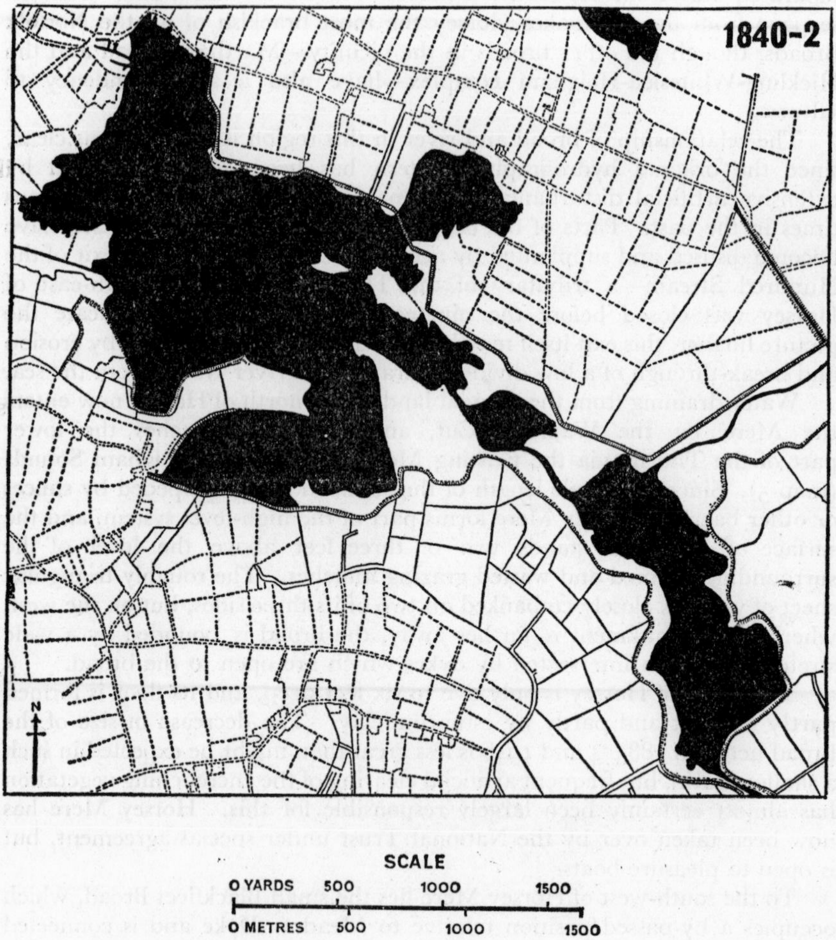

1840-2

N

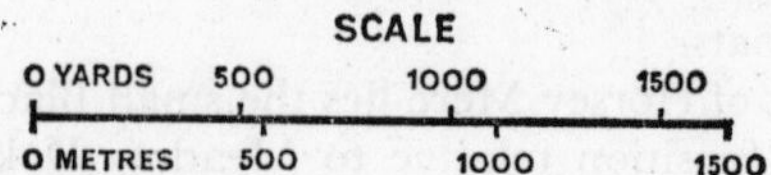

Map 23. Hickling Broad, Whiteslea and Heigham Sounds (*continued*)

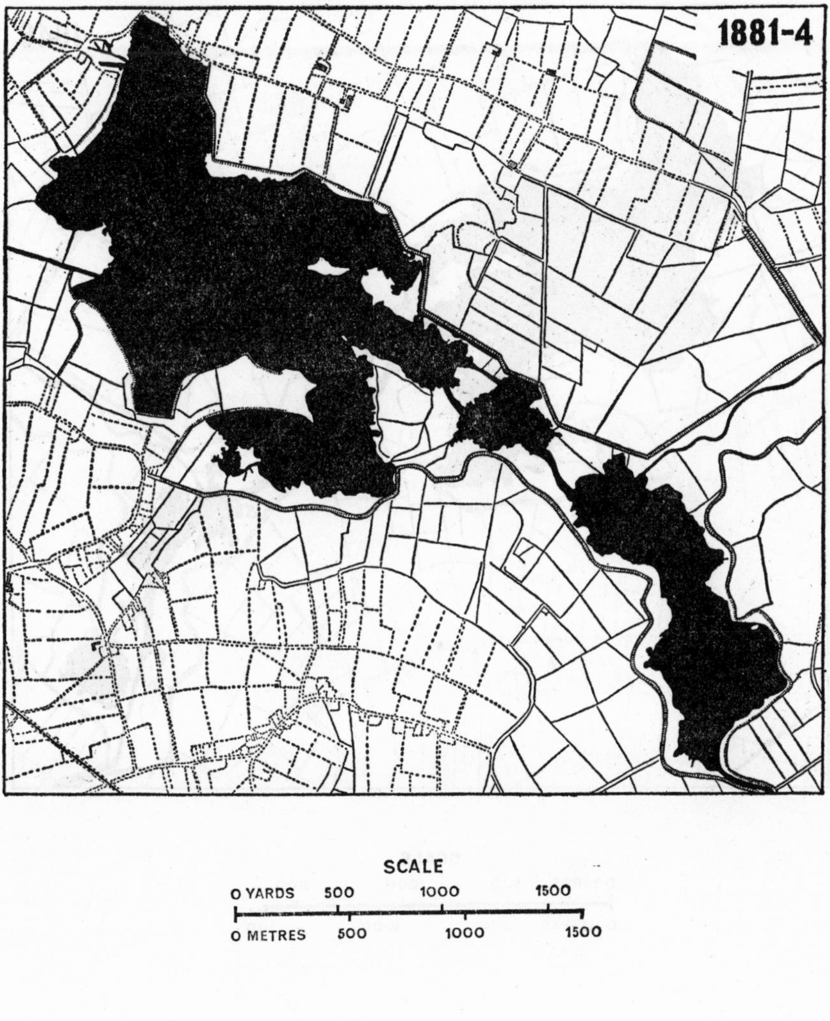

1881-4

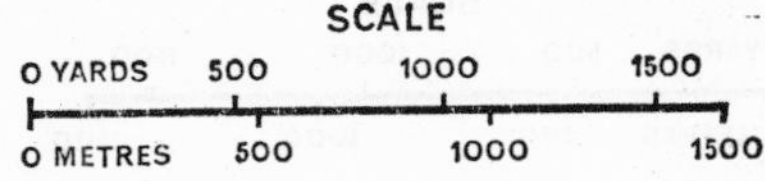

Map 23. Hickling Broad, Whiteslea and Heigham Sounds (*continued*)

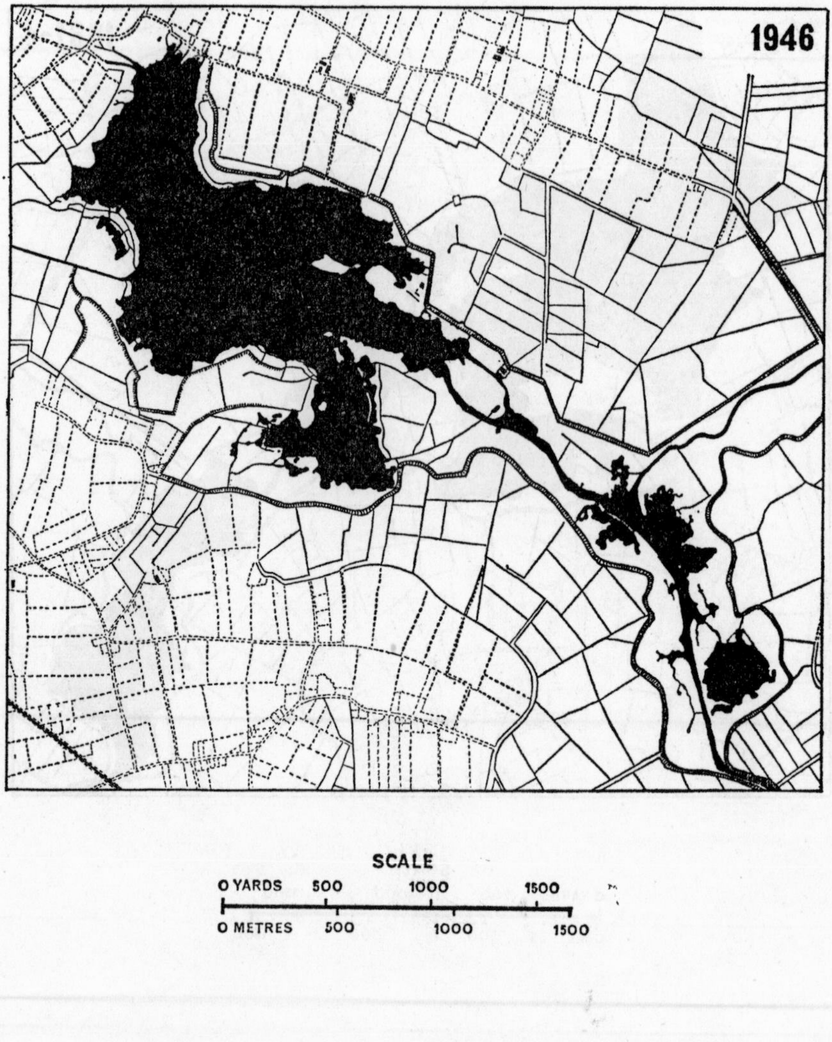

1946

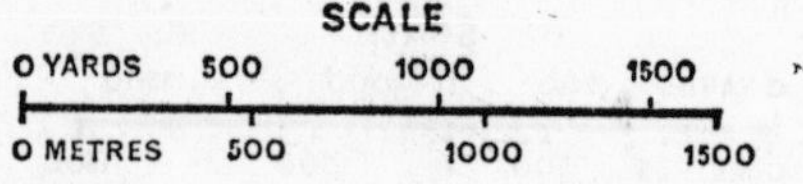

HICKLING BROAD, WHITESLEA and HEIGHAM SOUNDS

Finally, we come to the great expanse of Hickling—in some ways perhaps the best known of all the Norfolk Broads—and the associated stretches of Whiteslea and Heigham Sounds. Like Horsey, their waters stand high in the midst of drained alluvial flats, with an embankment separating the high-level broads from the low-level land around.

Borings have shown that the three units of the series—Hickling, Whiteslea and Heigham—have always been distinct from one another, separated by blocks of solid peat and clay cut through only by narrow channels. Although these three stretches together still represent the largest area of open water in broadland, their basins are the shallowest to be found, being rarely more than five to six feet deep in any part except the dredged sailing channels. However, steep-sided islands and peninsulas of undisturbed deposits project upwards from their level floors to show that, despite their shallowness, their basins have been excavated in the alluvium in the same way as the hollows forming the deeper and more typical broads.

In much of the western part of Hickling, the former shallow valley fill appears to have been removed in its entirety, so that here the marginal parts of the broad lie directly over the clayey sands and gravels of the original gently sloping glacial valley; but where the valley deepens towards the centre and towards the eastern end, the broad overlies brushwood peat in normal manner. In contrast, Heigham Sounds and parts of Whiteslea are underlain by estuarine clay, which extends up the valley as a thinning wedge roughly as far as the mouth of Hickling; and whereas the Hickling basin appears to have been made by the excavation of peat deposits beyond the limits of the clay, in Heigham Sounds the clay itself seems to have been the chief material which was removed.

Although the maps show that much overgrowth took place between 1840–2 and 1946, the total size of the open water is so great that the proportionate diminution in area is less striking than in many of the smaller broads. It is probably significant ecologically that organic mud accumulation and reedswamp encroachment (until the arrival of the coypu) seemed to be taking place more rapidly towards the south-east end of the system, which is traversed by the slowly-flowing headwaters from Waxham and Horsey, than in Hickling itself, which forms a blind arm in the present drainage pattern of the Thurne valley.

The Hickling-Whiteslea-Heigham chain of broads is particularly noted for its ornithological interest. The greater part of it is now a National Nature Reserve administered under an agreement between the Norfolk Naturalists' Trust and the Nature Conservancy, but there is free access to river craft.

APPENDIX B

INSECTS OF THE BROADS

by E. A. Ellis

GRASSHOPPERS (*Orthoptera*) by A. E. Ellis

Out of three families of grasshoppers, the long-horned bush crickets (Tettigoniidae), the little grouse-locusts or ground-hoppers (Tetrigidae) and the short-horned grasshoppers (Acrididae), are represented in the broads district by less than a dozen species. One of the Tettigoniids, *Conocephalus dorsalis*, an unobtrusive green insect with very long, slender antennae, is a common inhabitant of the fens around the broads, where it lives amongst sedges, rushes, long grass and bog myrtle, particularly where the vegetation is luxuriant. Though unable to fly, it can leap about amongst herbage with elusive agility and it is difficult to see owing to its protective coloration. The bush-cheep (*Pholidoptera griseoaptera*), the only other member of this family which occurs commonly in the district, frequents drier situations, such as hedges bordering the lokes and clumps of nettles, brambles and coarse herbage on the marsh walls. The bush-cheep, which is at any rate partly carnivorous and eats marsh snails on occasion, is more often heard than seen, being particularly vocal late on summer evenings, when the hedges resound with chirping. There is a ventriloquial quality in the ' song ' which makes it hard to track down the performer, and some people, who are deaf to high notes, are quite unaware of the presence of these insects. In general appearance the bush-cheep rather resembles a cricket, but is brown in colour, the hind legs are comparatively long, the anal cerci short and inconspicuous, the wings absent and the elytra, which in the male are sound-producing organs, reduced and scale-like.

Three of the four British species of ground-hoppers occur in the broads district: *Tetrix subulata*, *T. ceperoi* and *T. vittata*. These are the smallest of our grasshoppers, distinguished by the great extension of the pronotum (the shield covering the first segment of the thorax), which reaches to or beyond the tip of the abdomen and protects the folded wings, the elytra being vestigial. Tetrigidae differ from the majority of grasshoppers in hibernating, mature individuals being in evidence in early spring. They live on bare ground, the first two species in damp places and the last usually in dry habitats, though all have been found together. These insects are so well camouflaged that until they hop it is almost impossible to detect them against their normal background of soil, and as soon as they alight they disappear as though by magic. Their food consists of minute algae which grow on the surface of moist earth. *Tetrix ceperoi* was added to the British list in 1940, and in East Anglia has hitherto been recorded only from Surlingham. It closely resembles *T. subulata*, which is frequent in the broadland marshes. These little grasshoppers often leap accidentally into water, when they swim proficiently by the ordinary jumping action of the hind legs.

Amongst the Acrididae, *Omocestus viridulus*, the prevailing colour of which is green, is common in the fens and marshes, where its characteristic ' song ' is usually to be heard on sunny days in late summer. The ubiquitous and variable *Chorthippus bicolor* is sometimes found in its company, but prefers drier situations; a green variety which is not uncommon is liable to be mistaken at first sight for *O. viridulus*. It has been suggested that the colouring tends to match the background, and presumably varieties which are conspicuously out of harmony with their surroundings would tend to be weeded out by natural enemies, such as birds and hunting-wasps. This subject calls for further investigation in the field combined with controlled experiments. Another species of this genus, *Ch. albomarginatus*, occurs by some of the broads and rivers, usually within a few miles of the coast; its favourite habitat is short turf by the edges of footpaths. *Mecostethus grossus*, a large green and brown grasshopper with crimson and yellow hind legs, which inhabits wet fens amongst bog myrtle, sedges and rank grass, has been found at Irstead, Sutton, Barton, Catfield and Horning. It is a rare species, known from a few scattered localities in the south of England and in Ireland, and is recorded from Scotland. Though conspicuous in flight, this grasshopper is almost impossible to find amongst the dense vegetation it frequents. It varies greatly in size (body length 12 to 39 mm.), and is full grown in August and September.

STONE FLIES (*Plecoptera*)

Nearly all the British stone-flies breed in streams, rivers or lakes with stony beds; thus it is not to be expected that many species will occur in the broads or their slow-flowing rivers and dyke systems. The only common and widespread species here appears to be *Nemoura variegata*, which frequents the waterways and fens in spring. *Nemoura dubitans*, a rare and peculiarly East Anglian insect, has been noticed in early spring at Barton and Wheatfen Broads. *Leuctra geniculata* frequents the upper reaches of the broadland rivers.

MAYFLIES (*Ephemeroptera*)

Of the forty-seven British species of Ephemeroptera, only thirteen are known from the broads. This can be explained by the fact that most of these insects inhabit running streams and fast flowing rivers, while others are largely restricted to the slightly acidic waters of moorland tarns and lakes. The only large mayfly present here is *Ephemera danica* and this occurs mainly in the upper reaches of the local rivers and is present only on the fringe of broadland. The remaining species would be termed ' duns ' by fly-fishermen and are as follows: *Leptophlebia marginata*, *Habrophlebia fusca*, *Caenis robusta*, *C. horaria*, *Baetis pumilus*, *B. niger*, *B. vernus*, *B. tenax*, *B. bioculatus*, *Centroptilum luteolum*, *Cloen dipterum* and *C. simile*. Dr. T. T. Macan established that *Caenis robusta* occurred in Britain as the result of breeding specimens from nymphs collected in the Norfolk Broads in 1953; previously it was known to breed in slowly flowing waters in Holland. The tidal broads of the Yare are richer in ephemerids than those of the Bure and its tributaries, probably because there is greater aeration of the water due to rise and fall and currents in the former.

DRAGONFLIES (*Odonata*)

Of the large powerful fliers, the earliest to appear on the wing in May is *Brachytron pratense;* it is present in all parts of the district and is something of a wanderer. The teneral females have been observed to leave the sites of their emergence temporarily for several days immediately after first taking wing. The nymphs have been found in slightly brackish water on occasion. Mated specimens have been seen struggling in the water after losing control of their wings in a high wind. *Libellula quadrimaculata* appears normally towards the end of May and is common and well distributed. *L. depressa*, strictly a pond dragonfly, is rare in broadland; even the very slight movement of water in dykes draining the marsh levels appears sufficient to discourage it. The more slender-bodied *L. fulva*, on the other hand, is a familiar sight from the end of June until early August, quartering the marshes drained by the rivers Bure, Ant and Thurne; oddly enough, it is not known in the Yare valley and there is only a single record of its occurrence along the Waveney.

The metallic green *Cordulia aenea* is distinctly rare in broadland, having been noticed at Horning (where breeding was proved) and at Hickling, in June. *Orthetrum cancellatum*, which is on the wing during the same period as *Libellula fulva* and is apt to be confused with that species where the male is concerned, can be distinguished by its lack of brown patches at the bases of its wings. It is a commoner insect than *fulva* and its range extends to the Yare and Waveney and to the lower reaches of the Bure. It tends to be sedentary and to have a special fondness for settling on light-coloured objects. The males are not noticeably aggressive towards one another as they share flight-space over a restricted territory; they are seldom seen patrolling more than a few inches above the surface of the water. A nymph of *O. cancellatum* taken from a dyke adjoining the river Thurne was found to spend the winter in a state of complete inactivity under a layer of mud and algae, in company with three gammarids; in mid-March it became lively and ate the gammarids. When egg-laying, the female of this species is not normally attended by her partner; she strikes the surface of the water repeatedly with the tip of her abdomen and selects the middle of a dyke rather than the sides for this purpose.

The first *Aeshna* to appear is *Ae. isosceles* (Pl. XIV); it is usually on the wing by the middle of June and frequents waterways of the Ant and Thurne and dykes of the Bure below Acle. It is most abundant in the neighbourhood of Catfield and Hickling, where it survived the salt-water flooding of 1938, and its most characteristic breeding places are dykes and broads where the water-soldier (*Stratiotes aloides*) grows. Later in the summer its place is taken by the vigorous and ubiquitous *Aeshna grandis*, which is an exceedingly common broadland insect. When seen in flight, *isosceles* is distinguishable from *grandis* by its very large thorax, even when its other special features, the green eyes, duller wings and the yellow triangle on the second segment of its abdomen, cannot be discerned. The aggressively roving habit of *grandis* is lacking in *isosceles* and when the territories of the two overlap and sparring occurs, *grandis* has the advantage.

Aeshna juncea is seen from time to time along the Ant and Thurne, flying in August and September. It keeps very much to the waterside, maintaining a regular beat along the edges of reed-beds and over dykes and pools. *Ae. cyanea* occurs throughout the broads area, from July to September, and is very much of a wanderer, the males especially often travelling far from water. *Ae. mixta* is often common from late August to October and is fond of flying high along the sheltered side of a wood or carr, frequently alighting on the trees; but it also hunts along the margins of reedswamps fringing the broads; it is a well-known migrant, but also breeds here, at least occasionally.

By far the commonest of the darter dragonflies is *Sympetrum striolatum*, which abounds by all the broads, rivers and dykes from mid-July to the middle or even the end of October. It has been seen ovipositing in brackish pools on occasion. One of its favourite habits is to bask in the sunshine on bare patches of soil; it also perches frequently on tall plants, trees and fences. *S. sanguineum* is much rarer than *striolatum*, although it is locally abundant in a number of fens in some summers, notably in the Ant valley. This species migrates frequently and it is probable that breeding stations are established from time to time in Norfolk. Although the males of *sanguineum* and a large proportion of the males of *striolatum* have red abdomens, those of *sanguineum* can be recognised easily by their carmine tint and the club-shaped tip to the abdomen. The rare migrant *S. flaveolum*, distinguished by its yellow wing-bases, has colonised broadland occasionally in recent years; in one locality in the Ant valley a breeding colony is known to have persisted for at least three successive summers.

The more delicate Zygopterid dragonflies, fluttering only weakly over the water and marsh vegetation, are seen more readily at close quarters than most of the more active Anisopterids, and their glittering gauze wings and often bright blue or red thread-like bodies attract the eyes of even the most casual visitor exploring the broads. The red-bodied *Pyrrhosoma nymphula* is the first species to appear and continues on the wing from the beginning of May until the end of June; it is common and widespread. The only other red Zygopterid, *Ceriagrion tenellum*, which flies in July, is a Mediterranean species maintaining itself precariously in the British Isles; it has been noticed twice in the broads district (at Dilham in 1903 and at Acle more recently). *Ischnura elegans* abounds throughout the district, frequenting the broads themselves and most of the smaller waterways and marsh drains, including those where the water is brackish near the coast. Females of all the variously coloured forms described for this country occur here.

Agrion splendens, a metallic green-bodied insect, the male of which has dark, iridescent bands across its wings, belongs rather to the upper reaches of the rivers than to the sluggish waters of the broads, where it has only a patchy marginal distribution. The red-eyed *Erythromma naias*, appearing from June to August, is locally abundant at a number of places in all the main river areas of broadland. The female becomes completely submerged at times when ovipositing on water weeds, but is usually supported by the male holding on from above. *Enallagma cyathigerum* is one of the commonest of the small blue-bodied dragonflies and is particularly numerous in the neighbourhood of the Thurne and along parts of the Yare, flying from June to September. *Coenagrion puella* (June to August) and *C. pulchellum* (May to August) are both widely distributed and common; there seems to be a tendency for *puella* to become the more numerous at the localities farthest inland. *C. armatum* (Pl. XIV) is a very rare and local insect, in Britain confined to a small part of the broads, where it was noticed first in 1903, by F. Balfour Browne. It is on the wing usually from mid-May to mid-June and has its headquarters in the vicinity of the river Ant; a very few specimens have been recorded also from Hickling and one of the Bure Broads.

In compiling this account of the dragonflies, I have made extensive use of notes supplied by Messrs. E. T. Daniels and A. E. Ellis.

BUGS (Hemiptera: Heteroptera)

The list presented here is based on twenty years' study of these insects at Wheatfen Broad, where most types of broadland vegetation are represented. Records from other broads are included where available.

CYDNIDAE

Thyreocoris scarabaeoides: very local, largely a chalk insect, found here on banks where chalky boulder clay outwash flanks the river valleys.

Sehirus bicolor: rather local, associated with white deadnettle and stinging nettle on waste ground.

PENTATOMIDAE (Shield Bugs)

Eurygaster testudinarius: rare, Wheatfen and Upton Broads, in very wet fens.

Piezodorus lituratus: not uncommon, attached to gorse bushes.

Pentatoma rufipes: common on various trees.

Acanthosoma haemorrhoidale: found occasionally on sallows.

Elasmostethus interstinctus: on birch, alder and oak.

Elasmucha grisea: common on various trees, including alder and birch. The female broods over the young.

Picromerus bidens: a true fen insect, locally common; gregarious when young. Usually to be found in pairs from August to mid-October and often to be observed sucking the juices of caterpillars.

Troilus luridus: common on various trees and bushes and predatory on other insects, including ladybirds.

ARADIDAE

Aradus depressus: rare, on tree trunks.

NEIDIDAE

Neides tipularius: although typically an insect of dry grassland and sandhills, it has been found occasionally on marsh walls, associated with gorse bushes.

Berytinus minor: amongst grass roots on marsh banks.

LYGAEIDAE

Cymus claviculus: recorded from marshes in east Norfolk (Edwards).

C. melanocephalus: as above.

C. glandicolor: commonly associated with sedges, especially *Carex paniculata* and *C. appropinquata*, in fens.

Kleidocerys resedae: rather common on alder and birch.

Ischnodemus sabuleti: this insect has extended its range north-eastward from the Thames counties to reach East Anglia very recently. It made its first appearance in Suffolk at Flatford Mill in 1953 and its first in Norfolk at Wheatfen Broad in 1954, while in west Norfolk it was first noticed near Thetford in 1956. In all these localities it occurs gregariously on the rond-grass (*Glyceria maxima*) but is to be found attacking other grasses and sedges also, to a variable extent, where they are closely associated with the *Glyceria*. Brachypterous specimens reach maturity in July and macropterous specimens are rare at that time; in autumn the proportions are sometimes reversed. After walking through a marsh inhabited by these bugs, the writer has found some of the insects in his rubber boots and trouser turn-ups on reaching home; it is possible that naturalists have been responsible for the spread of *I. sabuleti* from one marshy locality to another in recent years and in this connection it may be pointed out that two of the East Anglian sites newly colonised are on nature reserves, while the third is in a locality frequently visited by botanists.

Chilacis typhae: locally abundant in ' pokers ' of both greater and lesser reed-maces. Adult and immature bugs may be found living together at all seasons, in varying proportions. A disintegrating seed-head of *Typha latifolia* examined in July was found to be harbouring eight imagines and about one thousand nymphs of *C. typhae*. The main exodus of mature insects takes place in August and September, when fresh seed-heads are ready for colonisation.

Heterogaster urticae: although more commonly associated with the small annual nettle in gardens, this insect is found here occasionally with the stinging nettle on river banks and staithes.

Pachybrachius fracticollis: a true fen insect, commonly associated with sedges, including *Carex elata* and *C. paniculata*.

Megalonotus praetextatus: typically an insect of dunes and dry grassland, but has been found here in damp woodland.

M. chiragra: another mainly coastal sand insect found rarely in a wood adjoining Wheatfen Broad, approximately thirteen miles inland.

Acompus rufipes: a characteristic fen species, widespread and abundant. Adults have been found in every month and the insects hibernate in marsh litter, flood-rubbish and sedge tussocks. Macropterous specimens are rare.

Stygnocoris rusticus: seen occasionally as a visitor to fen flowers.

S. pedestris: a common upland insect but rare in fens.

Peritrechus sylvestris: inhabits dry grassy places, but has been found hibernating in fen woodland.

Drymus sylvaticus:
D. brunneus: } common amongst dead leaves on the ground in woods and carrs.

Scolopostethus affinis:
S. thomsoni: } commonly present in waterside nettle-beds.

S. decoratus: has been found hibernating in carrs.

S. puberulus: mainly a coast insect, but found occasionally on inland marshes; it has been found hibernating in stems of reed-mace, with *S. thomsoni*.

Taphropeltus contractus: a single specimen taken at Wheatfen Broad by E. C. Bedwell.

Gastrodes grossipes: not uncommon on the bark of Scots pines, including those planted in exceptionally wet situations near broads.

PIESMIDAE

Piesma maculata: common on grassy banks and where fens are fringed by heathland and birch scrub.

P. quadrata: normally a salt-marsh insect, but found also on Chenopodiaceae on river and marsh banks inland.

TINGIDAE (Lace Bugs)

Acalypta carinata: rare, in moss on fens.

Derephysa foliacea: on marginal ground, rather rare, associated with ivy.

Tingis ampliata: common on thistles, including those of fens, and found hibernating in marsh litter.

T. cardui: common on spear thistles on drained marshes and banks; usually hibernating beneath the lower leaves of their host plants.

Monanthia humuli: common on water forget-me-not and often found hibernating in large numbers in sedge tussocks on fens.

REDUVIIDAE

Empicoris vagabundus: a delicate, very long-legged bug, much resembling a resting mosquito in form and said to prey upon gnats and other insects resting on tree trunks. It has been found in woods near some of the broads.

NABIDAE (Assassin Bugs)

Nabis ferus: common and widely distributed. Although usually considered an insect of dry habitats, this is not true of it here, where it frequents fens, carrs and woodland in some abundance. It attains maturity in July or August and hibernates.

N. flavomarginatus: rather rare in fens, where its prey includes the skullcap sawfly (*Athalia scutellariae*).

N. lativentris: common in woods and bushy places and not often found in the wetter parts of the marshes. The nymph looks very like an ant and matures in August, afterwards hibernating.

N. apterus: rather common on various trees, including those of the fen carrs. The rare macropterous form of the female was found at Wheatfen Broad in September 1941 following a hot summer in which this species was specially abundant.

N. limbatus: very common on the general vegetation of fens and often climbs bushes and trees in the carrs. Adults are seen from the end of July until the end of October, when they die, leaving eggs to carry the species through the winter.

N. lineatus: a true fen insect, fairly widely distributed but not common; the adults are found from August to October.

ANTHOCORIDAE

Temnostethus pusillus: rare, on lichen-encrusted trunks of ash trees.

Anthocoris confusus: very common and widely distributed on trees and at the flowers of marsh plants; it is predacious, feeding on aphids and mites.

A. nemoralis: common, especially on sallow bushes; occasionally found on marsh flowers; it attacks small insects and mites and has been known to feed on small spiders.

A. sarothamni: not uncommonly associated with broom, on which it attacks aphids.

A. nemorum: very common in all except purely aquatic habitats and found on all types of vegetation; the nymphs are predatory.

Tetraphleps bicuspis: a predaceous insect usually found on conifers; rare in fen carrs.

Orius niger, *O. majusculus* and *O. minutus:* small predacious bugs fairly common and widely distributed on trees and bushes in a variety of habitats.

Lyctocoris campestris: locally common in marsh litter and sometimes found on honeysuckle. It sucks the juices of other insects and mites and occasionally ' bites ' humans.

Xylocoris cursitans: found living under the bark of a variety of trees; it has been noticed only rarely here, probably because of its unobtrusive habits.

MIRIDAE

Pithanus markeli: fairly common in fens as well as in salt marshes and dry grassy places.

Pantilius tunicatus: not uncommon on the foliage of birch trees; also found on alders in the carrs.

Phytocoris tiliae, *P. longipennis*, *P. dimidiatus* and *P. reuteri* are all met with commonly on a variety of trees in wet as well as dry habitats.

Adelphocoris ticinensis: restricted to fens, where it is locally common and often closely associated with purple loosestrife, water-mint and bog myrtle. It is a conspicuously graceful red insect.

Calocoris ochromelas: common on oaks and found on various marsh plants near woods in spring and early summer.

C. norvegicus: common and widely distributed on herbaceous plants, in marshes as well as on the uplands.

Miris striatus: apparently rather rare, associated with oak and hawthorn.

Stenotus binotatus: rather common on low-growing plants in fens and on grassy banks.

Lygus pabulinus: very common in a wide variety of habitats, but most regularly associated with nettle-beds.

L. viridis: noticed occasionally on alders.

L. spinolae: not uncommon on various marsh plants and found occasionally on nettles and wild hops.

L. lucorum: noticed occasionally in fens, where it is sometimes attached to hemp agrimony, purple loosestrife and meadow-sweet.

L. pratensis: common and widely distributed over the marshes and in the undergrowth of carrs and woods; hibernating under dead leaves, sticks, moss, ferns and evergreens.

L. cervinus: an arboreal insect, found on sallows in the marshes as well as on a variety of trees in drier woodlands.

L. campestris: commonly associated with angelica.

L. kalmii: common on nettles and amongst fen vegetation and found on bog myrtle and alder. It often visits marsh flowers.

Poeciloscytus palustris: a fen insect, locally common on marsh bedstraw. The adults appear in July and usually die by mid-August, the males disappearing before the females.

Systratiotus nigrita: local, on goosegrass (*Galium aparine*) growing with nettles on staithes.

Liocoris tripustulatus: common in nettle beds in waterside habitats and has been found hibernating in reed-mace stems.

Camptobrochis lutescens: a fairly common arboreal insect.

Deraeocoris ruber: a predatory bug, apparently not common here in low-lying country. It is found occasionally in waterside nettle beds.

Rhopalotomus ater: this insect turns up in abundance periodically in fens, but cannot be relied upon to appear in the same locality two years running.

Capsodes gothicus: a rare insect in Norfolk; three specimens were found on water mint at Wheatfen Broad in August 1939.

Acetropis gimmerthali: local, in rushy fens.

Stenodema calcaratum: common and widespread on grasses in fens as well as in drier habitats. At Wheatfen Broad, where a prolonged study of this insect has been made, adult specimens have been found in the marshes throughout the year. They exhibit two colour-phases; brown imagines produced from August to October hibernate (both sexes) and reappear in late April or May. The females turn green in May and June; but though the males persist almost to the end of June, they remain brown. Adults from June-July larvae appear from mid-July onward and are mostly brown, but a proportion are green in both sexes. These green specimens do not live to hibernate and are presumably the parents of August-September larvae which are found.

S. trispinosum: locally common in fens, where it is found mainly on sedges and occasionally on grasses, including reed. It is pre-eminently a Norfolk Broads insect, but has been found also in a few localities in Cambridgeshire, Essex, Surrey and Suffolk. A lengthy study of its habits at Wheatfen Broad has shown that it is to some extent double-brooded. The adult insects are at first brown and are of this colour during their hibernation. At the beginning of April they become active and commonly resort to the sedge *Carex elata* as its flower spikes are developing. The females turn green very quickly, while the males remain brown and usually die by mid-May. The females later visit other sedges as they come into flower. Eggs are laid from May onward and larvae appear early in June. Adults of the new brood begin to appear in July; they are brown on emergence, but some of both sexes quickly turn green and produce a second brood, while others remain brown and do not breed until after hibernation.

S. laevigatum: common and widely distributed in grassy places and less frequently found in fens. Both sexes hibernate in the brown phase and the females turn green in late May and June; some males show a trace of green coloration in June. No green specimens have been seen later than July and there is no evidence that this insect is double-brooded.

Notostira erratica: Common in grassy places in both dry and damp situations.

Teratocoris antennatus: locally frequent in wet muddy situations, under reeds and rushes. It is also an insect of salt marshes.

T. saundersi: local, in the wetter parts of fens and often associated with the grass *Glyceria maxima* in the Yare valley.

Leptopterna dolobrata: common on grasses in fens from June to August.

Monalocoris filicis: common on various ferns, including lady, male and broad buckler ferns in the carrs; it has been found here occasionally on the marsh fern, *Thelypteris palustris*, in fens.

Bryocoris pteridis: less frequently found than the preceding species, but fairly widely distributed on male and buckler ferns, in carrs.

Dicyphus epilobii: common everywhere on great hairy willowherb.

D. stachydis: common on nettles and woundwort.

Camptoneura virgula: common on various trees and bushes.

Cyllecoris histrionicus: rather rare, on oaks.

C. flavoquadrimaculatus: common and widespread on oaks, in May and June.

Blepharidopterus angulatus: common on various trees and found chiefly on alders in the carrs.

Mecomma ambulans: local, in rushy fens and on ferns in the carrs.

Cyrtorhinus flaveolus: local, in the wetter parts of fens. It is associated with clumps of rushes.

Orthotylus flavinervis: rather local, on sallows and alders.

O. tenellus: collected once from buckthorn at Wheatfen.

O. nassatus: local, on sallows.

(A more comprehensive study of the species of *Orthotylus* living in this district needs to be undertaken since the publication of T. R. E. Southwood's account of the morphology and taxonomy of this genus in *Trans. Roy. Ent. Soc.*, 104, 415–49, 1953.)

Capsus meriopterus: common and widespread on most types of vegetation in a variety of habitats; it sucks the juices of plants and preys upon mites and insects; it has been found to suck eggs of the swallowtail butterfly (*Entomologist's Monthly Magazine*, 42, 280).

Malacocoris chlorizans: local, on various trees and shrubs, including alders in carrs.

Halticus apterus: local, in fens, where it has been found associated with tufted vetch on several occasions. It is a species with a markedly southern distribution in Britain and is not usually regarded as a marsh insect.

Harpocera thoracica: common in May and June in a variety of situations, including sallows and low-growing plants on fens.

Orthonotus rufifrons: rare, on nettles in damp woods.

Phylus melanocephalus: local, on oaks.

P. coryli: rather rare, on hazels.

Psallus ambiguus: fairly common and widespread but chiefly associated with apple trees.

P. betuleti: local, on birch.

P. variabilis: rather common on oak, but is found on a variety of other deciduous trees in the surrounding countryside.

P. lepidus: apparently uncommon, associated with ash.

P. varians: locally common on oak.

P. diminutus: found occasionally on oak.

P. roseus: locally abundant on sallow bushes.

P. salicellus: apparently rare; specimens swept in woodland at Wheatfen were probably associated with hazel.

Plagiognathus chrysanthemi: common and widely distributed on herbaceous plants of many kinds, including those growing in fens.

P. arbustorum: very common on nettles and found on many other kinds of plants all over the fens and in open spaces in carrs; it is most abundant in August.

Sthenarus roseri: a local fen insect found on sallows in the broads district (J. Edwards); not recorded from Wheatfen.

HYDROMETRIDAE (Water Measurers)

Hydrometra stagnorum: common and widespread round the margins of broads and on dykes. These slender, longlegged, blackish-brown insects lurk under waterside plants and creep out on the surface of the water in search of drowned and spent insects. They often hibernate many yards from the nearest water, sometimes climbing a little way up tree trunks in the carrs and hiding in crevices in the bark.

H. gracilenta: very local, in swampy carrs fringing broads of the river Ant, mainly where tussock sedges are growing in shallow water amongst alders and sallows. This species was first recorded as a British insect, found at Barton Broad, by G. A. Walton, 1938: A Water Bug new to Great Britain—*Hydrometra gracilenta* Horvath, *Entomologist's Monthly Magazine* 74, 272–5. It has since been noticed in a few other broadland localities, but appears to be absent from the more tidal broads, such as those of the Yare valley.

GERRIDAE (Pond Skaters)

Gerris thoracicus: common and widely distributed on still and slowly moving waters.

G. lacustris: very common and widely distributed.

G. odontogaster: locally common.

G. argentatus: local and fairly rare.

VELIIDAE

Microvelia reticulata: common and widely distributed on the surfaces of sheltered, weedy dykes and in sheltered bays of broads.

M. umbricola: locally abundant in somewhat shaded peaty ditches and inlets of broads in the Ant, Bure and Yare valleys. It was first recorded as a British insect by G. A. Walton in the *Journal of the Society for British*

Entomology 2, 26–33, in 1939, after colonies had been discovered in swamps bordering Barton Broad. Outside Norfolk, it has been found at Wicken Fen.

Velia currens: common on tidal ditches and tree-shaded waters, as well as in local streams.

NAEOGEIDAE

Naeogeus pusillus: a small bug associated with very wet moss and duckweed, recorded from east Norfolk by J. Edwards; there are no recent records of it from the fens of broadland, but it is an insect likely to be overlooked.

SALDIDAE

Salda littoralis: a salt-marsh insect, rare inland; found at Postwick, on the Yare, by J. Edwards.

S. mulleri: very rare; collected from fens at Ranworth and Brumstead many years ago.

S. morio: very rare; usually considered to be an insect of high moorland, but specimens were found running on mud in a *Glyceria maxima* marsh at Wheatfen Broad in July 1938 and June 1941.

Saldula orthochila: local; most usually inhabiting dry sandy tracks, but has been found occasionally in fens.

S. saltatoria: local, in muddy swamps where there are trampled paths.

Chartoscirta cincta: common in fens, running on wet mud and peat and often present in the more open parts of sallow carrs where the peat is covered by algae (*Vaucheria* spp.).

C. cocksii: this insect was known to J. Edwards from a site by the river Wensum, now built over, in Norwich. It has been sought for without success in the broads district in recent years.

APHELOCHEIRIDAE

Aphelocheirus montandoni: this aquatic bug is not uncommon in the river Wensum and tributary streams for some miles above Norwich. So far as is known, it does not frequent the broads, but in 1939 a colony was discovered temporarily inhabiting a clear ditch of brackish water on a strip of sub-maritime fen in the Waveney valley, at St. Olave's. The insect is typically an inhabitant of stony-bedded rivers, but has been found exceptionally in lakes and in brackish water. It is nearly always wingless, but macropterous specimens are produced from time to time and it appears likely that the brackish water colony at St. Olave's resulted from the stray arrival of one or more macropterous insects.

NAUCORIDAE

Ilyocoris cimicoides: rather common and widely distributed in dykes and broads.

NEPIDAE

Nepa cinerea (water scorpion): generally common in shallow, weedy pools and in the marsh ditches.

Ranatra linearis: local, in peaty broads and their associated backwaters and dykes; apparently absent from markedly tidal broads. It has not been found in the dykes intersecting the alluvial grazing marshes of the Breydon levels.

PLEIDAE

Plea leachi: locally abundant in weedy dykes and channels.

NOTONECTIDAE (Water Boatmen)

Notonecta glauca: common and widely distributed in broads and dykes throughout the year. Mass flights take place from time to time and numbers of these water boatmen have been found swimming in the sea close inshore near Great Yarmouth.

CORIXIDAE (Back-swimmers)

No extensive ecological study of the Corixidae has been undertaken here and such a survey might be expected to yield interesting results. The list which follows is compiled partly from district records made more than thirty years ago by James Edwards and H. J. Thouless (whose collections are in Norwich Castle Museum), a few more recent reports of captures published in *The Entomologist's Monthly Magazine*, and rather fuller details of the species found at Wheatfen Broad, Surlingham. Following each name, a brief indication of habitats favoured is given, based on the country-wide observations of T. T. Macan.

Corixa lateralis: in fouled waters and pools by the sea.

C. nigrolineata: often in shallow pools and favouring ' rich ' waters. Uncommon at Wheatfen.

C. concinna: an uncommon insect of slightly saline waters.

C. praeusta: a common and widely distributed species inhabiting waters where there is plenty of vegetable matter. Not uncommon at Wheatfen.

C. venusta: most usually found in running water.

C. semistriata: local, in fen pools. Scarce at Wheatfen.

C. limitata: usually found in ' productive ' ponds. Scarce at Wheatfen.

C. fossarum: in sheltered waters. Fairly common at Wheatfen. Recorded as abundant in the Thurne river in 1928.

C. falleni: in calcareous waters, including rivers. Common at Wheatfen, in broads and freshwater tidal dykes and channels, in base-rich waters.

C. distincta: in sheltered vegetation-rich waters, especially ponds. Common at Wheatfen.

C. stagnalis:
C. selecta: } usually in brackish waters.

C. linnei: in ponds, ditches and rivers. Scarce at Wheatfen.

C. sahlbergi: typically in stagnant small pools with much decomposing vegetation. Common at Wheatfen.

C. punctata: in ponds with rich vegetation. Fairly common at Wheatfen.

C. dentipes: in closed habitats with vegetation. Recorded from a dyke at Thurne, 1928. (H. R. P. Collett.)

C. panzeri: in lakes and rivers. Taken from the river Yare near the mouth of the Chet, 1928 (H. R. P. Collett).

C. dorsalis Leach (=*striata* of Kloet & Hincks' List): a common insect of open habitats, including slowly flowing rivers. This is by far the most abundant Corixid at Wheatfen.

The sampling of Wheatfen water bugs has been carried out at various times by Messrs E. T. Daniels and E. J. S. Brown.

Cymatia bonsdorffi: recorded by J. Edwards from the broads district.

C. coleoptrata: common and widely distributed.

Micronecta poweri:
M. scholtzi: } recorded from the district by J. Edwards.

HOPPERS (Hemiptera: Homoptera)

The main sources of our knowledge of these insects in the district are the records made by James Edwards in the latter part of the nineteenth century and in the first quarter of the twentieth, while additional information has been provided by recent studies undertaken in the vicinity of Wheatfen Broad. Only species found in fens and carrs are included and those specially characteristic of marsh habitats are marked with an asterisk. *W* indicates recent occurrence at Wheatfen.

CERCOPIDAE (Frog-hoppers)

Aphrophora salicis: rather local, on sallows. *W.*

**A. spumaria:* very common and widely distributed on alder. *W.*

**A. major:* locally common on bog myrtle, sallows and alder. *W.*

A. maculata: rather local, on oak, sallows and alder. *W.*

Philaenus leucophthalmus: abundant and extremely variable in colour and pattern. Inter-varietal pairing between specimens of twelve of the named varieties of this species has been studied at Wheatfen Broad and it has been found that the numbers of matings between contrasting forms and between non-contrasting forms are not significantly different. This, the familiar 'cuckoo-spit', insect of gardens and hedge-banks, is to be found on most kinds of herbaceous plants and bushes in fens. *W.*

Neophilaenus lineatus: very common on grasses. *W.*

N. exclamationis: not uncommon. *W.*

MEGOPHTHALMIDAE

Megophthalmus scanicus: fairly common. *W.*

M. scabripennis: rare, in sedge fen with bog myrtle. *W.*

TETTIGONIELLIDAE

* *Tettigoniella viridis:* abundant and widespread in reed-marshes and fens. *W.*

* *Euacanthus interruptus:* locally abundant in fens, as it is also on coastal dunes; in wet habitats it is often associated with the water forget-me-not. *W.*

BYTHOSCOPIDAE

Idiocerus stigmaticollis: common on willows. *W.*

I. varius: very local, on osiers.

I. lituratus: rather local, on willows and sallows. *W.*

I. elegans: local, on sallows.

* *I. confusus:* very common and widespread on sallows. *W.*

I. albicans: fairly common, especially on white poplar. *W.*

I. populi: local, on aspen. *W.*

I. fulgidus: very common, mainly on poplars. *W.*

Bythoscopus lanio: very common on oak. *W.*

* *Oncopsis alni:* frequent, on alder. *W.*

O. flavicollis: very common on birch.

O. rufuscula: on sallows.

Macropsis cerea: frequent on osiers and sallows.

M. virescens: on osiers and white willow.

M. impura: on sallows, not common.

M. scutellata: taken occasionally from sallows.

Agallia venosa: common and widely distributed. *W.*

JASSIDAE (Leaf-hoppers)

Aphrodes bicinctus: common and widely distributed. *W.*

A. albifrons: common and very variable. *W.*

A. flavostriatus: common and widely distributed. *W.*

* *Strongylocephalus agrestis:* locally common in marshes.

* *S. megerlei:* local, but widely distributed, at the roots of fen plants.

Deltocephalus costalis: Ranworth fen.

D. punctum, D. flori, D. pulicaris, D. abdominalis: all more or less common in a variety of habitats.

D. pascuellus: fairly common and widely distributed, but found only occasionally in fens. *W.*

* *D. maculiceps:* very local, in damp places. *W.*

Jassargus distinguendus: generally distributed.

* *Paralimnus phragmitis:* local, associated with reeds.

Jassus mixtus: on various trees, including those in carrs. *W.*

Limotettix striola: salt-marshes, also found at Hickling Broad.

**L. frontalis:* on grasses in damp places. *W.*
Athysanus grisescens: on grasses, common in fens. *W.*
A. plebeja: generally distributed on grasses.
**A. sahlbergi:* rather local, in fens and meadows. *W.*
A. sordida: more or less common grasses.
A. obsoleta: on grassland and common in fens. *W.*
A. brevipennis: very local, Wheatfen Broad.
Nocydia attenuata: on heaths and fens, local. *W.*
Thamnotettix splendidulus: generally distributed. *W.*
T. subfusculus: common, widely distributed. *W.*
T. dilutior: not uncommon on oak. *W.*
Cicadula quinquenotata: local, Ranworth Fen.
C. quadrinotata: common, widely distributed; often found in fens. *W.*
C. persimilis: local, Wheatfen Broad.
C. saturata: local, Hoveton Fen.
Macrosteles fieberi: local, on salt marshes and recorded occasionally from inland marshes. *W.*
M. opacipennis: local, Ranworth Fen.
M. sexnotatus: common. *W.*
**M. metrius:* common by ditches and riversides.
**M. septemnotatus:* local, in fens. *W.*

TYPHLOCYBIDAE

Erythroneura alneti: on alder.
Typhlocybe jucunda: common on alder.
T. decempunctata: common on sallows.
T. quercus: common on oaks.
T. geometra: on alder and willows.
T. aurovittata: common on oak. *W.*
T. salicicola: common on sallows.
**Cicadella vittata:* frequent on low plants in damp places. *W.*
C. urticae: very common on nettles. *W.*
C. simplex: fen at Hoveton.
C. cyclops: fen and carr at Wheatfen Broad.
C. stachydearum: on Labiatae, not uncommon. *W.*
C. thoulessi: Hoveton.
C. aurata: frequent on mints. *W.*
C. atropuncta: very common on nettles.
Empoasca smaragdula: abundant on willows.
Alebra albostriella: oak, Wheatfen Broad.
Dikraneura similis: common on grasses, including those in marshes.
D. citrinella: on grasses in damp places. *W.*

CIXIIDAE

Cixius pilosus: frequent, on various trees, including those of fen carrs. *W.*
**C. nervosus:* common on bushy fens. *W.*

DELPHACIDAE

**Araeopus pulchellus:* amongst sedges and rushes in fens, not uncommon. *W.*
Megamelus notula: on grasses in a variety of habitats.
M. fieberi: on grasses.
M. quadrimaculatus: Ranworth fen.
**M. venosus:* on grassy marshes and fens, local.
**Stenocranus longipennis:* on damp commons and fens. *W.*
Kelisia punctulum: amongst long grasses in damp places.
**K. scotti:* common at roots of reeds. *W.*
K. vittipennis: grasses, coastal and in fens. *W.*
**Chloriona smaragdula:* on reeds, Ranworth Broad.
**C. glaucescens:* on reeds, Ranworth Broad.
Eurysa lineata: common on fine grasses, such as *Festuca rubra.* *W.*
Conomelus limbatus: on grasses. *W.*
**Euconomelus lepidus:* local, at roots of rushes, broads and coast.
Delphax: of the more generally distributed species associated with grasses, the following occur in the broads district: *discolor*, *marginata*, *albo-carinata*, *elegantula*, *collina*, *forcipata*, *niveimarginata* and *leptosoma*. Those most commonly associated with grasses in damp habitats here include *discreta*, *obscurella*, *pellucida*, *lugubrina*, *adela* and *brevipennis*.

CHERMIDAE (Jumping Plant-lice)

**Livia juncorum:* common, forming galls on rushes. *W.*
Psyllopsis fraxinicola: common on various trees and bushes.
P. fraxini: on ash.
**Chermes alni:* common on alder. *W.*
**C. forsteri:* common on alder. *W.*
C. saliceti: on sallows.
Trichochermes walkeri: local, on common buckthorn. *W.*
**Trioza galii:* very common on *Galium palustre* and *G. uliginosum* (marsh and bog bedstraws) in fens. *W.*
T. urticae: common on nettles.

ALDER FLIES and SNAKE FLIES (Megaloptera)

From the end of April until late in June, alder flies are conspicuous by the waterside. They fly heavily on dusky, thickly netted, glistening wings when disturbed, but are seen most commonly at rest on bushes and other marsh vegetation. Their brown egg-masses are glued to these plants and the larvae enter the water, where they feed on small aquatic animals for two years before leaving the water to pupate and develop into winged insects. Only *Sialis lutaria* has been noticed about the broads, the other British alder fly (*S. fuliginosa*) requiring faster-running waters in its larval state. One kind of snake-fly (*Agulla xanthostigma*), has been found in damp woodlands adjoining the broads occasionally in June; the larva lives under loose bark, feeding on other insects there.

LACEWINGS (Neuroptera)

The small, smoky- and downy-winged sponge fly (*Sisyra fuscata*) is the only common lacewing with an aquatic larva here. The adults fly over the marshes at dusk throughout the summer, laying clusters of yellow eggs, covered by little webs, on waterside plants. The larvae enter the water and obtain their nourishment from freshwater sponges (chiefly *Ephydatia fluviatilis*). Of the terrestrial lacewings, *Micromus variegatus* and *Eumicromus paganus* are found regularly in the broadland fens. At Wheatfen Broad, Surlingham, where oak-ash woodland succeeds fen-carr, six species of *Chrysopa* (green lacewings) and two additional brown lacewings, *Hemerobius stigma* and *Kimminsia subnebulosa*, have been found.

SCORPION FLIES (Mecoptera)

Two kinds of scorpion flies, *Panorpa communis* and *P. germanica*, sit about on the nettles and other tall herbs of open spaces in the carrs and ditch and marsh banks. They appear in late May and June and again in autumn. Both have four black-spotted wings of equal length and yellow-and-black, orange-tailed bodies. Their flight is weak and shimmering and they more often sidle out of the way or drop to cover rather than take wing when disturbed. They may be seen devouring beetles, flies and harvest-spiders on leaves, but in some cases at least these insects have died from some other cause in the first instance; scorpion flies commonly clean up the remains of insects killed by entomogenous fungi of the genera *Empusa* and *Entomophthora*, in broadland habitats.

CADDIS FLIES (Trichoptera)

A thorough study of caddis flies in the broads has never been attempted. The list which follows has been compiled largely from the collector's records supplied by the late Mr. Claude Morley; the writer is also indebted to E. T. Daniels for some recent observations made chiefly in the Yare valley.

PHRYGANEIDAE

Phryganea grandis: this, the largest British caddis, is widely distributed in broads, where the larval cases are often constructed of reed leaves; the adults fly in May and June. *P. minor* has been identified at Wheatfen Broad on several occasions in June.

Agrypnia pagetana: common and widely distributed in spring and early summer and breeding in dykes, including those of brackish water near the coast. This insect was first described from specimens collected in marshes near Great Yarmouth and its specific epithet commemorates the name of C. J. Paget, an early nineteenth-century Yarmouth entomologist.

LIMNEPHILIDAE

This family is well represented here, the larvae living mostly in still or slowly moving waters.

Colpotaulius incisus: widely distributed and abundant in reedswamps and fens in spring and summer.

Grammotaulius nitidus: apparently rather rare; recorded from Wheatfen Broad and Horsey in July and August. *G. strigosus:* not uncommon in reedswamps, spring and summer.

Glyphotaelius pellucidus: generally distributed and very common, May to September.

Limnephilus rhombicus: common. *L. flavicornis:* fairly common and widely distributed, summer and autumn. *L. marmoratus:* very common; larvae have been found in brackish water of 8·3 parts per thousand chlorides near Great Yarmouth. *L. xanthodes:* more commonly seen on the broads than elsewhere in Britain and breeding in peaty fen pools and dykes; the adults appear in May and June and rest by day on sallows and alders. *L. lunatus:* widespread, emerging mainly in late summer and autumn. *L. politus:* widely distributed and not uncommon in autumn. *L. centralis:* rather common, June to August. *L. vittatus:* abundant and widespread, May to July and occasionally seen in autumn. *L. affinis:* common in the marshes and specially abundant in the neighbourhood of Breydon Water; the larvae are known to occur in brackish waters and the flies are on the wing from May to July; on 4 May, 1937, extraordinary numbers of these insects appeared in the coast town of Gorleston, adjoining Great Yarmouth, and it is thought probable that they had been blown off the marshes while flying at night rather than that their presence was due to immigration. *L. auricula:* extremely common and widespread in spring and again in autumn. *L. griseus:* found chiefly in marshes of the estuarine region, from spring to autumn; specimens were bred from larvae found living in a salt ditch of 23·4 parts per thousand chlorides near Great Yarmouth. *L. hirsutus:* common and widespread in summer. *L. luridus:* generally common in June. *L. sparsus:* recorded in every month from May to August at Wheatfen Broad, in the Yare valley. *L. fuscicornis:* recorded without specific locality from east Norfolk.

Anabolia nervosa: an autumnal insect, breeding in the upper and middle reaches of local rivers and in freshwater tidal broads and dykes.

Micropterna sequax and *M. lateralis:* breeding here and there in lowland becks.

Halesus radiatus: locally common in autumn, usually where waterways have a fair current.

Chaetopteryx villosa: an autumnal insect, associated chiefly with becks and the upper reaches of the rivers.

SERICOSTOMATIDAE

In this family, the larvae live in running water and make horn-shaped cases of sand grains or gravel. The species listed below are seldom noticed downstream of the lowest locks on the rivers of east Norfolk and exist only at the very fringe of broadland.

Sericostoma personatum: river Yare at Norwich and river Waveney at Geldeston Lock.

Notidobia ciliaris: common in suitable localities in May.

Goera pilosa: common in the upper reaches of rivers, May and June.

BERAEIDAE

Beraea pullata: fairly common in May and June alongside reed-fringed rivers and main dykes where there is a steady flow of water.

MOLANNIDAE

Molanna angustata: widespread, May to July, breeding in slowly moving waters and able to tolerate slightly saline conditions.

ODONTOCERIDAE (not represented)

LEPTOCERIDAE

Leptocerus nigronervosus: an up-river insect, recorded from Norwich, May 1938 (E.T.D.). *L. fulvus* and *L. senilis*, whose larvae feed on freshwater sponges, are common where there is running water. *L. aterrimus:* widely distributed and breeding commonly in fen ditches, flying chiefly in June.

Mystacides azurea, *M. longicornis* and *M. nigra:* these small, dusky-winged caddis flies breed in local rivers above their lowest locks and in some of the smaller streams or becks.

Triaenodes bicolor: fairly common, breeding in ditches, including those of salt marshes; *T. conspersa* recorded as generally common by C. Morley.

Erotesis baltica: one captured at Horning, 8th June, 1931 (C. Morley).

Oecetis furva and *Oe. lacustris:* rather rare.

Setodes tineiformis: recorded from Barnby Broad.

HYDROPSYCHIDAE

While several species of *Hydropsyche*, whose larvae live in fixed silken 'webs', occur in the upper reaches of local rivers, none has been recorded from any broad.

POLYCENTROPIDAE

The larvae inhabit silken webs, often attached to aquatic plants.

Plectronemia conspersa: normally an insect of brooks, this has been found living at Wheatfen Broad, where there are many freshwater tidal dykes and where conditions at sluices resemble those found in fast-running streams.

Polycentropus flavomaculatus: mainly an up-river insect.

Holocentropus picicornis: locally common in June. *H. stagnalis:* recorded from Horning and the neighbourhood of Horsey Mere; both species breed in standing waters; it is likely that *H. dubius*, common at Wicken Fen, will be found present about the broads.

Cyrnus trimaculatus: locally abundant in June; *C. flavidus:* known to be tolerant of brackish waters: recorded from the vicinity of Horsey Mere.

PSYCHOMYIDAE

The larvae in this family make immovable, usually flattish cases attached to twigs or stones, in both fast and sluggish streams and in lakes.

Tinodes waeneri: mainly an up-river insect, flying in May and June.

Lype phaeopa: recorded from fens at Horning and Catfield in summer.

RHYACOPHILIDAE

The larvae hide under stones and water-logged pieces of wood on the beds of streams.

Rhyacophila dorsalis: normally frequents the upper reaches of rivers and subsidiary streams, but has been noticed also in the vicinity of freshwater tidal channels in the Yare valley.

Agapetus fuscipes: becks, upper reaches of rivers and freshwater tidal channels in the Yare valley.

HYDROPTILIDAE

The larvae occupy very small movable cases, coated with silt or vegetable matter. The members of this family are extremely small and little noticed by entomologists: only two species have been recorded from the broads, viz.: *Agraylea multipuncta* and *Hydroptila sparsa.*

MOTHS and BUTTERFLIES (Lepidoptera)

In compiling the annotated list of broadland moths which follows, full use has been made of C. W. V. Gane's extensive records from the Bure-Ant-Thurne district (with Barton Broad as its collecting centre) and of records contributed by many visiting entomologists for the Yare valley (with Wheatfen Broad, Surlingham, as a centre of investigation); Mr. E. T. Goldsmith has allowed me to study his records for the Waveney valley, covering the last forty-five years. The classification adopted here is that of Kloet and Hincks' *Check List of British Insects* (1945) and the English names are those of R. South's *Moths of the British Isles* (1939 edition). Where no comment follows the name of an insect, the species is common and widely distributed in the district.

HEPIALIDAE

Gold Swift (*Hepialus hectus*); Common Swift (*H. lupulinus*).

Map-winged Swift (*H. fusconebulosus*); Orange Swift (*H. sylvinus*); Ghost Swift (*H. humuli*). These moths undertake short flights at sunset on summer evenings, when they may be seen darting from side to side with a pendulum-like motion above the vegetation of fens and marsh banks, especially along valley margins.

ARCTIIDAE

Dotted Footman (*Pelosia muscerda*): although almost confined to this district in Britain, this insect abounds in the fens associated with all five broadland rivers. The dark brown, velvety caterpillars feed on mouldy, decaying leaves in wet places under sallows and other bushes and the moths fly in August.

P. obtusa, new to Britain, was found near one of the broads in 1961.

Scarce Footman (*Eilema complana*): rare; Common Footman (*E. lurideola*).

Deal Footman (*E. pygmaeola*); occurs at Horsey.

Four-dotted Footman (*Cybosia mesomella*): rare and local.

Four-spotted Footman (*Lithosia quadra*): an irregular immigrant; specimens have been taken on east coast light vessels occasionally.

Dingy Footman (*L. griseola*): not uncommon in fens.

Round-winged Muslin (*Comacla senex*): very common in fens, where the caterpillars feed on mosses.

Rosy Footman (*Miltochrista miniata*): common in carrs, where the caterpillars feed on lichens encrusting the trees.

Cinnabar (*Hypocrita jacobaeae*): usually present within the district, but the caterpillars cannot be relied upon to appear in any particular locality in successive years, since the moths are wanderers largely dispersed by wind; marsh ragwort is the plant most commonly eaten by the caterpillars in damp habitats.

Ruby Tiger (*Phragmatobia fuliginosa*): locally common on fens in some years more than others.

Muslin (*Cycnia mendica*): rather rare.

Water Ermine (*Spilosoma urticae*): a fairly common and characteristic fen insect, the caterpillars feeding on water-mint, marsh ragwort and great water dock, especially in places which would be termed good snipe grounds. The pupae are found floating in considerable numbers on flooded marshes in winter and experiments have shown that nearly all the moths emerge successfully from pupae allowed to remain floating on water for weeks at a time. When it was common for horses to graze periodically on the marginal fens, the hairy caterpillars of the water-ermine were supposed to cause colic after being eaten accidentally by these animals. Buff Ermine (*Spilosoma lutea*); White Ermine (*S. lubricipeda*).

Garden Tiger (*Arctia caja*): the 'woolly bear' caterpillars are often abundant in very wet situations, such as the sides of marsh dykes, where they feed on many kinds of plants.

CYMBIDAE

Cream-bordered Green Pea (*Earias clorana*): locally common, the caterpillars feeding on sallows and osiers; in some years there is a small second brood.

Scarce Silver-lines (*Pseudoips bicolorana*): locally common.

Green Silver-lines (*Bena prasinana*): often common.

Large Marbled Tortrix (*Sarrothripus revayana*): rather rare.

CARADRINIDAE

The Miller (*Apatele leporina*): locally common in alder carrs, especially those of the Ant. Alder (*A. alni*): rare. Dark Dagger (*A. tridens*): rare. Grey Dagger (*A. psi*): widely distributed, but not very common. Poplar Grey (*A. megacephala*): rather rare. Knot Grass (*A. rumicis*): thinly but widely distributed in fens, where the caterpillars feed mainly on great water-dock.

Powdered Wainscot (*Simyra albovenosa*): rather common round most of the broads, where the hairy caterpillar feeds externally on the leaves of reeds and other reedswamp grasses, including *Glyceria maxima* and *Phalaris arundinacea* and often attacks the flowering plumes of reeds in August. The variety *ochracea* is almost as well represented as the typical form. This species is rare outside East Anglia.

Marbled Beauty (*Cryphia perla*): rather rare.

Copper Underwing (*Amphipyra pyramidea*): the larvae feed on most kinds of trees and shrubs in the carrs and the moths are very common in late summer and autumn. Mouse (*A. tragepogonis*): the caterpillars feed largely on sallow bushes; very common.

Frosted Orange (*Gortyna flavago*): fairly common.

Brown Rustic (*Rusina umbratica*): fairly common.

Small Rufous (*Caenobia rufa*): often abundant in fens, where the larvae bore in stems of rushes.

Brown-veined Wainscot (*Nonagria dissoluta*): extremely common, the larvae boring reed stems in such numbers that they spoil many reed beds in some summers. Reed Wainscot (*N. cannae*): common in reedswamps, where the larvae feed in stems of reed-maces (*Typha latifolia* and *T. angustifolia*) and much more commonly in bulrushes. Webb's Wainscot (*N. sparganii*): very rare; once taken at Barton Broad and known from one station in the Waveney valley. Bulrush Wainscot (*N. typhae*): a widely distributed British moth, common here; the larvae bore in stems of reed-maces.

Silky Wainscot (*Chilodes maritima*): local; the larva feeds on other caterpillars in reed stems. The moths emerge from reed stacks.

Small Yellow Underwing (*Panemeria tenebrata*): one of the few day-flying moths, common round the fringes of fens wherever its food-plant, mouse-ear chickweed (*Cerastium vulgatum*), is present.

Lesser Spotted Pinion (*Cosmia affinis*): rather local. Dun-bar (*C. trapezina*): common and extremely variable; the caterpillars often feed on sallow and at times devour other caterpillars.

Mottled Rustic (*Caradrina morpheus*). Uncertain (*C. alsines*): not very common. Rustic (*C. blanda*).

Old Lady (*Mormo maura*).

Double Kidney (*Zenobia retusa*): a sallow feeder, local. Olive (*Z. retusa*): rather rare, on poplar. The eggs, laid on terminal twigs, are at first bright yellow; they soon change to a greyish purple colour, remaining in this condition throughout the winter.

Bordered Sallow (*Pyrrhia umbra*): this is a coastal insect which wanders occasionally to broads lying nearest the sea.

Large Wainscot (*Rhizedra lutosa*): rather rare; the caterpillar feeds in reed rhizomes.

Small Wainscot (*Arenostola pygmina*): common; the larva feeds in stalks of sedges in fens and bogs. Fen Wainscot (*A. phragmitidis*): very common, the larva boring in reed stems. Fenn's Wainscot (*A. brevilinea*): in Britain this insect is confined to the broads and is locally abundant in reedswamps of the middle Bure and Ant. The caterpillar bores into the shoots of reeds and eventually emerges to feed on the leaves. For many years following its original discovery at Ranworth Broad in 1864 it was thought to be endemic, but its distribution is now known to extend across northern Europe to Siberia. The moth flies at dusk in July and August.

Small Dotted Buff (*Petilampa minima*): rather rare.

Treble-lines (*Meristis trigrammica*): widespread, but not very common.

Straw Underwing (*Thalpophile matura*).

Angle Shades (*Phlogophora meticulosa*).

Small Angle Shades (*Euplexia lucipara*): fairly common.

Bird's Wing (*Dipterygia scabriuscula*): rather rare.

Dusky Brocade (*Xylophasia remissa*): rather rare. Clouded-bordered Brindle (*X. crenata*). Light Arches (*X. lithoxylea*). Dark Arches (*X. monoglypha*): extremely common and migratory. Clouded Brindle (*X. hepatica*).

Small Clouded Brindle (*Apamea unanimis*): local and rather rare in fens.

Dusky Sallow (*Eremobia ochroleuca*): rare.

Haworth's Minor (*Celaena haworthi*): locally common where cotton-grass is present in fens. Crescent (*C. leucostigma*): the pale banded variety *fibrosa* is the common form here; the larvae feed in sedge stems. Common Rustic (*C. secalis*).

Rosy Rustic (*Hydraecia micacea*): very common, but least plentiful in marshy areas. Ear Moth (*H. oculea*). Double Lobed (*H. ophiogramma*): the moth is a frequent visitor to flowers of hemp agrimony and the caterpillar feeds on aquatic grasses.

Rosy Minor (*Miuna literosa*).

Cloaked Minor (*Procus furunculus*): rather rare away from the coast. Marbled Minor (*P. strigilis*). Middle-barred Minor (*P. fasciunculus*): common; the caterpillar feeds on various marsh grasses.

Bordered Straw (*Heliothis peltigera*): a rare immigrant.

Garden Dart (*Euxoa nigricans*). White-line Dart (*E. tritici*).

Turnip Moth (*Agrotis segetum*). Shuttle-shaped Dart (*A. puta*). Heart and Dart (*A. exclamationis*). Dark Sword Grass (*A. ypsilon*).

Portland Moth (*Actebia praecox*): rather rare.

Great Brocade (*Eurois occulta*): a northern insect which has appeared in the broads district in numbers from time to time, possibly as the result of migration from the Continent; a large influx took place in September 1931.

Pearly Underwing (*Peridroma saucia*): a fairly common immigrant.

Flame Shoulder (*Ochropleura plecta*).

Double Dart (*Graphiphora augur*).

Setaceous Hebrew Character (*Amathes c-nigrum*): extremely common and sometimes appearing in phenomenal numbers in September. Triple-spotted Clay (*A. ditrapezium*): rare. Double Square-spot (*A. triangulum*): rare. Square-spot Rustic (*A. xanthographa*). Six-striped Rustic (*A. umbrosa*). Square-spotted Clay (*A. stigmatica*): rare. Dotted Clay (*A. baja*).

Ingrailed Clay (*Diarsia festiva*). Purple Clay (*D. brunnea*): rather local. Small Square Spot (*D. rubi*). Large Yellow Underwing (*Triphaena pronuba*). Lesser Yellow Underwing (*T. comes*). Lesser Broad-border (*T. janthina.*) Least Yellow Underwing (*T. interjecta*): often flies by day.

Flame (*Axylia putris*).

Gothic (*Phalaena typica*): fairly common.

Broad-bordered Yellow Underwing (*Lampra fimbriata*).

Red Chestnut (*Cerastis rubricosa*): the moth is a frequent visitor at sallow bloom in spring.

Green Arches (*Anaplectoides prasina*): rather rare.

Dark Chestnut (*Conistra ligula*): fairly common. Chestnut (*C. vaccinii*).

Lunar Underwing (*Anchoscelis lunosa*): rare. Brown-spot Pinion (*A. liturna*).

Centre-barred Sallow (*Atethmia centrago*): rare.

Pink-barred Sallow (*Citrea lutea*): the caterpillar feeds on catkins and leaves of sallow bushes.

Sallow (*Cirrhia fulvago*).

Brick (*Agrochila circellaris*). Beaded Chestnut (*A. lychnidis*). Red-line Quaker (*A. lota*): fairly common, a sallow-feeder.

Suspected (*Parastichtis suspecta*): very common in August in some years; the larva feeds on birch and sallow. Dingy Shears (*P. ypsilon*).

Satellite (*Eupsilia transversa*): fairly common.

Green-brindled Crescent (*Allophyes oxyacanthae*): fairly common.

Shark (*Cucullia umbratica*): fairly common.

Golden Rod Brindle (*Lithomoia solidaginis*): a moorland insect, occurring here only as a rare wanderer.

Grey Shoulder-knot (*Graptolitha ornitopus*).

Merveille du Jour (*Griposia aprilina*): common in oak woods.

Minor Shoulder-knot (*Bombycia viminalis*): commonly associated with sallows and willows.

Brindled Green (*Dryobata protea*).

Flame Wainscot (*Senta flammea*): local in reedswamps of the Bure and Ant valleys; the larva feeds on reed leaves.

Obscure Wainscot (*Leucania obsoleta*): rare, recorded from Horning; the larva feeds on reed leaves. Striped Wainscot (*L. pudorina*): fairly common; the larva feeds on leaves of reed and other marsh grasses. Southern Wainscot (*L. straminea*): common; the larva feeds on various marsh grasses, including reed. Smoky Wainscot (*L. impura*): very common; the larva feeds on marsh and fen grasses. Common Wainscot (*L. pallens*): very common; the caterpillar feeds on many different grasses and is not restricted to marshy habitats. Clay (*L. lythargyria*): common, feeding on grasses in a variety of habitats. Brown-line Bright-eye (*L. conigera*): common on various grasses. Shoulder-striped Wainscot (*L. comma*): not uncommon, on marsh grasses. The caterpillars of the *Leucania* wainscots are external feeders and are camouflaged suitably by their body colours and stripe-like markings; in this they contrast strongly with the stem-boring larvae of the *Arenostola* and *Nonagria* wainscots and their allies, which are uniformly milk-white or pinkish in colour.

Clouded Drab (*Orthosia incerta*): the moth is a common visitor to sallow bloom in spring. Powdered Quaker (*O. gracilis*): fairly common; the larva feeds on many kinds of fen plants. Common Quaker (*O. stabilis*). Small Quaker (*O. cruda*): fairly common at sallow bloom. Hebrew Character (*O. gothica*): common at sallow bloom.

Antler (*Charaeas graminis*): a migrant arriving in large numbers in some years and absent in others.

Feathered Gothic (*Tholera popularis*). Hedge Rustic (*T. cespitis*).

Lychnis (*Hadena bicruris*): the caterpillars feed commonly on flowers of ragged robin at night. Campion (*H. cucubali*). Nutmeg (*H. chenopodii*): always common; but for a few years following the Horsey sea flood of 1938 it became very abundant, while quantities of goosefoot and orache flourished on the salted broadland marshes and provided a plethora of food for the larvae. Pale-shouldered Brocade (*H. thalassina*). Dog's Tooth (*H. sausa*): rather rare.

Bordered Gothic (*Heliophobus saponariae*): rare.

Bright-line Brown-eye (*Diataraxia oleracea*).

Broom Moth (*Caramica pisi*).

Grey Arches (*Pelia nebulosa*): rather rare.

Cabbage Moth (*Mamestra brassicae*).

Dot (*Melanchra persicariae*).

Beautiful Yellow Underwing (*Anarta myrtilli*): a heath insect which sometimes strays on to neighbouring fens.

PLUSIIDAE

Fan-foot (*Zanclognatha tarsipennalis*). Dotted Fan-foot (*Z. cribrumalis*): on fen grasses and sedges.

Common Fan-foot (*Herminia barbalis*): rather rare.

Pinion-streaked Snout (*Schrankia costaestrigalis*): a very common fen insect.

Buttoned Snout (*Hypena rostralis*): fairly common, the larvae feeding on wild hop in the carrs. Snout (*H. proboscidalis*).

Blackneck (*Ophiusa pastinum*): locally common in fens wherever the food plant, tufted vetch, is present.

Herald (*Scoliopteryx libatrix*): a characteristic insect of the fen carrs, where the larvae abound on sallows.

Clifden Nonpareil (*Catocala fraxini*): an irregular immigrant, possibly breeding in the district occasionally (e.g. on poplars near Barton Broad, where the moths appeared annually in fair numbers for several years in succession in the 1930's). Red Underwing (*C. nupta*): common on willows and poplars.

Mother Shipton (*Euclidimera mi*): common on fens and meadows.

Burnet Companion (*Ectypa glyphica*): fairly common on fens.

Silver Hook (*Eustrotia uncula*): a true fen insect of sedges and marsh grasses, common and double-brooded in most years.

Small Purple Barred (*Phytometra viridaria*): rare.

Straw Dot (*Rivula sericealis*): extremely common throughout the broadland marshes, where the larvae feed on coarse grasses.

Golden Plusia (*Polychrisia moneta*): not common, but widely distributed in local gardens.

Burnished Brass (*Plusia chrysitis*). Gold Spot (*P. festucae*): a common and characteristic marsh moth, often flying by day. The caterpillars feed on various sedges, reed and other marsh grasses, sweet flag and yellow flag iris. Plain Golden Y (*P. iota*): rather rare. Beautiful Golden Y (*P. v-aureum*): rare. Silver Y (*P. gamma*): a regular immigrant, often visiting fen flowers in large numbers in late summer and autumn.

Spectacle (*Abrostola tripartita*).

LYMANTRIIDAE

Scarce Vapourer (*Orgyia gonostigma*): frequent and widely distributed in fens and carrs; the larvae usually occur singly and spin thick webs in which they hibernate; they have been found feeding on sallow, buckthorn, meadowsweet and great water dock near the broads. Vapourer (*O. antiqua*).

Pale Tussock (*Dasychira pudibunda*): the caterpillars feed on the leaves of most kinds of trees in wet as well as dry habitats.

Yellowtail (*Euproctis chrysorrhaea*): the caterpillars are often plentiful on sallow bushes in addition to the usual hawthorns. Brown-tail (*E. phaeorrhaea*): an irregular immigrant, sometimes breeding in the district for a few years in succession.

White Satin Moth (*Leucoma salicis*): rather rare and appearing only intermittently in a way which suggests that it is an occasional immigrant breeding impersistently here.

Black Arches (*Lymantria monacha*). Gipsy (*L. dispar*): known to have been locally abundant on bog myrtle in the broads in the early nineteenth century; it had vanished from the area by 1860 and has never returned.

STERRHIDAE

Purple-bordered Gold (*Sterrha muricata*): locally common in fens where its food plant, marsh cinquefoil, is present. Satin Wave (*S. subsericeata*): rare. Riband Wave (*S. aversata*). Small Fan-footed Wave (*S. biselata*). Small Scallop (*S. emarginata*): the larvae feed on marsh and bog bedstraws in fens and several pretty varieties of the moth occur here.

Cream Wave (*Scopula remutaria*). Lesser Cream Wave (*S. immutata*): an extremely common fen insect; the larvae feed on meadowsweet and valerian. Small Blood-vein (*S. imitaria*). Tawny wave (*S. rubiginata*): this typical Breckland insect has wandered (wind-blown?) to the broads occasionally.

Mocha (*Cosymbia annulata*): rare.

Blood-vein (*Calothysanis amata*): specially common in damp localities.

GEOMETRIDAE

Common Emerald (*Hemithes strigata*).

Small Grass Emerald (*Chlorissa viridata*): rare, Horning and Barton Broad.

Blotched Emerald (*Comibaens pustulata*): rather rare in a few damp oak woods here.

Little Emerald (*Jodis lactearia*): the larvae feed most frequently on sallows here.

Large Emerald (*Geometra papilionaria*): common where birches grow in the carrs.

Grass Emerald (*Pseudoterpna pruinata*): rather rare.

HYDRIOMENIDAE

Small Seraphim (*Mysticoptera sexalata*): local, on sallows.

V-Pug (*Chloroclystis coronata*): local, on hemp agrimony and purple loosestrife. Green Pug (*C. rectangulata*).

Ling Pug (*Eupithecia goosensiata*): rather rare. Wormwood Pug (*E. absinthiata*): very common, chiefly on hemp agrimony in fens. Valerian Pug (*E. valerianata*): rather local on valerian in fens. White-spotted Pug (*E. albipunctata*): very common on flowers of angelica. Common Pug (*E. vulgata*). Toadflax Pug (*E. linariata*). Marsh Pug (*E. pygmaeata*): local; its normal food plant is the common stitchwort of hedgerows, but the moth occurs in fens occasionally where marsh stitchwort is present. Brindled Pug (*E. abbreviate*): fairly common, on oak.

Dentated Pug (*Anticollix sparsata*): rare, on yellow loosestrife.

Treble-bar (*Anaitis plagiata*).

Scallop Shell (*Calocalpe undulata*): rather rare, on sallows.

Dark Umber (*Philereme transversata*): locally common on buckthorn.

Phoenix (*Lygris prunata*): common on wild currant bushes in the carrs. Chevron (*L. testata*): the larvae feed at night on small sallow bushes; very common. Spinach (*L. mellinata*): common on wild currant bushes. Barred Straw (*L. dotata*).

Blue-bordered Carpet (*Plemyria bicolorata*): common, alder and birch.

Common Carpet (*Epirrhoe alternata*).

Oblique-striped (*Mesotype virgata*): this moth breeds typically on lady's bedstraw in Breckland and on east coast dunes. Specimens taken from time to time in various parts of the broads district are almost certainly wind-drifted.

Purple Bar (*Lyncometra ocellata*).

Autumn Green Carpet (*Chloroclysta miata*).

July Highflyer (*Hydriomena furcata*); May Highflyer (*H. impluviata*): rather rare, on alder.

Common Marbled Carpet (*Dysstroma truncata*). Dark Marbled Carpet (*D. citrata*).

Water Carpet (*Lamptropteryx suffumata*): rare and local, on bedstraws in fens.

Broken-barred Carpet (*Electrophaes corylata*): fairly common on sallows.

Tissue (*Triphosa dubitata*): rather rare, on buckthorn.

Marsh Carpet (*Coenotephria sagittata*): formerly breeding on meadow rue in fens near the river Yare at Brundall; it has not been seen in the district for many years. Streamer (*C. derivata*): rather rare, on wild roses.

Yellow Shell (*Euphyia bilineata*).

Small Rivulet (*Perizoma alchemillata*): local. Grass Rivulet (*P. albulata*): local, on yellow rattle in fens.

Beautiful Carpet (*Mesoleuca albicillata*): rather rare in woods.

Gem (*Nycterosea obstipata*): a rare immigrant.

Dark Spinach (*Pelurga comitata*).

Winter Moth (*Operophtera brumata*). Northern Winter Moth (*O. fagata*).

Dingy Shell (*Euchoeca obliterata*): locally common on alder.

November Moth (*Oporinia dilutata*).

Dark-barred Twin-spot Carpet (*Xanthorhoe ferrugata*). Red Twin-spot Carpet (*X. spadicearia*). Flame Carpet (*X. designata*): common in carrs. Large Twin-spot Carpet (*X. quadrifasciata*): rare (typically a Breckland insect). Silver-ground Carpet (*X. montanata*). Garden Carpet (*X. fluctuata*).

Shaded Broad-bar (*Ortholitha limitata*).

Twin-spot Green Carpet (*Calostigia didymata*). Green Carpet (*C. pectinataria*).

Oblique Carpet (*Orthonama vittata*): commonly breeding on marsh bedstraw in fens and reedswamps.

BREPHIDAE

Orange Underwing (*Brephos parthenias*): very local, on birch.

SELIDOSEMIDAE

Brimstone Moth (*Opisthograptis luteolata*).

Latticed Heath (*Chiasma clathrata*): this little moth is often mistaken for a butterfly as it flies by day over fens in spring and late summer.

V-moth (*Itama wauaria*): common on wild currant bushes.

Grey Birch (*Ectropis punctulata*): rather local, on birch and alder.

Brussels Lace (*Cleora lichenaria*): rather rare; the caterpillars are coloured like the tree lichens on which they feed in the carrs. Mottled Beauty (*C. repandata*). Willow Beauty (*C. rhomboidaria*).

Common Heath (*Ematurga atomaria*).

Waved Umber (*Hemerophila abruptaria*).

Spring Usher (*Erannis leucophaearia*): local, on oak. Dotted Border (*E. progemmaria*). Mottled Umber (*E. defoliaria*). Brindled Beauty (*Lycia hirtaria*).

Oak Beauty (*Biston strataria*): rather rare. Peppered Moth (*E. betularia*): common on various trees; the melanistic form *carbonaria* has been present in this non-industrial area for at least fifty years and has become increasingly common, but not to the exclusion of the normal form. The grime of cities, against the background of which *carbonaria* is aptly camouflaged, is simulated by sooty moulds (*Cladosporium*) which develop on the honeydew secreted by aphids on various trees. Sallow bushes round the broads become very sooty in appearance from this cause in some summers and undergrowth plants in the carrs are often blackened by mouldy honeydew in the same way. It will be seen that the advantages afforded by black pigmentation in the mutant peppered moth are not confined to city environments.

Magpie or Currant Moth (*Abraxas grossulariata*): not so common as formerly; the caterpillars are found occasionally on wild currant bushes in the carrs.

Scorched Carpet (*Ligdia adustata*): rather rare, on spindle.

Clouded Border (*Leraspilis marginata*): extremely common, breeding on sallows.

Clouded Silver (*Bapta punctata*): fairly common. White-pinion Spotted (*S. bimaculata*): local (the food plant, wild cherry, is present in some broadland carrs).

Brown Silver-line (*Lithina chlorosata*): fairly common.

Common White Wave (*Cabera pusaria*). Common Wave (*C. exanthemata*).

Swallow-tailed Moth (*Ourapteryx sambucaria*).

Light Emerald (*Campaea margaritata*).

Scorched Wing (*Plagodis dolabraria*): rather rare.

Bordered Beauty (*Epione repandaria*).

Early Thorn (*Selenis bilunaria*). Purple Thorn (*S. tetralunaria*): rare.

Canary-shouldered Thorn (*Deuteronomos alniaria*). September Thorn (*D. erosaria*). Dusky Thorn (*D. fuscentaria*).

Scalloped Hazel (*Gonodontis bidentata*).

Scalloped Oak (*Crocallis elinguaria*).

POLYPLOCIDAE

Buff Arches (*Habrosyne derasa*).

Peach Blossom (*Thyatira batis*).

Satin Carpet (*Tethes fluctuosa*): rare, on birch. Lesser Satin Moth (*T. duplaris*). Poplar Lutestring (*T. or*): rare. Figure-of-Eighty (*T. octogesima*): locally common on poplar.

Frosted Green (*Polyploca ridens*): rather rare, on oak.

SPHINGIDAE

Humming-bird Hawk (*Macroglossa stellatarum*): an irregular but occasionally common immigrant. It is seen visiting fen flowers, but the larva has not been found locally on any of the bedstraws of wet habitats.

Small Elephant (*Deilephila porcellus*): rare and not known to breed in marshes here. Elephant (*D. elpenor*): plentiful and widespread; the larvae feed on marsh and bog bedstraws, marsh willowherb and rosebay, and when almost full-fed they tend to consume a variety of other plants, including marsh pennywort and bogbean.

Privet Hawk (*Sphinx ligustri*): although this has become the commonest hawk moth in Norfolk during the past twenty years, the larvae are rarely found on the wild deciduous privet which abounds in many of the broadland carrs.

Death's-head (*Acherontia atropos*): in some years when immigrants of this species invade East Anglia in large numbers, a few larvae are found feeding on bittersweet (*Solanum dulcamara*) near the broads.

Eyed Hawk (*Smerinthus ocellatus*): common in the district, but the larvae are not often found on sallows in the fen carrs. It is possible that winter flooding drowns buried pupae in such places, where this species is concerned.

Lime Hawk (*Dilina tiliae*): fairly common. The larvae feed on alder and birch foliage in many of the carrs and pupation takes place in rotten tree stumps very often instead of in the ground which is liable to winter flooding.

Convolvulus Hawk (*Herse convolvuli*): a fairly regular late summer immigrant in small numbers.

Poplar Hawk (*Laothoe populi*): formerly very common, but noticeably scarcer in this area in recent years.

NOTODONTIDAE

Small Chocolate-tip (*Clostera pigra*): locally abundant on fens where dwarf willow grows. Chocolate-tip (*C. curtula*): rare.

Pebble Prominent (*Notodonta ziczac*): common on sallows. Iron Prominent (*N. dromedarius*): very common, the larvae feeding on alder and birch continuously throughout the summer.

Lesser Swallow Prominent (*Pheosia gnoma*): a birch insect, locally abundant in some years. Swallow Prominent (*P. tremula*).

Pale Prominent (*Pterostoma palpina*): common; double-brooded, on willows and poplars.

Puss Moth (*Cerura vinula*): fairly common; the larvae appear more frequently on isolated white willows and poplars in the open marshland than on sallow trees and bushes in carrs. Poplar Kitten (*C. hermelina*): rather rare. Sallow Kitten (*C. furcula*): the larvae are plentiful on sallows round the broads and in some years there is a second brood. Alder Kitten (*C. bicuspis*), rare.

Buff-tip (*Phalera bucephala*).

SATURNIIDAE

Emperor Moth (*Saturnia pavonia*): the larvae are common on meadow-sweet in fens throughout the district.

DREPANIDAE

Chinese Character (*Cilix glaucata*).

Scalloped Hook-tip (*Drepana lacertinaria*): rare. Pebble Hook-tip (*D. falcataria*): locally abundant on birch and alder. Oak Hook-tip (*D. binaria*): rather rare.

CRAMBIDAE

Crambus uliginosellus: locally common in the wetter parts of fens. *C. silvellus:* fairly common in fens. *C. selasellus:* common in fens and grassy marshes.

C. paludellus: one of the special East Anglian fen insects, found in reed-swamps of the Bure and Ant broads, where it is locally common.

Chilo phragmitellus: the larvae, like certain of the wainscot moths, feed in stems of reed and occasionally in those of the broad-leaved rond-grass (*Glyceria maxima*) in many broadland localities.

PYRAUSTIDAE

Acentropus niveus: local, but widely distributed. The larvae are aquatic, but air-breathing and live usually between spun floating leaves of pondweeds (often *Potamogeton natans*). Pupation occurs under the water. The white-winged male moths seldom fly more than a few inches above the water and the females, some of which have extremely small wings, usually sit on floating weeds.

Schoenobius gigantellus: local in reedswamps; the larvae bore in reed stems. *S. mucronellus:* locally plentiful in fens, where the larvae feed in sedge stems.

China Marks (*Cataclysta lemnata*): very common; the larvae make portable cases of duckweed leaves.

Brown China Marks (*Nymphula nymphaeata*): common in broads and large marsh drains; the aquatic larvae cut out portions of water-lily leaves to make flat cases like those of certain caddis larvae; at first, they appear to absorb the oxygen needed for respiration directly through the skin while submerged; later, reserves of air are held inside their leaf-cases. *N. stratiotata:* rather common; the larvae are wholly aquatic and obtain their oxygen from the water; they spin webs among various aquatic plants and are not restricted to association with the water-soldier (*Stratiotes aloides*). *N. stagnata:* common, with aquatic larvae living in spun floating leaves of bur-reeds.

LASIOCAMPIDAE

Oak Eggar (*Lasiocampus quercus*): fairly common in the district, but the caterpillars are seldom seen in wet habitats.

December Moth (*Poecilocampa populi*): fairly common.

Small Eggar (*Eriogaster lanestris*): like the Lackey, this species is given to sudden abundances in certain years and is scarce or even absent here at other times.

Pale Oak Eggar (*Trichiura crataegi*): rather rare.

Lackey (*Malacosoma neustria*): in some years the caterpillars are extremely numerous on sallow bushes round the broads; in other years few or none can be found.

Drinker (*Philudoria potatoria*): exceedingly and regularly common throughout the area, where the caterpillars feed on various marsh and fen grasses and may be found even in the wettest reedswamps at times. The moths fly in July and are often active on dull days as well as at night. Despite their plumpness, the females are powerful fliers and it is a wonderful experience to watch numbers of these large moths dashing and hovering over the marshes at dusk, when they are egg-laying.

Lappet (*Gastropacha quercifolia*): widely distributed but not very common. The well-camouflaged caterpillars may be found occasionally on sallow bushes.

HETEROGENEIDAE

Festoon (*Cochlidion avellana*): local, on oak.

ZYGAENIDAE

Five-spot Burnet (*Zygaena trifolii*): common in fens, June, where the larvae feed on marsh bird's-foot trefoil. Six-spot Burnet (*Z. Filipendolae*): local, in fens, July.

Forester (*Procris statices*): very local here in fens.

COSSIDAE

Reed Leopard (*Phragmatoecia castaneae*): extremely rare and collected on only a very few occasions at Ranworth, Hickling, Catfield and Horsey. Although the larva is a reed stem-borer, there must always remain some doubt as to the true status of this insect in the broads, because specimens were introduced at Ranworth by C. G. Barrett in 1873 and those discovered subsequently in the district may all have come from this stock.

Leopard (*Zeuzera pyrina*): fairly common.

Goat Moth (*Cossus cossus*): many caterpillars of this ubiquitous tree-borer feed in the trunks of willows and old sallows in broadland, where they are commonly attacked by greater spotted woodpeckers.

In dealing with moths of the superfamilies *Tortricoidea* and *Tinaeoidea* in the remaining part of this list, reference is made only to insects specially characteristic of the fens and carrs and in some cases having a restricted distribution embracing only the broads and the fenland, so far as Britain is concerned.

Tortricoidea

PHALONIIDAE

Phalonia alismana: the larvae feed in stems of water-plantain. *P. walsinghamana:* local; larvae in seed capsules of red-rattle.

TORTRICIDAE

Tortrix viburnana: local, on bog myrtle. *T. rusticana:* on bog myrtle. *T. costana:* common, the larvae feeding on many kinds of marsh plants.

Peronea emargana: common on sallows. *P. lorquinana:* rather rare, on purple loosestrife in fens. *P. aspersana:* rather common on meadowsweet. *P. shepherdana:* abundant on meadowsweet. *P. comariana:* local, on marsh cinquefoil. *P. schalleriana:* on sallows. *P. hastiana:* common on sallows.

EUCOSMIDAE

Ancylia paludana: very local, on marsh pea in fens. *A. siculana:* frequent on buckthorn and alder buckthorn in carrs.

Eucosma nisella: common on sallow catkins and young leaves. *E. demarniana:* local, on alder and sallow catkins. *E. triquetrana:* local, on birch and alder. *E. semifuscana:* common and very variable, on sallows. *E. sordidana:* common on alder.

Argyroploce doubledayana: the broads are the *locus typicus* of this species, which was discovered at Ranworth by Barrett in 1872. The moth is restricted in Britain to fens in east Norfolk and Cambridgeshire.

Tinaeoidea

GELECHIIDAE

Aristotelia arundinetella: the larvae are leaf-miners of sedges. *A. palustrella:* local, in fens and marshes; the larvae have been found in rootstocks of great water dock. *A. divisella:* local, fens. *A. subdecurtella:* a highly localised fen species, on purple loosestrife.

Taygete lathyri: on marsh pea.

Gelechia sororculella: on sallow shoots. *G. muscosella:* on sallow catkins, very local.

Stomopteryx ligulella: larvae in spun leaves of marsh bird's-foot trefoil; common.

COSMOPTERIGIDAE

Cosmopteryx lienigiella: a rare leaf-miner of the reed, found in the broads and the Cambridgeshire fens.

Limnaecia phragmitella: common, the larvae feeding in the fluffy 'pokers' of the reed-mace (*Typha latifolia*).

Mompha propinquella: the larvae form blotch-mines in leaves of great hairy willowherb.

OECOPHORIDAE

Depressaria angelicella: locally abundant in shoots of angelica. *D. conterminella:* common, on sallows.

SESIIDAE

Large Red-belted Clearwing (*Aegeria culiciformis*): rare. Currant Clearwing (*A. tipuliformis*): rare.

Lunar Hornet (*Sphecia bembeciformis*): rare, the larvae feeding in twigs of grey sallow in fen carrs.

GLYPHIPTERIGIDAE

Choreutis myllerana: fairly common, on skull-cap.

Glyphipteryx schoeniscolella: local, on black bog-rush.

ELACHISTIDAE

Elachista paludum: the larvae are common leaf-miners of sedges. *E. cerusella:* the blotch-mines of the larvae are rather commonly seen in leaves of reed and reed canary-grass.

YPONOMEUTIDAE

Willow Ermine (*Yponomeuta rorella*): in the summer of 1936, hundreds of white willows in the Waveney valley portion of broadland were defoliated by the caterpillars of this species. The damage was so extensive and spectacular that it attracted wide notice. Many of the trees were stripped bare of leaves and their branches and trunks were shrouded and festooned by vast communal webs containing thousands of larvae. Local authorities took measures for controlling what was regarded as a new pest in this part of England, but a plague of the caterpillars occurred locally again in the following summer. Although *Y. rorella* was not recognised in East Anglia until 1936, a Beccles entomologist, Mr. E. T. Goldsmith, had observed colonies of the caterpillars on willows in the neighbourhood of that town from about 1931 onward, so that the original invaders may have been quite few in number. In the early part of August 1937 large numbers of the moths were captured on the Outer Dowsing Light Vessel, thirty miles off the Norfolk coast, on two nights, showing that *Y. rorella* is capable of extending its range by long-distance flights. From 1938 onward, the insects became established in other parts of the broads and reached west Norfolk and the fens; but no further 'plague' has been reported. In the Waveney valley, the larvae were found to be parasitised commonly by *Herpestomus brunnicornis* (Grav.), one of the Ichneumonidae.

COLEOPHORIDAE

Coleophora viminetella: common on grey sallow, the larvae living in leaf-cases. *C. caespititiella:* very common on the flower-heads of rushes, the larvae living in white silken cases.

GRACILARIIDAE

Lithocolletis quinqueguttella: leaf-mining on creeping-willow. *L. stettinensis:* mining the upper sides of alder leaves. *L. froelichiella:* mining the undersides of alder leaves.

EPERMENIIDAE

Cataplectica fulviguttella: very common, the larvae feeding on developing fruits of angelica.

Epermenia illigerella: the larvae commonly spin sticky webs on the leaves and umbels of angelica.

PLUTELLIDAE

Orthotaelia sparganella: locally common, the larvae burrowing in the soft stems of bur-reed, yellow flag and broad-leaved sweet-grass.

LYONETIIDAE

Opostega auritella: a rather rare and localised fen insect; the larvae are miners in stems of marsh marigold. *O. crepusculella:* commonly associated with water-mint.

Bucculatrix frangulella: a common leaf-miner of buckthorn and alder buckthorn. *B. cidarella:* mining leaves of alder.

ADELIDAE

Adela cuprella: rather local, the larvae living in cases fashioned from pieces of fallen sallow leaves in the carrs.

STIGMELLIDAE

Stigmella alnetella: a common leaf-miner of alder. *S. salicii:* very common, mining leaves of grey sallow.

In addition to the swallowtail (see chapter 9), the following butterflies occur in broadland:

Wall (*Pararge megera*): common, with broods emerging in May and August.

Grayling (*Eumenis semele*): breeding in the coast dunes and to be seen visiting flowers on adjoining fens in the vicinity of Horsey and Winterton, July and August.

Hedge Brown (*Maniola tithonus*): very plentiful in some years, rare in others; single-brooded, July–August.

Small Heath (*Caenonympha pamphilus*): common, double-brooded and to be seen on the wing from mid-May until autumn.

Meadow Brown (*Maniola jurtina*): common, June–October.

Ringlet (*Aphantopus hyperanthus*): very common and not affected by wet summers so unfavourably as the other Satyrid butterflies in this area; single-brooded and on the wing from the end of June until mid-August.

Small Pearl-bordered Fritillary (*Argynnis selene*): often plentiful where bog violet grows, in June; occasionally there is a partial second brood.

Pearl-bordered Fritillary (*A. euphrosyne*): rare, May and June; almost confined to the coastal fringe.

Dark Green Fritillary (*A. aglaia*): mainly an insect of the sand dunes, but seen visiting marsh thistles on fens in July in a few broadland localities.

Silver-washed Fritillary (*A. paphia*): thinly distributed but increasing in wooded parts of the area.

Red Admiral (*Vanessa atalanta*): an immigrant, fluctuating in numbers from year to year.

Painted Lady (*V. cardui*): an immigrant, appearing in large numbers less frequently than the red admiral.

Small Tortoiseshell (*Aglais urticae*): very common and breeding freely on nettle-beds everywhere; often double-brooded.

Large Tortoiseshell (*Nymphalis polychlorus*): rare in most years, but locally plentiful from time to time. The larvae have been seen feeding on sallows overhanging the water at the edge of a broad, where their habit of dropping to the ground before pupation proved disastrous.

Camberwell Beauty (*N. antiopa*): this butterfly has appeared in the broads district on a great many occasions, usually towards the end of August. L. F. Newman has put forward the theory that all the *antiopa* met with in Britain have been shipped with timber from Scandinavia to east coast ports. Specimens have been taken on light-vessels off the Norfolk coast and more often in the open country of East Anglia than in the ports where the Baltic timber is unloaded; but whether or not this insect is migratory remains uncertain.

Peacock (*N. io*): breeding commonly everywhere in nettle beds; single-brooded.

Comma (*Polygonia c-album*): now a fairly common insect and generally distributed; the caterpillars have been seen feeding on wild hops, wild red-currant bushes in carrs and most frequently on nettles. This butterfly reached Norfolk from the west in 1935 and by 1938 had become well established in all parts of that country. Its numbers fluctuate from year to year, but it holds its own firmly.

White Admiral (*Limenitis camilla*): this insect spread to Norfolk in 1933 and colonies became established in a number of suitable woods in the broads district within the next five years, but there has been a noticeable decline in their numbers recently.

Silver-studded Blue (*Plebeius argus*): present in small numbers on some heath-clad commons in the district.

Common Blue (*Polyommatus icarus*): the caterpillars feed on the marsh bird's-foot trefoil in fens as well as on the common bird's-foot trefoil of drier habitats; in places subject to winter flooding, it appears likely that the hibernating larvae are mostly drowned and the insect is able to build up a strong fen population only after a succession of dry years.

Holly Blue (*Lycaenopsis argiolus*): common in some years, rare in others.

Small Copper (*Lycaena phlaeas*): round the broads, where the caterpillars feed on common sorrel, this butterfly is abundant in dry summers and comparatively scarce in wet years.

Purple Hairstreak (*Thecla quercus*): common in oak woods throughout the district.

Large White (*Pieris brassicae*): migratory swarms which cross the North Sea to the East Anglian coast fairly regularly at intervals between May and the end of August are often seen passing over the broads and visiting flowers in the marshes.

Small White (*Pieris rapae*): like *P. brassicae*, this species is only a passage migrant and wandering visitor and is not known to breed in the marshes.

Green-veined White (*P. napi*): a common resident and true inhabitant of fens and water-meadows, where the caterpillars of two successive broods each summer feed almost exclusively on the cuckoo-flower (*Cardamine pratensis*). Migratory flocks are also seen occasionally. The late Professor F. W. Oliver recorded that on one occasion he saw a great many of these butterflies caught by leaves of round-leaved sundews in a boggy part of broadland.

Orange-tip (*Euchloe cardamines*): despite its specific epithet, this butterfly does not lay its eggs commonly on *Cardamine pratensis* in fens near the broads, but breeds mainly on garlic mustard along the hedgerows. It is a butterfly of inland meadows and waysides rather than of the broads.

Clouded Yellow (*Colias croceus*): an irregular migrant from the south, seldom appearing here before June. In favourable years it visits the fens and is attracted by their flowers, but there is no evidence that its caterpillars feed on any of the leguminous plants of wet places.

Brimstone (*Gonepteryx rhamni*): a common resident, the caterpillars occurring on both common and alder buckthorns in the carrs. In early spring, male brimstones often appear far from their native haunts following hibernation and there is a certain amount of evidence to indicate that they make cross-country journeys to the broadland localities where their food-plants and the females await them. From early September onward, a preponderance of females has been noted in the fens, suggesting that some of the males have wandered away or else gone into hibernation sooner.

Dingy Skipper (*Erynnis tager*); Grizzled Skipper (*Syrichtus malvac*): localised and uncommon. Seen more frequently in meadows of the Waveney valley than elsewhere in the broads area.

Small Skipper (*Adopaea sylvestris*): a single-brooded insect, appearing on the wing commonly from the beginning of July until late August on all the grassy fens.

Large Skipper (*Ochlodes venata*): very common throughout the summer as a visitor to flowers in the marshes.

BEETLES (Coleoptera)

While numerous records of beetles taken here have been published in collectors' lists for more than a century past, no intensive studies of the marsh beetles have ever been undertaken, so that comparatively little is known of the distribution and numerical or bulk significance of the various species represented. The area offers splendid opportunities for such studies; but at the moment it is not possible except in a few cases to give any indication of how the beetle fauna of fens and reedswamps surrounding the broads compares significantly with that of the much better studied Wicken Fen in Cambridgeshire, although many species found at Wicken are known to be present in the broads. Even Balfour Browne's bionomic investigation of the water-beetles involved the sampling of only a small part of the district within easy working distance of the old Sutton Broad Laboratory; the dyke systems and broads of the Yare and Waveney valleys were neglected entirely. During the past twenty years, records have been kept of Coleoptera collected at all seasons from the reedswamps, fens and carrs of Wheatfen Broad, in the Yare valley, by the writer and visiting entomologists. These records have been used freely in the preparation of the account which follows and reference has been made also to numerous collections undertaken by the late H. J. Thouless in the Bure valley earlier in the present century. Lists of beetles taken from a number of other broadland localities have been published from time to time in *The Entomologist*, *The Entomologist's Monthly Magazine* and other journals; these also have been consulted, together with the late C. G. Doughty's manuscript account of the Coleoptera of Great Yarmouth and its neighbourhood (1929). While it is impracticable to furnish a full list of the species occurring in the district, attention is drawn to as many as possible of the more characteristic beetles of broadland habitats, including some that have a wide range as well as those more strictly localised.

CARABIDAE

The only species of *Carabus* common in the marshes is the shining bronze-coloured *C. granulatus*, which frequents the river banks and marsh walls and the margins of fens. *Cychrus caraboides* var. *rostratus*, which squeals when handled, occurs in the fen carrs where there is plenty of rotten wood. Carabids of damp ground here include *Leistus spinibarbis*, *L. fulvibarbis*, *L. terminatus*, *Nebria brevicollis*, *Notiophilus substriatus*, *N. biguttatus*, *Elaphrus cupreus*, *E. riparius*, *Loricera pilicornis*, *Dyschirius globosus*, *Asaphidion flavipes*, *Bembidion litorale*, *B. lampros*, *B. nitidulum*, *B. transparens* var. *clarki*, *B. normannum*, *B. quadrimaculatum*, *B. unicolor*, *B. guttula*, *Oodes helopioides*, *Badister bipustulatus*, *B. sodalis*, *Acupalpus meridianus*, *Bradycellus ruficollis*, *Trichocellus cognatus*, *T. placidus*, *Anisodactylus binotatus*, *Amara plebeja*, *A. similata*, *A. vulgaris*, *A. aenea*, *A. familiaris*, *Stomis pumicatus*, *Feronia caerulescens*, *F. vernalis* *F. nigra*, *F. nigrita* (very abundant in fens), *F. anthracina*, *F. minor* (common in fens), *F. strenua*, *F. diligens* (abundant in fens), *F. madida*, *F. cristata*, *Calathus piceus*, *Agonum mulleri*, *A. viduum* (common in fens), *A. fuliginosum*, *A. piceum*, *A. gracile*, *A. thoreyi* var. *puellum*. *Colliuris melanura*, a species confined to fens, is commonly associated with reed-beds everywhere in the district. The long, narrow-bodied Lebiini are represented by numerous species in fens and flood refuse, including *Risophilus monostigma*, *R. atricapillus*, *Dromius longiceps*, *D. linearis*, *D. agilis*, *D. meridionalis*, *D. quadrimaculatus*, *D. quadrinotatus*, *D. sigma*, *D. melanocephalus* and *D. notatus*.

WATER BEETLES

The area is particularly rich in water beetles and the number of species represented is large because most types of habitat favoured by these insects exist here. While there are few streams, many of the marsh drains carrying water to outfall pumps and sluices possess fairly fast-running currents at times and tides create little spates of movement in narrow channels connected with certain broads, chiefly in the Yare valley. There are slow rivers moving through peat and silt lands. The broads themselves vary in depth, and in the character of their bottom deposits and aquatic vegetation. There are large and small marsh drains in both peaty and silty grounds. Waterlogged portions of fens attract beetles characteristic of rush-grown peat pools and wet moss. Finally, numerous dykes in marshes near the coast are frequented by brackish-water species. A list of water beetles recorded from the broads is given below. After the name of each species a rough indication of its distributional frequency is provided:

c=generally common and widespread
f=of fairly wide distribution and moderately common
r=known from only a very few localities

The types of habitats occupied are denoted thus:

R=rivers, stream-like freshwater tidal waterways
L=open broads
D=freshwater ditches (fen drains usually with plenty of aquatic vegetation)
P=silt ponds and silty ditches
F=shallow mossy and peaty pools in rush fens
S=brackish pools and ditches

HALIPLIDAE (mainly algal feeders)

Peltodytes caesius	c				P		
Haliplus confinis	c		L	D	P		
obliquus	c			D	P		S
lineatocollis	c			D	P		S
ruficollis	c			D	P		S
heydeni	r			D			
fluviatilis	r	R			P		
lineolatus	f			D			
immaculatus	r			D			
wehnckei	f		L	D	P		
fulvus	c		L	D			
flavicollis	c		L		P		
mucronatus	r			D			
variegatus	c					F	

HYGROBIIDAE (carnivorous)

Hygrobia hermanni	f				P		

DYTISCIDAE (carnivorous)

Noterus clavicornis	c			D	P		
capricornis	c			D	P		S
Laccophilus minutus	c	R		D	P		
hyalinus	c	R		D	P		S
Hyphydrus ovatus	c	R		D	P		S
Bidessus unistriatus	f			D	P		
Hygrotus inaequalis	c			D	P		S
decoratus	r			D			
versicolor	f			D			
confluens	r				P		
parallelogrammus	r						S
impressopunctatus	f			D	P		
Deronectes duodecimpustulatus	f		L	D			S
assimilis	c		L	D	P		S
depressus	f		L				
Oreodytes halensis	r				P		
Hydroporus pictus	c			D	P		S
granularis	c			D	P	F	
lepidus	f	R		D		F	
dorsalis	c			D			
lineatus	c		L	D	P		
scalesianus	r					F	
neglectus	f			D	P		
tristis	r			D		F	
umbrosus	c			D		F	
angustatus	c			D		F	
gyllenhalii	c			D		F	
striola	c			D		F	
palustris	c			D	P		S
incognitus	f			D		F	
erythrocephalus	c			D	P	F	
melanarius	r					F	
memnonius	c			D	P	F	
obscurus	f					F	
nigrita	c			D		F	
pubescens	c			D		F	
planus	c			D	P		
tessellatus	f			D			
ferrugineus	r	R					
Laccornis oblongus	f					F	

Agabus paludosus	r	R					
unguicularis	c		L	D	P		
nebulosus	c			D	P		
conspersus	r						S
striolatus	r	R					
labiatus	r					F	
(*undulatus*, introduced to the broads from Askham Bog, Yorkshire, in 1906, by F. Balfour Browne)						F	
sturmii	c		L	D	P		
chalconotus	c					F	
bipustulatus	c			D	P	F	
Platambus maculatus	r	R	L				
Ilybius fuliginosus	c	R	L		P		S
ater	c			D	P	F	
quadriguttatus	c			D	P	F	
guttiger	c					F	
aenescens	r					F	
fenestratus	c			D	P		
Copelatus haemorrhoidalis	c			D	P	F	
Rantus grapii	c			D	P	F	
exsoletus	c			D		F	
pulverosus	c			D	P		
frontalis	f	R	L				S
bistriatus	r					F	
aberratus	r			D			
Colymbetes fuscus	c			D	P	F	
Dytiscus semisulcatus	c		L	D	P		
marginalis	c		L	D	P		
circumflexus	f						S
circumcinctus	r				P		
dimidiatus	r			D			
Hydaticus transversalis	c			D		F	
Graphoderus cinereus	r			D			
Acilius sulcatus	f		L	D	P	F	

GYRINIDAE (Whirligig beetles, swimming at the surface)

Gyrinus minutus	r					F	
natator var. *substriatus*	c			D	P		
suffriani	c			D		F	
bicolor	f		L	D		F	
caspius	f		L				S
colymbus	r					F	
marinus	c		L	D	P		S
aeratus	f	R	L	D			
opacus	r	R					

HYDROPHILIDAE (larvae carnivorous, adults mainly vegetarian)

The beetles of this family crawl slowly over water weeds and are to be found where these abound, in dykes, the shallower parts of broads and in mossy fen pools. In some instances brackish water is frequented to some extent, or even exclusively. Species present in a variety of aquatic habitats are listed below with 'V' following the name; 'S' indicates that the insect has been found in brackish water in this district.

Ochthebius dilatatus	c	V	S
bicolon	f		S
minimus	c	V	S
nanus	f	V	S
pusillus	c	V	S
marinus	c	V	S
Hydraena testacea	c	V	
palustris	f	V	
riparia	c	V	
Limnebius truncatellus	c	V	(often in wet moss)
papposus	c	V	(„)
nitidus	f	V	(„)
aluta	c	V	(„)
Helophorus nubilus	c	V	(often found out of water)
rufipes	r	V	S
alternans	f		S
aquaticus	c	V	S
brevipalpis	c	V	S
minutus	c	V	
flavipes	c	V	S
dorsalis	r	V	
nanus	r	V	
Hydrochus elongatus	f	V	
brevis	f	V	
angustatus	c	V	S
Coelostoma orbiculare	c	V	S
Hydrobius fuscipes	c	V	S
Limnoxenus niger	r		S
Anacaena globulus	c	V	S
limbata	c	V	S
bipustulata	c	V	
Laccobius minutus	r	V	
biguttatus	c	V	S
striatulus	c	(mainly in ponds)	
alutaceus	c	V	S
Helochares lividus	r	V	
punctatus	c	V	S

Enochrus melanocephalus	c	V	S	
bicolor	r		S	
testaceus	c	V	S	
coarctatus	c	V		
ochropterus	c	V	S	
Cymbiodyta marginella	c	V	S	
Chaetarthra seminulum	c	V	S	(often in wet moss)
Hydrophilus piceus	f	V	S	

(this, the largest of British water beetles, is rather scarce and local here and is found most frequently in silty dykes).

Berosus luridus	f	V	S

Terrestrial Hydrophilidae found in moss, rotting leaves, etc., in the fens and carrs include *Cercyon ustulatus*, *C. haemorrhoidalis*, *C. melanocephalus*, *C. lateralis*, *C. pygmaeus*, *C. unipunctatus*, *C. quisquilius*, *C. atricapillus*, *C. granarius*, *C. tristis*, *C. convexiusculus*, and *C. analis*, while *C. marinus* is found near the coast.

STAPHYLINIDAE

This family is represented by a very large number of species in marshy country, those of the genera *Stenus* and *Tachyporus* being specially abundant in fens and flood refuse. One small orange-and-black species, *Paederus riparius*, is a characteristic inhabitant of the reed-swamps. The larvae of marsh Staphylinidae feed largely on minute fungi of decaying vegetation on the ground.

LAMPYRIDAE

The glow-worm (*Lampyris noctiluca*) is locally abundant in many of the fens of broadland, where it preys upon a variety of snails. Both larval and adult glow-worms are commonly attacked by a pale pink powdery fungus (*Isaria fumoso-rosea*) in this district (Pl. XII).

CANTHARIDAE

Many beetles of this family are common visitors to fen flowers in summer, rejoicing in sunshine and flying very freely. Their predaceous larvae are to be found crawling about fen litter and in sedge tussocks as well as amongst moss and decaying wood in the carrs. *Silis ruficollis*, black, with an orange thorax, is the most typical fen species; others seen on the flowers include *Cantharis rustica*, *C. nigricans*, *C. pellucida*, *C. livida*, *C. figurata*, *C. rufa*, *C. pallida* and *C. fulvicollis*; *Rhagonycha fulva*, *R. testacea*, *R. limbata* and *R. lignosa*; *Malthinus fasciatus* and *Malthodes dispar*.

MALACHIIDAE

The brilliant blue-green and red beetles of this family are conspicuous on flowers in and near fens in summer; the most usual species seen are

Malachius marginellus and *M. bipustulatus*, *Ceraphetes terminatus* and *Anthocomus rufus*.

ELATERIDAE (Click-beetles)

The species breeding in fens and carrs include: *Adelocera murina*, *Hypnoides riparius* (the most typical marsh click-beetle), *Limonius minutus*, *Athous hirtus*, *A. vittatus* and *A. haemorrhoidalis*, *Corymbites siaelandicus*, *C. incanus*, *Agriotes acuminatus*, *A. pallidulus*, *A. obscurus* (with wire-worm larvae at plant roots), *Dolopius marginatus*, *Adrastus nitidulus* and *Denticollis linearis*.

HELODIDAE

The fen species include *Microcara testacea*, *Cyphon variabilis*, *C. padi* (in abundance), *C. coarctatus* and *Scirtes hemisphaericus*.

NITIDULIDAE

Kateretes bipustulatus is commonly associated with sedges and meadowsweet in fens. Several species of *Meligethes* are to be found in flowers of most marsh plants throughout the summer.

RHIZOPHAGIDAE

Rhizophagus bipustulatus lives under the bark of dead trees in the carrs.

CUCUJIDAE

Psammoecus bipunctatus abounds in the fens and many specimens are to be found hibernating in the tops of sedge tussocks and under dead leaf bases of reed-mace. *Pediacus dermestoides* occurs under the bark of dead alders.

EROTYLIDAE

Triplax russica and *Dacne rufifrons* have been found in bracket-fungi on trees in carrs.

CRYPTOPHAGIDAE

These extremely small beetles have not received adequate study in this area. *Atomaria nitidula*, *A. mesomela* and *A. fuscata* have been recorded from fens and reedswamps.

PHALACRIDAE

Phalacrus brisouti and *P. nigrinus* are present in fens. *Olibrus corticalis* is common in carrs and visits marsh flowers with *O. liquidus*, which is often abundant in fen litter. *Stilbus testaceus* is not uncommon under trees.

LATHRIDIIDAE

The beetles of this family are associated with moulds on rotting wood and leaves. Fen carr species include *Lathridius lardarius* and *L. nodifer*, *Enicmus minutus* and various *Corticaria* and *Corticarina* spp.

MYCETOPHAGIDAE

Mycetophagus quadripustulatus and *M. multipunctatus* live in bracket-fungi on various trees.

ENDOMYCHIDAE

The bright red, black-spotted *Endomychus coccineus* occurs locally in carrs and on willows planted beside the marsh roadways, where its larvae feed on woody fungi. The beetle is apt to be taken for a somewhat elongate and very glossy ladybird.

COCCINELLIDAE (Ladybirds)

This family is well represented in broadland habitats. The small reddish brown *Coccidula rufa* is to be found in fens throughout the year, with the comparatively rare *C. scutellata*, and *Rhyzobius litura*. The following true ladybirds occur here: *Hippodamia 13-punctata*: (rare, in fens and hibernating in litter). *Adonia variegata:* an occasional visitor only; has been found on angelica flowers in the marshes in autumn. *Anisosticta 19-punctata:* this might well be called the ' reed ladybird ', since it is a marsh insect most commonly associated with reeds; the adults are found throughout the year; eggs are laid in May and the greyish larvae feed on aphids on reed leaves in June, to produce a new generation of the ladybirds in mid-July. The adults are to some extent mycophagous and browse on moulds (especially *Cladosporium* sp.) which develop on dying leaves and stems of plants. They hibernate in hollow stems and leaf-sheaths of reed, reed-mace and sedge.

Aphidecta obliterata: usually associated with conifers, but finds its way on to fens occasionally.

Micraspis 16-punctata; a small faintly yellow, black-spotted ladybird often extremely common in upland field-crops, lives also to a small extent in fens, where it may be found in every month, mainly by searching grassy edges of marsh walls. This species hibernates gregariously and vast numbers are to be found massed under flood refuse on occasion.

Adalia 10-punctata: occurs usually in small numbers throughout the year and is found on trees and bushes in carrs rather than on herbaceous plants in wet places. *A. bipunctata:* very abundant and widespread in some years, the adults appearing in every month and breeding May to July. In spring and early summer the insects feed mainly on the aphids of bushes and trees and in late summer on those of herbaceous plants, including those of marsh country. Two generations are produced in favourable summers, when enormous numbers of these ladybirds emerge on aphis-infested willows and are dispersed over the countryside. The males visit angelica flowers for nectar.

The familiar seven-spotted red ladybird, *Coccinella 7-punctata*, is found in the adult state in every month of the year and breeds in April, May and June. A large emergence usually takes place about mid-July. This insect feeds on aphids on a great variety of trees, shrubs and low-growing plants in all kinds of situations and it is not uncommon in fen country, where it is seen chiefly on trees and bushes, except in late summer and autumn, when males very commonly visit angelica flowers for nectar. Specimens not uncommonly hibernate fully exposed on twigs in the carrs, where they may be seen beaded with frost in hard weather; but most of them seek shelter in hedges and undergrowth during the winter. The smaller *C. 11-punctata* is not uncommon round the margins of fens, but is more often associated with gorse bushes; it has been found hibernating in flood refuse and on sedge tussocks. *C. hieroglyphica* is a heath insect only rarely appearing in the marshes.

Halyzia 16-guttata: a large reddish-brown ladybird ornamented with yellowish spots. It is a characteristic insect of fen carrs and other valley woodlands, but is seldom abundant. The adult insects have been noticed on various trees and bushes in such habitats from February to the end of June.

Thea 22-punctata: a very common and widely distributed yellow ladybird, appears fairly regularly in fens, but in small numbers as a rule; specimens are found hibernating in marsh litter and under fallen leaves in the carrs.

Calvia 14-guttata: a medium-sized red-brown insect with white spots and occurs in various types of woodland, including the carrs. This species breeds later in the summer than other ladybirds and the main emergence takes place in September.

Propylea 14-punctata: the common yellow-and-black 'anchor-marked' ladybird, is abundant all the year round. It is an early breeder and a large emergence takes place at the end of June. The adults and larvae prey upon aphids on all sorts of trees, shrubs and herbaceous plants in a variety of situations, including carrs, fens and reedswamps. The males are common visitors to angelica flowers in August and September.

Anatis ocellata; associated with conifers, has been found occasionally here on Scots pines planted near the broads.

Chilocorus renipustulatus: a highly glossy black ladybird ornamented with two red spots. It is common on the trunks of ash trees and on branches of alder, buckthorn and grey sallow in the carrs; it has been found also on bog myrtle here. The adults have been seen in every month except July.

Exochomus 4-pustulatus: rather like the last species mentioned, is somewhat smaller and has four red spots. It is found on trunks and branches of various trees and bushes in the carrs and is often associated with ash and Scots pine. It breeds from March to May.

OEDEMERIDAE

Oedemera nobilis has been found visiting umbelliferous flowers with *Oe. virescens* and in flowers of great bindweed in August. Neither insect appears to be at all common.

PYTHIDAE

Vincinzellus viridipennis and *Rhinosimus planirostris* occur under bark in the carrs.

PYROCHROIDAE

The scarlet cardinal beetle, *Pyrochroa serraticornis*, which breeds in rotten oak wood, is often to be seen sitting about on marsh plants.

MELOIDAE

In some years, the metallic green blister beetle, *Lytta vesicatoria* is seen feeding on wild privet as well as on privet in local gardens, in large numbers. Then several years may pass without one being noticed anywhere in the district.

Meloe proscarabaeus is the only oil beetle found occasionally on grassy marsh banks here in spring.

RHIPIPHORIDAE

Metoecus paradoxus, parasitic in the nests of social wasps, occurs here in variable numbers from year to year.

MORDELLIDAE

The beetles of this family are nearly all visitors to hawthorn blossoms and their larvae feed in woody and herbaceous stems. The beetles are also attracted by the flowers of umbellifers, wild currants in the fen carrs and flowers of common buckthorn. The species recorded from broadland localities include *Mordellistena pumila*, *Anaspis rufilabris*, *A. frontalis*, *A. pulicaria*, *A. regimbarti*, *A. lurida*, *A. humeralis* and *A. maculata*.

MELANDRYIDAE

Tetratoma fungorum, a small blue beetle with an orange thorax, breeds commonly in the birch bracket fungus (*Polyporus betulinus*). *Melandrya caraboides* and *Conopalpus testaceus* are associated with rotten wood.

LAGRIIDAE

Lagria hirta is a common visitor to many fen flowers and breeds in dead leaves carpeting damp ground under trees.

ALLECULIDAE

Isomira murina is found on fen flowers occasionally.

SCARABAEIDAE

Geotrupes spiniger, *G. stercorarius* and *G. stercorosus* are the common large dung-beetles of the grazing marshes here; in addition, *G. mutator* has been noticed occasionally. Most of the numerous British species of *Aphodius* have been recorded from this area. All the cockchafers appear to avoid breeding in waterlogged soils.

LUCANIDAE

The small stag-beetle, *Dorcus parallelipipedus*, breeds commonly in decaying trunks of ash trees in some of the carrs.

CERAMBYCIDAE

Only a few kinds of long-horn beetles are at all common here. *Grammoptera ruficornis*, a familiar insect on hawthorn blossoms, is also a frequent visitor to flowers of buckthorn in the carrs in June. *Strangalia maculata* breeds commonly in birch and sallow boughs and the beetle visits fen flowers in summer; *S. quadrifasciata*, whose larvae feed in alder wood, is a somewhat rare insect of fens in the Bure valley. *Molorchus minor*, breeding in conifers, visits marsh flowers in suitable localities. The large, fragrant musk beetle, whose larvae live in stems of grey sallow, is extremely rare in Norfolk; at the present time its only east Norfolk habitat appears to be in the vicinity of Surlingham Broad.

Clytus arietis, the zebra beetle, is extremely plentiful, breeding in dead boughs of sallow and birch. *Leiopus nebulosus*, associated with dying oak boughs, is found only very locally. *Agapanthia villosoviridescens*, a true fen species, is widely distributed and fairly common; it is most frequently seen on hemp agrimony here, but the larvae are said to live in stems of thistles and hogweed.

CHRYSOMELIDAE

The metallic ' reed-beetles ' (Donaciinae) are well represented. The larvae feed on submerged roots and rhizomes of aquatic and reed-swamp plants and obtain their oxygen for respiration by tapping the air-filled spaces between the cellular tissues of their host plants. Cocoons are formed in late summer and these also are attached in such a way that they have access to air supplies from the plants underwater. The beetles develop quickly, but remain quiescent in their cocoons from autumn until late spring before emerging. One species, *Macroplea mutica*, var. *curtisii*, continues to live underwater when it reaches the adult state; it is able to do this because the surface of its body is covered with a golden pile of short, bent hairs which hold a thin layer of gas. This plastron mechanism, as it is called, enables the insect to make use of oxygen in the surrounding water for respiration. Similar mechanisms have been perfected by only a very few other kinds of aquatic insects, of which the most notable example is the water bug *Aphelocheirus*. *M. m. curtisii* is found crawling on the pondweed *Potamogeton pectinatus* in slightly brackish ditches near Great Yarmouth and at Hickling Broad; the cocoons have been found attached to rootstocks of common reed; the beetles are active in May and June.

Donacia clavipes is attached to the reeds at the edges of most of the broads;

the beetles feed on reed leaves from May until August. *D. crassipes* is associated throughout its life with white and yellow water-lilies and has been found in the neighbourhood of Ranworth Broad. *D. versicolorea* is wholly attached to the pondweed *Potamogeton natans*, on which it is locally common, the beetles appearing from May to August. *D. semicuprea* is found in great abundance feeding on the leaves of broad-leaved rond-grass (*Glyceria maxima*) from May to July; the leaves become scarred extensively with small bleached patches and in some parts of the Yare valley acres of the grass damaged in this way can be seen in most years; the larvae of this species are associated most commonly with the *Glyceria*, but also feed on bur-reed (*Sparganium* spp.). *D. sparganii* beetles visit yellow water-lily flowers in summer in a few places here, but the larval host has not been identified. *D. aquatica*, associated with bur-reed (*Sparganium*) and great spearwort (*Ranunculus lingua*) has been noticed occasionally in some of the broads in July. *D. impressa*, attached to bulrush (*Schoenoplectus lacustris*) appears to be rare in this district. *D. marginata*, on the common bur-reed (*Sparganium ramosum*), is fairly common in June and July; *D. bicolora*, also on this host, appears to be rare. *D. obscura* has been found locally on flowers of the sedge *Carex rostrata* in swampy parts of the fens. *D. thalassina*, on lesser reed-mace and common club-rush, is one of the rarer species here. *D. simplex*, another bur-reed insect, is common and widespread; the beetle is active from June to August. *D. cinerea*, attached to both great and lesser reed-maces, is not uncommon at Hickling, Sutton and Ranworth Broads, from May to August.

Plateumaris discolor is associated with the cotton-grass *Eriophorum angustifolium* in at least one broadland locality. *P. sericea*, an exceedingly common and variable species, which may be gold, bronze, fiery copper-coloured, green, blue or violet, is conspicuous everywhere in the marshes in early summer; it is most commonly seen on yellow flag (*Iris pseudacorus*), but feeds also on marsh marigold (*Caltha palustris*), sedges (*Carex* spp.), reed (*Phragmites*), reed-mace (*Typha*), bur-reed (*Sparganium*), broad-leaved rond-grass (*Glyceria maxima*) and bulrushes (*Schoenoplectus* and *Scirpus*). *P. braccata* is attached to the reed (*Phragmites*) and is common in the wetter reed beds throughout the area, including places where the water is brackish, in June and July. *P. affinis*, associated with the sedge *Carex nigra*, has been recorded from Ranworth.

Lema cyanella (on thistles), *L. lichenis* (on grey sallow) and *L. melanopa* are common in the fens, and hibernate in marsh litter.

The only common fen-dwelling species of *Chrysolina* is *C. polita*, which feeds on water-mint and gipsywort, on which the larvae abound in early summer. The metallic green *Gastrophysa viridula* and the blue-and-orange *G. polygoni* are rather common on docks and *Polygonum* spp. in marsh habitats, as are *Phaedon cochleariae* (on Cruciferae), *P. armoraciae* (on *Callitriche* spp.), *Hydrothassa marginella* (on buttercups), *Prasocuris junci* (on water speedwells) and *P. phellandrii* (often on marsh marigold). The very large reddish *Chrysomela populi* is locally common on the creeping willow (*Salix repens*) here. *Phyllodecta laticollis* is common on grey sallow. *Timarcha tenebricosa* is rare, on goosegrass (*Galium aparine*) on marsh staithes.

Galerucella viburni commonly strips the leaves from guelder-rose bushes in the fen carrs here, year after year, in early summer. *G. pusilla* is rather local, on purple loosestrife. *G. tenella* is common everywhere on meadowsweet. *G. nymphaeae* feeds on water-lilies, marsh cinquefoil and meadowsweet. *Galeruca tanaceti* is widely distributed, but not common, on water-mint. *Lochmaea capreae* abounds on sallow and alder. *Phyllobrotica quadrimaculata* is locally common in fens, feeding on skullcap (*Scutellaria galericulata*). Marsh species of flea-beetles, mainly attacking Cruciferae, include *Phyllotreta vittula* (on watercress), *P. undulata*, *P. exclamationis* and *P. atra*. *Aphthona lutescens* is common on purple loosestrife and marsh cinquefoil, *A. euphorbiae* on hemp agrimony and *A. coerulea* on yellow flag. The genus *Longitarsus* is represented here by *L. pellucidus* (chiefly on clovers), *L. succineus* (on hemp agrimony), *L. rubiginosus* (on great bindweed), *L. nasturtii* (on cresses) and *L. holsaticus* (on red-rattle, *Pedicularis palustris*).

Haltica lythri is abundant almost everywhere on hairy willowherb (*Epilobium hirsutum*) and is found locally on purple loosestrife; the brilliantly metallic blue beetles hibernate in marsh litter and may be seen swarming out in the early spring sunshine in great numbers where the willowherb is established on river banks. *Crepidodera transversa* is associated with rushes. *Hippuriphila modeeri* feeds on the horsetail *Equisetum arvense* at the upland margins of fens. *Chalcoides aurea*, *C. fulvicornis*, *C. aurata* and *C. plutus* are all small metallic beetles present on the foliage of sallows and osiers. *Chaetocnema concinna* is found amongst dead leaves in the carrs and *C. sahlbergii* is associated with sedges. *Psylliodes affinis* and *P. dulcamarae* occur on woody nightshade, *P. picina* has been noticed on purple loosestrife and *P. napi* is common on Cruciferae in marshes.

Of the tortoise beetles, *Cassida viridis* is locally common on water-mint, *C. rubiginosa* is widespread on thistles and *C. vittata*, usually a salt-marsh insect, is found occasionally on fens inland, despite the fact that its known food plants are glasswort (*Salicornia* spp.) and sea spurrey (*Spergularia* spp.).

BRUCHIDAE

Bruchus loti is not uncommon on marsh bird's-foot trefoil.

CURCULIONIDAE (Weevils)

The list provided here is by no means exhaustive, but is intended to give a fair picture of the occurrence of many common and widespread weevils in fens and carrs adjacent to the broads, while including also most of the species more strictly associated with aquatic and waterside plants.

Caenorhinus germanicus and *C. aeneovirens*, on oak. *Byctiscus betulae*, on birch.

Apion hydrolapathi and *A. curtirostre*, on docks (especially *Rumex hydrolapa-*

thum); *A. vicinum*, on water-mint; *A. confluens*, on Compositae; *A. ulicis* and *A. striatum* on gorse; *A. ervi*, *A. pomonae*, *A. virens*, *A. nigritarse*, *A. apricans* and *A. varipes* on various low-growing Leguminosae.

Otiorrhynchus ovatus is commonly found in moss round the edges of fens. The metallic and mostly green scale-dusted leaf weevils (*Phyllobius parvulus*, *P. virideaeris*, *P. oblongus*, *P. pyri* and *P. maculicornis*), are common on oaks and sallows, while *P. calcaratus* is found on alders and *P. pomaceus* abounds on nettles. *Polydrusus pterygomalis* is not uncommon on various trees, especially birch and sallow. *Liophloeus tessulatus* occurs locally on Umbelliferae. The dull brown weevils of the genus *Sitona* are represented by numerous species associated with Leguminosae. *Tanymecus palliatus*, mainly a coast insect, has been found associated with thistles in the marshes. *Lixus paraplecticus* has been recorded on angelica here. *Bagopus diglyptus* has been found at Sutton Broad only. *Hydronomus alismatis* is usually found on horsetails (*Equisetum* spp.). *Tanysphyrus lemnae* abounds on duckweed everywhere and may often be seen crawling underwater. *Dorytomus taeniatus* is very common on sallow. *Notaris acridulus*, *Thryogenes nereis* and *T. festucae* are all common on sedges. *Acalypta carpini*, a rare fen species, occurs on sallow. *Anthonomus rubi*, var. *brunneipennis* is associated locally with marsh cinquefoil. The long beaked weevils of the genus *Curculio* include *C. venosus*, *C. villosus* and *C. glandium* on oak and *C. salicivorus* on sallow. *Alophus triguttatus* abounds on ribwort plantain. *Phytonomus rumicis* on docks and *P. nigrirostris* and *P. posticus* on trefoils, are widespread. *Cryptorhynchidius lapathi* is present on alder. *Limnobaris t-album* and *L. pilistriata* are peculiarly slender weevils of sedge fens, the first being common and the second rare.

Coeliodes dryados is attached to oak. *Cidnorhinus quadrimaculatus* abounds on nettle. *Ceuthorhynchus pyrrhorhynchus*, *C. cochleariae* and *C. erysimi* feed on various Cruciferae and *C. melanostictus* is rather common on water-mint and gipsywort. *Tapinotus sellatus* is extremely local, on yellow loosestrife in a few fens of the Bure valley and at Alderfen Broad. *Poophagus sisymbrii* is common on watercress. *Stenopelmus rufinasus* has been found living on the little water fern (*Azolla filiculoides*) on a few occasions at Wroxham, Horning and Acle. *Nanophyes marmoratus* is common on purple loosestrife. *Mecinus pyraster* attacks ribwort plantain and *Gymnetron villosulum* forms galls on water speedwell. Water figwort is commonly infested with three kinds of weevils, *Cionus alauda*, *C. scrophulariae* and *Cleopus pulchellus*.

SCOLYTIDAE

Hylesinus fraxini, the ash bark beetle, abounds in ash trees of the Yare valley carrs. *Trypodendron domesticum* occurs in decaying birch and alder.

Hymenoptera

1. SYMPHYTA (Sawflies)

These insects have not been studied comprehensively in the broads district, but the local sawfly fauna, so far as it has been investigated, resembles closely that of Wicken Fen in Cambridgeshire. Most of the species listed below have been found in fens and carrs at Wheatfen Broad, Surlingham (1934–56); a few records have been added from fens of the Bure and its tributaries and from those of the Waveney valley. The names used are those of Kloet and Hincks' *Check List*.

Pamphilus sylvaticus
Hartigia linearis
Cephus tabidus, *pallipes*, *pygmaeus*, *cultratus*
Arge rustica, *ustulata*, *ciliaris*, *ochropus*, *cyaneocrocea*, *malanochroa*
Cimbex femorata
Trichiosoma lucorum
Abia sericea
Tenthredo maculata, *mesomelas*, *temula*, *atra*, *livida*, *scrophulariae*, *arcuata*, *viridis*, *picta*
Aglaostigma aucupariae
Tenthredopsis nassata (several varieties)
Macrophya ribis, *duodecimpunctata*, *blanda*, *annulata*, *rapae*
Loderus vestigialis
Dolerus pratensis, *aericeps*, *anticus*, *gonager*, *puncticollis*, *anthracinus*, *picipes*, *nigratus*, *sanguinicollis* v. *fumosus*
Monsoma pulverata
Monostegia abdominalis
Eriocampa ovata
Allantus togatus
Emphytus calceatus, *cinctus*
Protemphytus tener, *carpini*
Ametastegia equiseti, *glabrata*
Empria excisa, *liturata*, *tridens*, *longicornis*
Rhadinoceraea micans
Blennocampa pusilla, *ruficrurus*, *geniculata*
Phymatocera aterrima
Tomostethus nigritus
Eutomostethus luteiventris, *ephippium*, *funereus*
Stethomostus fuliginosus
Athalia lineolata, *cordata*, *glabricollis*, *lugens*, *scutellariae*
Pseudohemitaxonus sharpi
Strongylogaster lineata
Selandria serva, *sixii*
Aneugmenus stramineipes

Melisandra morio
Metallus pumilus
Profenusa pygmaea
Fenusa ulmi, *pusilla*
Heterarthrus vagans, *nemoratus*, *microcephalus*
Caliroa limacina, *cinxia*, *annulipes*, *varipes*
Endelomyia aethiops
Cladius pectinicornis
Priophorus eradiatus
Hemichroa alni
Hoplocampa crataegi
Platycampus luridiventris
Croesus septentrionalis
Euura saliceti
Pontania leucosticta, *viminalis*, *proxima*, *bridgmanii*
Dineura stilata
Holcocneme caeruleocarpa
Pteronidea miliaris, *ribesii*, *myosotidis*, *segmentaria*, *viridescens*, *oligospi.a*, *capraea*, *brevivalvis*
Amauronematus viduatus
Nematinus luteus
Pachynematus albipennis, *xanthocarpus*
Pristiphora pallipes, *fulvipes*, *pallidiventris*

2. PARASITICA (Ichneumons, gall-wasps, chalcids and proctotrupids)

The parasitic Hymenoptera have received little serious study in the broads district and since most records of their occurrence here were made more than half a century ago by the late J. B. Bridgman, the reader is referred to his various lists of Norfolk Hymenoptera published in the *Transactions of the Norfolk and Norwich Naturalists' Society* and the *Victoria History of Norfolk*.

Among the insects parasitised by ichneumons are the larvae of caddis flies, while certain chalcids choose hosts among the water bugs, dragonflies and water beetles. Nearly all kinds of terrestrial arthropods are victims of at least one of the parasitica and some species of ichneumons are in the habit of attacking many different hosts. These insects may often be found visiting fen flowers in spring and summer and the females of many ichneumons hibernate on the fens in sedge tussocks, reedy litter and the hollow stems of marsh plants, while others hide in moss or under bark. The ichneumon *Trogus lapidator*, which parasitises the swallowtail butterfly, appears to be rare, fortunately.

3. ACULEATA (Ants, wasps, bees, etc.)

Formicidae (Ants)

Only one of the red ants, *Myrmica laevinodis*, lives here in fens subject to regular flooding, often making its nests in peaty tussocks of sedges. *M. ruginodis* is present in fairly damp situations here and there on marsh tracks and embankments, while *M. scabrinodis* prefers still drier habitats. The black ant (*Lasius fuliginosus*) lives in association with dead standing trees in some of the fen carrs. The yellow meadow ant (*L. flavus*) makes its hillocks on some of the grazing marshes, but avoids fens. *L. niger* abounds, as elsewhere, in gardens and houses of the district. The large black ant (*Formica fusca*) with its variety *rubescens* colonises marsh walls to some extent, and is found also in gardens.

Pompilidae

Only one of the spider-hunting wasps, *Priocnemis perturbator*, appears to frequent fens at all commonly.

Vespidae

Mason wasps visiting marsh flowers include *Odynerus spinipes*, *O. melanocephalus; Ancistrocerus callosus*, *A. parietum*, *A. trimarginatus*, *A. parietinus*, *A. antilope* and *Symmorphus sinuatissimus*. The hornet (*Vespa crabro*) is thinly distributed over the area and nests occasionally in decayed tree stumps in the carrs. Of the social wasps, *Vespula rufa* affects the most marshy situations for nesting, but *V. vulgaris* and *V. germanicus* often occupy nests in marsh walls and rotten tree stumps in carrs.

Sphecidae

A great many of the bigger wasps inhabit dry sandy country, but some are quite common about the broads, visiting fen flowers (especially angelica in late summer) and preying upon flies, froghoppers and other insects in damp situations. These include *Passaloecus insignis*, *Crabro cribrarius*, *Ablepharipus podagricus*, *Acanthocrabro vagabundus*, *Hoplocrabro quadrimaculatus*, *Clytochrysus cavifrons* and *C. chrysostigmus*, *Solenius continuus*, *Corynopus coarctatus*, *Nysson spinosus*, *N. trimaculatus* and *N. dimidiatus*, *Gorytes mystaceus*, *Hoplisus quadrifasciatus*, *Mellinus arvensis* and *M. sabulosus*.

Apidae

While most kinds of bees from the surrounding countryside visit flowers in the marshes at some time, very few breed in wet situations. Two species only may be regarded as true fen insects; these are *Prosopis pectoralis*, which uses empty cigar-galls in reeds as its brood-chambers and *Macropis labiata*, which breeds in the hollow stems of marsh plants and collects pollen largely from flowers of the yellow loosestrife. Other bees known to breed in the close vicinity of broads, either burrowing in wood or in the mossy or grassy banks, include the following: *Halictus calceatus*, *H. tumulorum*, and *H. smeathmanellus*, *Sphecodes gibbus*, *S. crassus* and *S. miniatus*, *Andrena rosae*, *A. varians*, *A. armata* and *A. dorsata*, *Nomada obtusifrons*, *N. lathburiana and N. sheppardana*, various species of *Megachile*, *Stelis punctulatissima*, *Chelostoma florisomne* and the humble-bees, *Bombus terrestris*, *B. lapidarius*, *B. ruderatus*, *B. hortorum*, *B. sylvarum*, *B. agrorum* and *B. muscorum* (with the cuckoo-bees, *Psithyrus rupestris*, *P. campestris* and *P. vestalis*).

FLIES (*Diptera*)

No thorough ecological study of even a single family of Diptera has ever been undertaken in the broads district and we owe most of our knowledge of these insects to a few visiting collectors who have published lists of their captures in various broadland localities, in entomological journals and in the *Transactions of the Norfolk and Norwich Naturalists' Society*. In preparing the account which follows, use has been made also of a number of unpublished records of Diptera collected at Wheatfen Broad, in the Yare valley, since 1933.

TIPULIDAE

Craneflies abound in marsh pastures and throughout the fens and damp woodlands. Fifteen species of *Tipula*, five of *Nephrotoma* and two of *Prionocera* are known here. Their leather-jacket larvae are present in soil, wet peat and rotten wood. *Tipula paludosa* appears in great numbers on the drained grazing levels in summer; *T. maxima*, the longest-winged British fly, inhabits the carrs. The true fen species include the dusky-winged *T. nigra*, the grey-bodied *Prionocera turcica* and the rare *P. proxima*, first noticed as a British insect at Catfield in 1920. *Cylindrotoma distinctissima*, whose caterpillar-like larvae feed on leaves of marsh marigold, is fairly common. *Phalacrocera replicata*, with aquatic larvae feeding on mosses, has been found in some of the more swampy parts of fens. Limoniine gnats of many kinds breed in the marshes and carrs and may be seen dancing rhythmically in smoky columns over waterside bushes towards dusk on summer evenings.

TRICHOCERIDAE

Winter gnats (*Trichocera* spp.) may be seen on the wing at all seasons, about the fen banks and over the drained grazing marshes; it is unusual to find them in the wetter areas.

ANISOPODIDAE

In this family, only one species, *Anisopus punctatus*, frequents fens in abundance; there its larvae feed in wet decaying vegetable matter.

PTYCHOPTERIDAE

Superficially resembling craneflies, with shining bodies and spotted wings, these are characteristic insects of the carrs. Their aquatic larvae, equipped with long breathing tubes like the rat-tailed maggots of drone-flies, feed amongst wet decaying leaves. *Ptychoptera contaminata* and *P. albimana* are widely distributed; *P. scutellaris* occurs typically in alder carrs and *P. lacustris* appears to have been noticed at Wheatfen Broad only.

PSYCHODIDAE

The small moth-flies or owl-midges abound in the fens and reedswamps, where their white larvae and dusky cylindrical pupae may be found everywhere in rotting mats of vegetation. Typical fen species include *Clytocerus ocellaris*, *Pericoma nubila* and *P. fusca.*

CULICIDAE

The mosquitoes are well represented. All the British species of *Anopheles* occur here. *A. claviger* is generally distributed and breeds chiefly in shallow water under trees; its population usually reaches peak abundance in July and there is another slightly smaller peak in September. *A. algeriensis* breeds freely in the shallow backwaters of Hickling and Barton Broads, which are its main strongholds in Britain. *A. plumbeus*, with larvae living in water-filled hollows in trees, is rare here. *A. maculipennis* is only fairly common in broadland; the variety *atroparvus*, capable of transmitting malaria, is restricted to ditches of brackish water near the coast, while the innocuous var. *messae* occurs farther inland. *Theobaldia annulata* is widespread and usually the earliest mosquito to bite in spring, when it emerges from hibernation. *T. fumipennis* breeds in shallow water at Horsey and *T. morsitans* is present locally at several of the broads. *Taeniorhynchus richiardii*, whose larvae tap their supplies of oxygen from submerged parts of water plants, has been found near broads of the Ant, Thurne and Yare. *Aedes vexans* is present in fens; *A. annulipes* breeds mainly in swamp-carrs; *A. dorsalis* is restricted to brackish marsh ditches near the coast, in company with *A. detritus*. *A. cinereus* is a small reddish mosquito breeding in reedy pools on the marshes; it is an aggressive biter, but rarely moves out in to the open, so that people going about the broads in boats usually remain unmolested unless they happen to step ashore. The innocuous gnat, *Culex pipiens* is generally common and the biting *C. molestus* has so far been noticed only in the vicinity of Norwich.

CHIRONOMIDAE

The non-biting midges, most of which have aquatic larvae, have not been the subject of critical study in this area, although they occur in great abundance. Swarms of them rise from the water to dance high in the air at sunset and it is usual for swallows, martins, swifts and bats to assemble over the broads to feed on them in summer. Certain early species are taken by black terns here during their spring migration. It has been found that some Chironomid larvae usually associated with decaying stems of reedswamp plants in the broads also burrow into soft wood in the bottoms of boats moored on the broads.

CERATOPOGONIDAE

The minute biting midges of this family are a source of annoyance to humans who loiter in marshy places on warm summer evenings, *Culicoides pulicaris* being the chief culprit, but the insects are nothing like so troublesome here as on the northern moors.

SIMULIIDAE

These small, black, hump-backed flies have aquatic larvae, but the adults range far from water on occasion. *Simulium erythrocephalum* attacks cattle on the grazing marshes and *S. equinum* bites the ears of horses; but neither is a major pest in this area.

BIBIONIDAE

No flies of this family appear to breed in very wet situations. The larvae in most cases feed gregariously in organic soils, under moss or at roots. Several species of *Bibio* are common visitors to umbelliferous flowers in fens and some breed along the marsh walls.

SCATOPSIDAE

Ectaetia platyscelis and *Aldrovandiella halterata* are the most noteworthy broadland representatives of this family of small blackish flies breeding in dung and rotting vegetation.

MYCETOPHILIDAE

Fungus-gnats do not appear to be common in marshes. The yellow-bodied, black-winged *Sciara thomae* is the only conspicuously common species seen swarming at the water's edge in late summer.

CECIDOMYIIDAE

The gall midges and their allies have not been studied at all adequately here and would well repay closer investigation. The more familiar species include the following. *Lasioptera rubi*, producing stem galls on wild raspberry; *Thomasiella arundinis* with reddish yellow larvae in thickened shoots of reed; *Rhabdophaga marginemtorquens*, in rolled leaf-margins of common osier; *R. rosaria*, producing large leafy rosette-galls on white willow and grey sallow; *Dasyneura ulmariae* forming yellow galls on leaves of meadowsweet; *D. urticae*, galling leaf-bases of nettle; *Giraudiella inclusa*, inhabiting 'rice-grain' galls within the outer sheathing leaves of the cigar-galls of *Lipara lucens* (Chloropidae) on the common reed; *Helicomyia saliciperda*, breeding in willow twigs; *Cystiphora sonchi*, producing rounded blotch-galls on leaves of corn sowthistle on marsh walls; *Wachtliella persicariae* with red larvae in rolled leaf-margins of *Polygonum amphibium; Iteomyia capreae*, forming leaf galls on sallows; *Ametrodiplosis thalictricola*, in swollen flower-buds of meadow rue; *Pseudhormomyia granifex* producing groups of galls resembling wheat grains at the bases of sedge stalks (especially those of *Carex acutiformis* in this district).

STRATIOMYIDAE

Many of these gaily marked soldier-flies are present in fens adjacent to the broads; many of the larvae are aquatic and others live in wet peaty soil. The flies are common visitors to fen flowers, especially those of marsh ragwort, angelica and milk parsley. Species found here include *Beris clavipes*, *B. vallata*, *B. geniculata*, *Chorisops tibialis*, *Microchrysa polita*, *M. flavicornis*, *Geosargus iridatus*, *G. bipunctatus*, *Chloromyia formosa*, *Stratiomys furcate*, *S. potamida*, *Odontomyia argentata*, *O. angulata*, *O. ornata*, *O. viridula*, *Nemotelus pantherinus*, *N. uliginosus*, *N. notatus*, *N. nigrinus*, *Oxycera trilineata*, *O. pulchella*, *O. formosa* and *Pachygaster atra*.

RHAGIONIDAE

The down-looker fly (*Rhagio scolopacea*) is common beside woods along the valley margins; *R. tringaria* and *lineola* are noticed occasionally in fens; *Chrysopilus cristatus* is a very common fly in the fens and *C. aureus* only a little less so.

TABANIDAE

Clegs and horse-flies breed freely in the fens and swampy carrs and the females of many species bite humans viciously in sultry weather. The gay yellow-and-black *Chrysops*, with metallic fiery eyes (known here as harlequin flies) include *C. caecutiens*, *C. quadratus* and *C. relictus*, the last being the most abundant. The grey cleg, *Haematopota pluvialis*, is notoriously common and *H. crassicornis* is rather rare. *Tabanus autumnalis*, the largest horse-fly present, is seen chiefly in the grazing marshes of the estuarine region; *T. bromius* is rather rare, being more generally associated with inland meadows; *T. bisignatus* abounds in spring and early summer and is followed by *T. tropicus* and *T. distinguendus*, equally common in the fens. *T. fulvus* has been recorded from Sutton Broad.

BOMBYLIIDAE

The furry bee-fly, *Bombylius major*, of humming-bird hawk-moth mien, visits many kinds of flowers in spring and is the only common representative of its family here. The larva parasitises solitary-bees.

THEREVIDAE

These dagger-shaped furry flies, whose white wireworm-like predatory larvae live in the soil, are represented in broadland by the ubiquitous *Thereva nobilitata*, the marsh-dwelling *T. bipunctata* and the mainly coastal *T. annulata*.

ASILIDAE

The robber-flies seize and suck the juices of other insects. The large hairy-legged yellow-and-black *Asilus crabroniformis* appears occasionally in broadland habitats, but specimens met with are generally thought to have been blown from higher and drier heath country. The slender black *Leptogaster cylindrica* is rather common in fens and rough marshes; the blue-black *Laphria marginata* is rare, in damp woodlands; *Dioctria rufipes*, *D. baumbaueri* and *D. linearis* are found in grassy places.

EMPIDIDAE

These hunt and devour other flies. The species of *Platypalpus* run over leaves and grip their prey by means of spiny leg-pincers: *P. annulatus*, *P. candicans* and *P. pallidiventris* frequent the broads. The delicate black *Bicellaria spuria* occurs in fens. Great numbers of small black flies of the genus *Hilara* fly over waterways in summer, their flocks travelling up and down the dykes with a shuttle-like rhythm. Mated couples in these flocks commonly carry prey in the form of a small insect, caught earlier and fastened with silk by the male as an offering to his bride. Small green Chironomid midges are a common prey, but the *Hilara* males sometimes pick up small fragments of water-weeds and germinating seeds of sallow instead of insects from the surface of the water. *Hilara fuscipes*, *H. maura*, *H. nigrina* and *H. monedula* have been identified from the broads and doubtless many more species occur.

Larger predatory flies of the genus *Empis* are common here and include *E. stercorea*, *E. trigramma*, *E. livida*, *E. tessellata*, *E. pennaria* and *E. aestiva*. *Rhamphomyia*, a genus of smaller, mostly grey flies of the waterside is represented by *R. nigripennis*, *R. umbripennis*, *R. flava*, *R. culicina* and *R. spinipes*.

DOLICHOPODIDAE

These highly active ' long-headed ' flies run about over wet mud and water, where they prey upon small insects. Most of them have metallic brassy or coppery-green bodies. One of the largest species common on the broads is *Poecilobothrus nobilitatus*, the males of which may be recognised by the broad smoky bands across their wings. *Dolichopus* is represented by numerous species, including *D. vitripennis*, *D. atratus*, *D. fallenii*, *D. picipes*, *D. lepidus*, *D. laticolor*, *D. plumipes*, *D. pennatus*, *D. popularis*, *D. urbanus*, *D. signatus*, *D. griseipennis*, *D. nitidus*, *D. nubilus*, *D. simplex*, *D. longitarsus*, *D. brevipennis*, and *D. ungulatus*. Other Dolichopodids present are: *Hercostomus nanus*, *Gymnopternus chalybeus*, *G. celer*, *G. metallicus*, *G. aerosus*, *G. assimilis*, *G. cupreus*, *Hypophyllus obscurellus*, *Hydrophorus litoreus*, *H. viridis*, *H. praecox*, *H. bipunctatus*, *Thrypticus bellus*, *Syntormon monilis*, *Chrysotus cupreus*, *C. gramineus*, *Argyra diaphana*, *A. argentina*, *A. leucocephala*, *Campsicnemus scambus*, *C. curvipes*, *Sympycnus annulipes* and *Micromorphus albipes*.

DORILAIDAE

These small slow hovering flies, whose larvae are internal parasites of leaf-hoppers, are rather common in fens and reedswamps; the species of *Dorilas* found here include *D. littoralis*, *D. sylvaticus*, *D. xanthopus*, *D. haemorrhoidalis*, *D. confusus* and *D. zonatus*.

SYRPHIDAE

The hover-flies, drone-flies and their allies are represented here by numerous species whose larvae feed on aphids and many others which breed in decaying vegetable matter, peaty soil and shallow pools. Syrphid flies are common visitors to marsh flowers in summer and are very conspicuous on the flowering umbels of angelica and milk parsley in August. The species listed from the fens and carrs of the broads include the following: *Myathropa florea*, *Eristalinus sepulchralis*, *Tubifera* (*Eristalis*) *tenax*, *T. intricaria*, *T. arbustorum*, *T. horticola*, *T. pertinax*, *Lejops vittata*, *Anisimyia lineata*, *A. transfuga*, *Parhelophilus frutetorum*, *P. versicolor*, *P. consimilis*, *Helophilus hydridus*, *H. pendulus*, *Chrysochlamys cuprea*, *Zelima segnis*, *Z. sylvarum*, *Tropidia scita*, *Syritta pipiens*, *Brachyopa scutellaris*, *Rhingia macrocephala*, *Volucella pellucens* v. *bombylans*, *Neoascia podagrica*, *N. aenea*, *N. dispar*, *Chilomyia illustrata*, *C. funebres*, *C. vulpina*, *C. fraterna*, *C. impressa*, *C. albitarsis*, *C. proxima*, *Cartosyrphus paganus*, *Orthoneura splendens*, *Chrysogaster hirtella*, *C. chalybeata*, *C. solstitialis*, *Sulcatella tarsata*, *S. metallina*, *Cheilosia granditarsa*, *C. rosarum*, *Melanostoma mellinum*, *M. scalare*, *Platycheirus manicatus*, *P. timeo*, *P. scutatus*, *P. albimanus*, *P. fulviventris*, *Stenosyrphus umbellatarum*, *Sphaerophoria scripta*, *S. menthastri*, *Episyrphus balteatus*, *Ischyrosyrphus laternarius*, *Epistrophe eligans*, *Pipiza noctiluca*, *Phalangus virens*, *P. flavitarsis*, *Chrysotoxum festivum*, *C. bicinctum*, *Xanthogramma pedissequum*, *Scaeva* (*Catabomba*) *pyrastri*, *S. selenitica*, *Metasyrphus latifasciatus*, *M. consisto*, *M. luniger*, *Syrphus lucorum*, *Syrphidis ribesii*, *S. vitripennis*.

CONOPIDAE

These flies in many cases look very much like wasps and their larvae are internal parasites of aculeate hymenoptera. *Conops quadrifasciatus* and *C. flavipes* are the species met with most frequently here, but all are somewhat rare; others present include *Physocephala rufipes*, *Thecophora atra*, *Sicus ferrugineus*, *Myopa buccata* and *M. testacea*.

PLATYSTOMATIDAE

Platystome seminationis is common among trees and bushes in damp situations and *Rivellia syngenesiae* has been noticed in fens.

OTITIDAE

These smallish flies with prettily variegated wings are common in marshes; the local species include *Otites guttata*, *Meliera crassipennis*, *M. picta*, *Ceroxys urticae*, *Herina frondescentiae* (abundant in fens) and *Seioptera vibrans*.

PALLOPTERIDAE

Palloptera trimacula and *P. saltuum* occur in the marshes.

DRYOMYZIDAE

Dryomyza flaveola and *Neuroctena anilis* breed commonly in decaying vegetation in damp places.

TRYPETIDAE

The small picture-winged flies of this family include leaf-miners and species with larvae feeding in flower-heads of Compositae. Broadland representatives include *Urophora jaceana*, *Euribea zoë*, *Philophylla heraclei*, *Myiolia caesio*, *Trypeta cylindrica*, *T. tussilaginis*, *T. ruficauda*, *Xyphosia miliaria* and *Tephritis bardanae*.

LONCHAEIDAE

Lonchaea chorea and *L. tarsata* are rather common in the grazing marshes and rather less so in fens.

LAUXANIIDAE

These flies appear mainly in damp shady situations and their larvae feed on rotting vegetation. The local species include *Lauxania cylindricornis*, *Tricholauxania praeusta*, *Minettia fasciata*, *Cnemacantha rorida* and *Peplomyza litura*.

TYLIDAE

Trepidaria adusta and *T. petronella* are common stilt-legged flies preying on small insects in the marshes.

PSILIDAE

Fen species include *Loxocera aristata* and *Psila fimetaria*.

SEPSIDAE

Nemopoda nitidula is a common visitor to umbelliferous flowers.

SCIOMYZIDAE

Most of these are sluggish marsh flies with aquatic larvae. Species found here include: *Sciomyza griseola* (in fens), *Ditaenia cinerella* (chiefly in reed-swamps), *Pherbellia schoenherri*, *Tetanocera hyalipennis*, *T. silvatica*, *T. elata*, *T. ferruginea*, *T. robusta*, *Lunigera chaerophylli*, *Dictya umbrarum*, *Trypetoptera punctulata*, *Pherbina communis*, *P. coryletti*, *Elgiva sundewalli*, *Ilione albiseta*, *Limnia unguicornis*, *L. fumigata*, *Sepedon sphegeus* (often on yellow flag, *Iris pseudacorus*) and *S. spinipes*.

CHAMAEMYIIDAE

Chamaemyia herbarum is common on waterside plants where its larvae feed on aphids.

HELOMYZIDAE

Tephrochlamys rufiventris is generally common; its larvae develop in animal and vegetable refuse.

ANTHOMYZIDAE

Anthomyza gracilis is an inquiline (guest fly) in the cigar galls of *Lipara lucens* on reed.

OPOMYZIDAE

Opomyza germinationis, breeding in grasses, is very common.

EPHYDRIDAE

These are smallish flies of the waterside and may often be seen sitting about on wet mud. *Notiphila uliginosa* often visits flowers of the yellow water-lily and *N. brunnipes* those of the white water-lily; *N. cinerea* and *N. supposita* occur round the margins of broads. *Hydropota griseola* is a common leaf-miner of duckweeds. *Ephydra riparia*, typically a salt-marsh insect, is not uncommon about the broads. *Scatella stagnalis* and *Limnella quadrata* frequent fen ditches.

SPHAEROCERIDAE

These small flies run over dung, decaying vegetation and fen litter. Species found here in marshes include *Borborus ater*, *Trichiaspis similis*, *Collinellula lutosa* and *Limosina rufilabris*.

CHLOROPIDAE

Cigar-like malformations of reed shoots are seen commonly in the marshes here. These conspicuous galls are formed by a plump, slow-moving Chloropid fly, *Lipara lucens*. The reeds are parasitised in early summer and the galls are at first green and leafy; they are most noticeable in winter, after the leaves have dropped. The gall-makers emerge through the tips of the thickened shoots in May and June. Their larvae are commonly parasitised by the Pteromalid wasp (*Stenomalus liparae*) and the Braconid wasp (*Polemochartus liparae*); these eat their way out of the sides of the galls, leaving circular holes. Several kinds of inquilines or guest flies breed in the tightly sheathed leaves of the cigar-galls; they include the gall midge (*Giraudiella inclusa*) which makes small subsidiary galls resembling rice grains; two Chloropidae, *Cryptonevra flavitarsis* and a small black *Oscinella* resembling the common frit fly of cereal crops and lastly, *Anthomyza gracilis*. The *Giraudiella* is in turn parasitised by a Chalcid wasp, *Geniocerus flavimanus* and another small Hymenopteron, *Platygaster vestinus*. Galls vacated by their original occupants are often used as brood-chambers by solitary-bees (*Prosopis pectoralis*) and the bees in turn are parasitised by Evaniid wasps (*Gasteruption assectator*). If the reed galls are collected at the beginning of May and kept under observation in an insect cage they will usually produce most of the species just mentioned.

The other Chloropidae of fens include *Conioscinella frontella*, many species of *Meromyza* and *Chlorops*, *Platycephala planifrons* (locally common in reed stems), *Cryptonevra diadema* and *Diplotoxa messoria*.

CORDILURIDAE

Cordilura pubera, *C. pudica*, *C. ciliata* and *C. umbrosa* are all more or less common in the marshes. *Parellelomma albipes* may be found on bushes near water. *Cnemopogon apicalis* has predatory larvae which feed on the larvae of stem-boring insects in reeds. *Amaurosoma flavipes* is a fairly common fen insect. The yellow, hairy dung fly, (*Scopeuma stercorarium*) abounds everywhere and is predaceous on other insects; dead specimens, killed by entomogenous moulds (*Empusa*) are often to be seen attached to the tops of thistles and other tall plants in the marshes in large numbers during the summer. *Norellisoma spinimanum* has larvae feeding in stems of docks. *Cleigastra nigrita* and *Gimnomera tarsea* are associated with reeds.

LARVAEVORIDAE

It is to be regretted that no special study has been made of the part played by these flies in controlling the population of other insects in this area. The larvae are internal parasites of Lepidoptera (mainly) and other invertebrates, but we know little of their local status, as regards specific hosts. The adult insects are common visitors to fen flowers, especially to those of angelica and milk parsley in late summer and these include the following species: *Phryxe vulgaris*, *Exorista simulans*, *Germaria angustata*, *Varichaeta radicum*, *Linnaemyia vulpina*, *Eriothrix rufomaculatus*, *Larvaevora fera*, *Thelaira leucozona*, *Pelatachina tibialis* and *Dexiosoma caninum*.

CALLIPHORIDAE

Most of the common blowflies, greenbottles and grey fleshflies familiar in the countryside generally are to be found visiting fen flowers. *Protocalliphora azurea*, a brilliantly metallic bluebottle, breeds commonly in swallows' nests, where its larvae suck the blood of the nestlings. *Lucilia bufonivora* is found attacking frogs and toads here occasionally, but seems to be rather rare.

MUSCIDAE

Few flies of this family are specially characteristic of marsh habitats and most of the species noticed in the fens are also common elsewhere. *Graphomyia maculata* may be mentioned as an exception, as its predatory larvae are more or less aquatic. *Mesembrina meridiana*, a large fly with orange wing-bases, is commonly seen sitting about on marsh gateposts; its larvae prey upon the grubs of other insects in dung.

HIPPOBOSCIDAE

Blood-sucking bird-flies occurring here include the common *Ornithomyia avicularia* (attacking many different kinds of birds), *Stenepteryx hirundinis*, on house- and sand-martins and *Crataerina pallida* on the swift.

APPENDIX C

A NOTE ON BROADLAND MARSHING TOOLS

(See Pl. XXII)

by E. A. Ellis

Bile or *Boil:* a loop of briar (with the thorns removed), hazel or sallow fixed to a scythe in such a way that it pushes swathes of cut marsh litter clear of the blade.

Bottom-cutter: a kind of scythe resembling a shore-cutter, but with the blade set more obliquely; it is used for cutting weeds on the beds of waterways.

Caner: a scythe with the blade set at right-angles to the stick, used for clearing dyke weeds.

Didle or *Dydle:* there are several types—flat-bottomed, scuttle-shaped, or in the form of a scraper with a shallow bag-net attached. The commonest form consists of a shovel bent and socketed at right-angles to a long handle. All are used for pulling mud out of dykes. Ice-dydles used for skimming ice from Surlingham Broad in the nineteenth century were shallow, wire-netted hoops about two feet across, mounted on long poles; the ice was collected in wherries, some being stored in an ice-house near the broad and some being shipped to Yarmouth and stored there until it was required for the refrigeration of fish and other perishable foods.

Dyke Crome: usually a converted muck-fork, the round or square tines, four or six in number, being bent by a blacksmith so that they can be used to draw weeds and mud out of dykes. A ' mavish ' is a dyke-crome with a strip of iron forming a hoe-like cutting bar across the ends of the tines; it may be regarded as a kind of dydle.

Dyke Rake: this implement is now seldom seen; it measures about 2 ft 6 in. across and is set with twelve or fourteen long curved teeth and mounted on a very long handle. Its function is to gather up floating weeds, including those that have been cut adrift from below.

Reed- or *Cane-sickle:* this is made usually from a shortened scythe-blade, which is mounted on a short, straight handle. It is the favourite implement for cutting reeds in winter, the reeds being grasped in one hand and cut as low as possible with the sickle in the other. Where the reed is ' double wale ' (the ranks being made up of stems produced in two successive years), the mower may hold the bunches at the top immediately after cutting, to shake out the older, shorter stalks which have lost the ' feather '; but in some cases the whole crop is taken as it stands. The reeds are tied into bundles with string or with the green leaves of tussock sedge (*Carex paniculata*). Strictly speaking, six bunches or sheaves of reed go to the fathom, so that a true hundred fathoms will contain six hundred bunches. In some parts of broadland, e.g. at Hickling, a fathom consists of only five bunches; but the reeds are then sold by the 'long hundred' (120 fathoms), so that the buyer still receives six hundred bunches.

Scoop or *Slubbing-spade:* this is fashioned all in one piece out of a section of willow trunk; it is about the size of an average garden spade and has a cot-handle (T-shaped). It is shod with sheet iron or steel from an old scythe blade, riveted on, and a leather hood is attached across the top. This implement is used for throwing water and mud out of dammed sections of dykes, the operation being termed slubbing or bottom-fying. The 'slub' is thrown straight out in the same thrust with which it is collected in the scoop; the leather hood prevents most of the mud and water from shooting backwards off the scoop. The traditional method of damming lengths of dyke for bottom-fying consists of knocking in double rows of boards, or placing double rows of boards across the dyke, supported by stakes, and sealing the 'joints' with turf sods, rammed tight.

Scythe: when a scythe is used for mowing marsh litter, the edge of the blade is set high. Sometimes a 'bile' (q.v.) is attached as a labour-saving device. A scythe is not generally used for cutting reeds for thatching purposes in winter, largely because its use involves extra trouble in gathering up the reeds afterwards as they lie with butt ends and ear ends criss-crossed untidily. Scythed green litter of mixed fen vegetation used to be made into marsh hay in July; when dry, it was made into large cocks and afterwards poled away, one cock at a time, on a pair of deal poles about twelve feet long. These had the upper surface flat and the lower surface curved like a sledge runner and the ends were thinned to make handling comfortable.

Shears: used formerly for cutting bottom weeds in the larger waterways. Were formed of two old scythe blades welded together with their cutting edges facing outward on either side and fixed to a pole, for towing behind a marsh boat. A man in the stern used to haul and release the implement alternately as the boat moved forward.

Shore- or *Side-cutter:* a kind of scythe with the blade set at a very wide angle, used for slicing off rooted waterside vegetation which is afterwards pulled on to the bank with a crome. The best shore-cutters are made from long, thin, rivet-backed blades.

Stock-cutter: a half-moon knife mounted on a handle about five feet long. It is used for sheer-slicing the shores of dykes, giving them a neat finish. It is of value also in cutting 'grups' or small foot-drains that take surface water from turf fens. Some stock-cutters are made from stack-knives.

BIBLIOGRAPHY

GEOLOGY AND PHYSIOGRAPHY

BADEN-POWELL, D. F. W. (1948). The chalky boulder clays of Norfolk and Suffolk. *Geol. Mag.* 85: 279.

(1953). Correlation of Pliocene and Pleistocene marine beds. *Nature,* 172 : 762.

BLAKE, J. H. (1890). The geology of the country near Yarmouth and Lowestoft. *Mem. Geol. Surv.*

BOSWELL, P. G. H. (1921). The surface and dip of the Chalk in Norfolk. *Trans. Norf. Norw. Nat. Soc.* II : 22.

(1935). The geology of Norfolk. *Brit. Ass. Rep.* (1935), Appendix: 58.

CHATWIN, C. P. (1937). East Anglia. *Brit. Reg. Geol.*

DAVIES, H. C. (1931). Tides of the river Bure. *Trans. Norf. Norw. Nat. Soc.* 13 : 14.

FISHER, O. (1866). On the denudation of Norfolk. *Geol. Mag.* 3 : 316.

FUNNELL, B. M. (1955). The geology of the Bungay district. *Trans. Suff. Nat. Soc.* 9 : 115.

GODWIN, H. (1938). The origin of roddons. *Geog. J.* 91 : 241.

(1940 a). Fenland pollen diagrams. *Phil. Trans. Roy. Soc. Lond.* B 230 : 239.

(1940 b). Postglacial changes of relative land- and sea-level in the English Channel. *Phil. Trans. Roy. Soc. Lond.* B. 230 : 285.

(1940 c). Pollen analysis and forest history of England and Wales. *New Phyt.* 39 : 370.

(1943). Coastal peat beds of the British Isles and North Sea. *J. Ecol.* 31 : 199.

(1945). Coastal peat beds of the North Sea region as indices of land- and sea-level changes. *New Phyt.* 44 : 29.

GODWIN, H. and CLIFFORD, M. H. (1938 a). Origin and stratigraphy of Fenland deposits near Wood Walton, Hunts. *Phil. Trans. Roy. Soc.* B. 299 : 323.

(1938 b). Origin and stratigraphy of deposits in Southern Fenland. *Phil. Trans. Roy. Soc.* B. 229 : 363.

GODWIN, H. and TALLANTIRE, P. A. (1951). Hockham Mere, Norfolk. *J. Ecol.* 39 : 285.

GRANTHAM, R. B. (1869). A description of the broads. *Q. J. Geol. Soc. Lond.* 25 : 258.

GREEN, CHARLES (1956 a). Changing coastline: conflict of land and sea in East Anglia. *The Times,* 12/3/56.

(1956 b). The birth of broadland. *Eastern Daily Press,* 20/3/56.

(1961 a). East Anglian coast-line levels since Roman times. *Antiquity,* XXXV, 21–8.

(1961 b). Broadland fords and causeways. *Norfolk Archaeology*, xxxii (4), 316–31.

GREEN, CHARLES and HUTCHINSON, J. N. (1965) Relative land and sea levels at Great Yarmouth. *Geog. J.* 131 (1).

GREEN, C., LARWOOD, G. P. and MARTIN, A. J. (1954). The coastline of Flegg. *Trans. Norf. Norw. Nat. Soc.* 17 : 327.

GREGORY, J. W. (1892). The physical features of the Norfolk Broads. *Natural Science*, 1 : 347.

GUNN, J. W. (1867). On recent formations in the valleys of Norfolk. *Geol. Mag.* 4 : 519.

GURNEY, R. (1911 a). Some observations on the waters of the river Bure and its tributaries. *Geog. J.* 37 : 292.

(1911 b). The tides of the river Bure and its tributaries. *Trans. Norf. Norw. Nat. Soc.* 9 : 216.

(1932). Some notes on the tide at Stokesby. *Trans. Norf. Norw. Nat. Soc.* 13 : 142.

HARMER, F. W. (1902). A sketch of the later tertiary history of East Anglia. *Proc. Geol. Ass.* 17 : 416.

INNES, A. G. (1911). The tidal action of the Bure and its tributaries. *Trans. Norf. Norw. Nat. Soc.* 9 : 244.

JENNINGS, J. N. (1950). The origin of the Fenland meres. *Geol. Mag.* 87 : 217.

(1952). The origin of the Broads. *Roy. Geog. Soc. Lond. Research Series No. 2.*

(1955). Further pollen data from the Norfolk Broads. *New Phyt.* 54 (2) : 199.

JENNINGS, J. N. and LAMBERT, J. M. (1951). Alluvial stratigraphy and vegetational succession in the region of the Bure valley broads I: surface features and general stratigraphy. *J. Ecol.* 39 : 106.

(1953). The origin of the broads. *Geog. J.* 93 : 408.

JOLLY, H. L. P. (1939). Recent coastal changes in south-eastern England II: supposed land subsidence in the south of England. *Geol. J.* 93 : 408.

LAMBERT, J. M. (1954). The past, present and future of the Norfolk Broads. *Trans. Norf. Norw. Nat. Soc.* 17 : 223.

LAMBERT, J. M., JENNINGS, J. N., SMITH, C. T., CHARLES GREEN and HUTCHINSON, J. N. (1960). The making of the broads: a reconsideration of their origin in the light of new evidence. Roy. Geog. Soc. *Research Memoir*, No. 3.

LARWOOD, G. P. and MARTIN, A. J. (1954). Stratigraphy and fauna of the Easton Bavents cliff sections near Southwold, Suffolk. *Trans. Suff. Nat. Soc.* 8 : 157.

MARR, J. E. (1900). *The scientific study of scenery:* 165 & Note D.

MARRIOTT, W. and GRIBBLE, T. G. (1904). The Breydon Viaduct at Great Yarmouth. *Proc. Inst. Civ. Eng.* 157 : 268.

MOSBY, J. E. G. (1939 a). Recent coastal changes in south-east England. *Geog. J.* 93 : 415.

(1939 b). Norfolk Land Utilisation Survey Report No. 70. *Land of Britain.*

PALLIS, M. (1911). On the cause of the salinity of the broads of the river Thurne. *Geog. J.* 37 : 284.

PRESTWICH, J. (1860). On the presence of the London Clay in Norfolk. *Q. J. Geol. Soc. Lond.* 16 : 449.

REID, C. (1882). The geology of the country around Cromer. *Mem. Geol. Surv.*

(1913). *Submerged Forests.*

ROBBERDS, J. W. (1826). *Geological and historical observations on the eastern valleys of Norfolk.*

(1827). Reply to Mr. Taylor's remarks. *Phil. Mag.* ser. 2, v. 2 : 192.

SAINTY, J. E. (1949). The origin of the broads. *Trans. Norf. Norw. Nat. Soc.* 16 : 369.

(1952). The Geology of Norfolk. *Trans. Norf. Norw. Nat. Soc.* 17 : 149.

STEERS, J. A. (1927). The East Anglian Coast. *Geogr. J.* 69 : 24.

(1942). The Physiography of East Anglia. *Trans. Norf. Norw. Nat. Soc.* 15 : 231.

(1949). The coastline of East Anglia. *New Naturalist*, 6 : 6.

(1953). *The sea coast.* London (Collins' *New Naturalist*).

(1961). Chapter of Physiography in *Norwich and its Region* (ed. Briers, F.), p. 31.

TAYLOR, J. E. (1872). The Norfolk Broads and meres geologically considered. *Trans. Norf. Norw. Nat. Soc.* 1, Pt. 3, 30.

TAYLOR, R. C. (1827 a). On the geology of east Norfolk. *Phil. Mag.* Ser. 2, v. 1 : 277.

(1827 b). On the natural embankments formed against the German Ocean. *Phil. Mag.* Ser. 2, v. 2 : 327.

(1827 c). On the geological features of the eastern coast of England. *Phil. Mag.* Ser. 2, v. 2 : 327.

WEST, R. G. (1955). The Glaciations and Interglacials of East Anglia; a summary and discussion of recent research. *Quaternaria* 2 : 45.

(1956). The Quaternary deposits at Hoxne, Suffolk. *Phil. Trans. Roy. Soc. Lond.* 239 : 265.

WEST, R. G. and DONNER, J. J. (1956). The glaciations of East Anglia and the Midlands: a differentiation based on stone orientation measurements of the tills. *Q. J. Geol. Soc. Lond.* 112 : 69.

WOOD, S. V. (1867). Correspondence *re* Lacon's Brewery bore at Yarmouth. *Geol. Mag.* 4 : 560.

WOODWARD, H. B. (1879). The scenery of Norfolk. *Trans. Norf. Norw. Nat. Soc.* 3 : 439.

(1881). The geology of the country around Norwich. *Mem. Geol. Surv.*

WOODWARD, S. (1833). *An outline of the geology of Norfolk.*

BOTANY and ECOLOGY

AINSWORTH, G. C. and SAMPSON, K. (1950). The British smut fungi (*Ustilaginales*). *Commonwealth Myc. Inst., Kew.*

BARRY, D. H. and JERMY, A. C. (1953). Observations on *Najas marina*, I. *Trans. Norf. Norw. Nat. Soc.* 17 : 294.

BISBY, G. R. and MASON, E. W. (1940). List of Pyrenomycetes recorded for Britain. *Trans. Brit. Myc. Soc.* 24 : 127.

BURRELL, W. H. (1914) in Nicholson's *Flora of Norfolk:* mosses and liverworts, 179.

CLAPHAM, A. R., TUTIN, T. G. and WARBURG, E. F. (1952). *Flora of the British Isles.* Cambridge.

DENNIS, R. W. G. (1949). A revision of the British Hyaloscyphaceae. *Commonwealth Myc. Inst.*, Kew.

(1956). A revision of the British Helotiaceae. *Commonwealth Myc. Inst.*, Kew.

ELLIS, E. A. (1935). Flora of Norfolk: Rust Fungi (Uredinales). *Trans. Norf. Norw. Nat. Soc.* 13 : 489.

(1935 a). Wheatfen Broad, Surlingham. *Ibid.* 13 : 422.

(1941). The natural history of Wheatfen Broad, Surlingham, Part 3, Micro-fungi. *Ibid.* 15 : 191.

(1945). Marsh sowthistle in east Norfolk and Lothingland. *Ibid.* 16 : 77.

(1949). The broads as a relict marsh. *New Naturalist*, 6 : 28.

(1956). *Symphyosirinia*, a new genus of inoperculate Discomycetes. *Ibid.* 18, Pt. 3 (Mycology) : 1.

(1956 a). Entomogenous fungi in Norfolk. *Ibid.* 18, Pt. 3 (Mycology) 23.

ELLIS, M. B., E. A. and J. P. (1951). British marsh and fen fungi, I and II. *Trans. Brit. Myc. Soc.* 34 : 147 and 497.

GELDART, A. M. (1906). *Stratiotes aloides. Trans. Norf. Norw. Nat. Soc.* 8 : 181.

GODWIN, H. and TURNER, J. S. (1933). Soil acidity in relation to vegetational succession at Calthorpe Broad. *J. Ecol.* 21 : 235.

GRIFFITHS, M. B. (1927). Studies in the phytoplankton of the lowland waters of Great Britain, V: the phytoplankton of some Norfolk Broads. *J. Linn. Soc. Lond. Bot.* 47 : 595.

GROVE, W. B. (1935, 1937). *British stem and leaf fungi.* Cambridge.

GURNEY, R. (1949). Vegetational changes. *Eastern Daily Press*, 26/8/49.

HOWARD, H. J. (1948). The Mycetozoa of sand-dunes and marshland. *S.E. Nat. and Antiq.* 53 : 26.

JENNINGS, J. N. and LAMBERT, J. M. (1949). The shrinkage of the broads. *New Naturalist*, 6 : 26.

KITTON, F. (1877). Fauna and Flora of Norfolk: Diatomaceae. *Trans. Norf. Norw. Nat. Soc.* 2 : 336.

(1884). *Ibid.* 3 : 754.

LAMBERT, J. M. (1946). The distribution and status of *Glyceria maxima* (Hartm.) Holmb. in the region of Surlingham and Rockland Broads, Norfolk. *J. Ecol.* 33 : 230.

—— (1947 a). A note on the physiognomy of *Glyceria maxima* reed-swamps in Norfolk. *Trans. Norf. Norw. Nat. Soc.* 16 : 246.

—— (1947 b). *Glyceria maxima* (Hartm.) Holmb. in Biol. Flora Brit. Is. *J. Ecol.* 34 : 310.

—— (1948). A survey of the Rockland-Claxton level, Norfolk. *J. Ecol.* 36 : 120.

—— (1951 a). The ecological status of the Bargate Nature Reserve. *Trans. Norf. Norw. Nat. Soc.* 17 : 123.

—— (1951 b). Alluvial stratigraphy and vegetational succession in the region of the Bure valley Broads: III, classification, status and distribution of communities. *J. Ecol.* 39 : 149.

—— (1957). Diminishing broads. *The Times*, 11/7/1957.

—— (1961). The chief Norfolk habitats. In *Norwich and its Region* (ed. Briers, F.), p. 51.

LAMBERT, J. M. and JENNINGS, J. N. (1951). Alluvial stratigraphy and vegetational succession in the region of the Bure valley Broads: II, detailed vegetational-stratigraphical relationships. *J. Ecol.* 39 : 120.

LISTER, G. (1925). *A monograph of the Mycetozoa.* 3rd edition. Brit. Mus. Lond.

MANNING, S. A. (1944). The natural history of Wheatfen Broad, Surlingham: Lichens. *Trans. Norf. Norw. Nat. Soc.* 15 : 420.

MASON, E. W. and ELLIS, M. B. (1953). British species of Periconia. *Commonwealth Myc. Inst.* No. 56.

NICHOLSON, W. A. (1914). *A Flora of Norfolk.* Norwich.

PALLIS, M. (1911). The river valleys of East Norfolk; their aquatic and fen formations. In Tansley, A.G., *Types of British Vegetation*, 214.

—— (1956). *The Impermeability of Peat and the Origin of the Norfolk Broads.* Glasgow.

—— (1961). *The Status of Fen and the Origin of the Norfolk Broads.* Glasgow.

PETCH, T. (1948). A revised list of British entomogenous fungi. *Trans. Brit. Myc. Soc.* 31 : 286.

RAMSBOTTOM, J. and BALFOUR BROWNE, F. L. (1951). List of British Discomycetes. *Trans. Brit. Myc. Soc.* 34 : 38.

RICHARDS, P. W. and WALLACE, E. C. (1950). An annotated list of British mosses. *Trans. Brit. Bryol. Soc.* 1 : part 4.

SALISBURY, E. J. (1933). The East Anglian Flora. *Trans. Norf. Norw. Nat. Soc.* 13 : 191.

STANT, M. Y. (1953). Variations in reed structure in relation to thatching. *Kew Bulletin*, 2 : 231.

WAKEFIELD, E. M. and BISBY, G. R. (1941). List of Hyphomycetes recorded for Britain. *Trans. Brit. Myc. Soc.* 25 : 49.

WALTERS, S. M. (1956). *Eriophorum gracile* Roth. *Proc. Bot. Soc. Brit. Is.* 2 : 23.

WATSON, W. (1953). *Census catalogue of British Lichens*. Brit. Myc. Soc.

WILSON, M. and BISBY, G. R. (1954). List of British Uredinales. *Trans. Brit. Myc. Soc.* 37 : 61.

ZOOLOGY

BRADY, G. S. and ROBERTSON, D. (1870). The Ostracoda and Foraminifera of tidal rivers. *Ann. Mag. Nat. Hist.* 4th series, 6 : 1.

BRIDGMAN, J. B. (1877–94). Fauna and Flora of Norfolk: Hymenoptera. *Trans. Norf. Norw. Nat. Soc.* 2 : 275, 617; 3 : 367; 4 : 523, 690; 5 : 61, 603.

BROWNE, F. BALFOUR (1904). A bionomical investigation of the Norfolk Broads (dragonflies). *Trans. Norf. Norw. Nat. Soc.* 7 : 661.

(1905). A study of the aquatic Coleoptera and their surroundings in the Norfolk Broads district. *Ibid.* 8 : 58.

(1906). ditto, second paper. *Ibid.* 8 : 290.

(1940). *British Water Beetles* 1 and 2. London, Ray Soc.

DAVIS, R. A. (1956). The coypu. *Agriculture*, 63 : 127.

EDWARDS, J. (1884–1914). Fauna and Flora of Norfolk: Hemiptera. *Trans. Norf. Norw. Nat. Soc.* 3 : 700; 4 : 702; 5 : 650; 6 : 528; 7 : 746; 8 : 840; 9 : 812.

ELLIS, A. E. (1926). *British Snails*. Oxford.

(1941). The Mollusca of a Norfolk Broad. *J. Conchol.* 21 : 224.

(1942). The natural history of Wheatfen Broad, Surlingham, part 4: woodlice and harvestmen. *Trans. Norf. Norw. Nat. Soc.* 15 : 291.

(1949). A broadland slug. *Ibid.* 16 : 388.

ELLIS, E. A. (1940 and 1942). The natural history of Wheatfen Broad, Surlingham, parts 2 and 5. Heteroptera. *Trans. Norf. Norw. Nat. Soc.* 15 : 115 and 301.

(1945). The rond-snail (*Assiminea grayana*) in East Anglia. *Ibid.* 16 : 82.

(1951). The introduction of the large copper butterfly at Wheatfen Broad, Norfolk. *Ibid.* 17 : 84.

GURNEY, E. and R. (1908). *The Sutton Broad freshwater laboratory.*

GURNEY, R. (1929). The freshwater Crustacea of Norfolk. *Trans. Norf. Norw. Nat. Soc.* 12 : 550.

HARTLEY, P (1940). The food of coarse fish. *Fresh-water Biol. Ass., Sci. Pub.* No. 3.

HOLMES, P. J. and PRYOR, M. G. M. (1938). Barnacles in Horsey Mere. *Nature*, 142 : 795.

HURRELL, H. E. (1927). The ecology of the fresh-water Polyzoa in East Anglia. *J. Roy. Micr. Soc.* June 1927 : 135.

(1943). Pond life. *Trans. Norf. Norw. Nat. Soc.* 15 : 319.

KLOET, G. S. and HINCKS, W. D. (1945). *A check list of British insects.*

LAURIE, E. M. O. (1946). The coypu (*Myocastor coypus*) in Great Britain. *J. Anim. Ecol.* 15 : 22.

LUBBOCK, R. (1879). *Observations on the Fauna of Norfolk.* 2nd ed., edited by T. Southwell. Norwich.

MACAN, T. T. and WORTHINGTON, E. B. (1951). *Life in lakes and rivers.* Collins, *New Naturalist*, London.

MANN, K. H. (1954). A key to the British freshwater leeches. *Freshwater Biol. Assoc. Sci. Pub.*, No. 14.

MORLEY, C. and ATMORE, E. A. (1915). The Diptera of Norfolk and Suffolk. *Trans. Norf. Norw. Nat. Soc.* 10 : supplement.

RIVIERE, B. B. (1930). *A history of the birds of Norfolk.* London.

ROBERTSON, M. (1911). Transmission of flagellates living in the blood of certain freshwater fishes. *Phil. Trans. Roy. Soc.* B. 202 : 29.

RUDD, A. J. (1937). The freshwater fishes of Norfolk. *Trans. Norf. Norw. Nat. Soc.* 14 : 149.

(1944). Norfolk fishes. *Ibid.* 15 : 377.

SHEPHEARD, T. (1937). The otters of Norfolk. *Ibid.* 14 : 138.

SOAR, C. D. (1905). The hydrachnids of the Norfolk Broads. *Ibid.* 8 : 83.

STEVENSON, H. (1866, 1870 and 1890). *Birds of Norfolk* (3 vols.).

TURNER, E. L. (1922). The status of birds in broadland. *Trans. Norf. Norw. Nat. Soc.* 11 : 228.

WALTON, G. A. (1938). A water bug new to Britain: *Hydrometra gracilenta* Horvath. *Ent. Mo. Mag.* 74 : 272.

(1939). *Microvelia umbricola. J. Soc. Brit. Ent.* 2 : 26.

WRIGHT, H. G. S. (1957). The rotifer fauna of East Norfolk. *Trans. Norf. Norw. Nat. Soc.* 18, part 5 : 1.

HISTORY, RURAL ECONOMY and MISCELLANEOUS WORKS ON MAN AND NATURE IN BROADLAND

BELL, S. A. (1933). *A yachtsman's guide to the broads.*

BIRD, M. C. H. (1909). The rural economy, sport and natural history of East Ruston Common. *Trans. Norf. & Norw. Nat. Soc.* 8 : 631.

BLOMEFIELD, F. (1805–10). *History and antiquities of Norfolk.*

BOARDMAN, E. T. (1940). The development of a broadland estate at How Hill, Ludham, Norfolk. *Trans. Norf. Norw. Nat. Soc.* 15 : 5.

BOARDMAN, H. C. (1933). Reed thatching in Norfolk. *Archit. J.* 67 : 563.

BUXTON, A. (1939–44). The Norfolk sea floods of February 1938 and effects seen in after years. *Trans. Norf. Norw. Nat. Soc.* 14 : 349; 15 : 22, 150, 259, 332, 410.

CLARKE, R. R. (1940 a). Norfolk in the Dark Ages, A.D. 400–800, Part ii. *Norfolk Archaeology* 27 : 249.

(1940 b). A bronze cauldron and other antiquities from north-east Suffolk. *Proc. Suff. Inst. Arch.* 23 : 219.

(1960). The broads and the medieval peat industry. *Norfolk Archaeology*, 32 (2) : 209.

(1960). *East Anglia*. London.

DALEY, P. V. (1935). *Broadland : the rivers and broads of Norfolk and Suffolk.* Norwich.

DAVIES, G. C. (1883). *Norfolk broads and rivers.*

DUTT, W. A. (1903, 1930). *The Norfolk Broads.* London.

EVERITT, N. (1902). *Broadland sport.* London.

GODWIN, H. and M. E. (1933). British Maglemose harpoon sites. *Antiquity*, 7 : 1.

GREEN, C. (1952). Excavations at Roman port in East Anglia. *The Times*, Feb. 2, 1952.

GURNEY, R. (1920). A bronze shield from Sutton, Norfolk. *Proc. Prehist. Soc. E. Anglia* 3 : 209.

HAMILTON, C. R. and MILLER, G. C. M. (1935 and subsequent editions). *Hamilton's map and chart of the broads.* Norwich.

LAMBERT, J. M. and SMITH, C. T. (1960). The Norfolk Broads as man-made features. *New Scientist*, 31/3/60.

MORRIS, A. S. (1947). The Saxon shore fort at Burgh Castle. *Proc. Suff. Inst. Arch. & Nat. Hist.* 5 : 100.

MOTTRAM, R. H. (1952). *The broads.* London.

PAGET, C. J. and J. (1834). *Sketch of the natural history of Yarmouth and its neighbourhood.*

PATTERSON, A. H. (1892). *Broadland scribblings.* Norwich.

(1895). *Man and nature on the broads.* London.

(1904). *Notes of an East Coast naturalist.* London.

(1905). *Nature in eastern Norfolk.* London.

(1907). *Wild life on a Norfolk estuary.* London.

(1909). *Man and nature on tidal waters.* London.

(1920). *Through Broadland in a Breydon punt.* Norwich.

(1923). *The cruise of the 'Walrus' on the broads.* London.

(1929). *Wildfowlers and poachers.* London.

(1930). *A Norfolk naturalist.* London.

(1930 a). *Through broadland by sail and motor.* London.

RACKHAM, W. L. L. (1931). *In and around Norwich, broadland, Yarmouth, etc.* Norwich.

ROBINSON, L. A. (1936). *Yachting on the broads.* Lowestoft.

SOUTHWELL, T. (1887). Notes on some annual customs and regulations with regard to the freshwater fisheries of the county of Norfolk. *Trans. Norf. Norw. Nat. Soc.* 4 : 433.

WOODWARD, S. (1847). *History and antiquities of Norwich Castle.*

INDEX